PUFFIN BOOKS

Editor: Kaye Webb

COME HITHER
VOLUME II

D0529203

Cover design by Erik Blegvad

COME HITHER

VOLUME II

*

A COLLECTION OF

RHYMES AND POEMS

FOR THE YOUNG
OF ALL AGES

*

MADE BY

WALTER DE LA MARE

*

WOOD-ENGRAVINGS BY
DIANA BLOOMFIELD

PUFFIN BOOKS

in association with Longman Young Books

Puffin Books: a Division of Penguin Books Ltd,
Harmondsworth, Middlesex, England
Penguin Books Australia Ltd, Ringwood, Victoria, Australia

—

First published by Constable 1923
Published in Puffin Books 1973

—

This edition copyright © Alfred A. Knopf, Inc., 1957

—

Made and printed in Great Britain
by Richard Clay (The Chaucer Press), Ltd,
Bungay, Suffolk
Set in Monotype Fournier

Contents

'Like Stars upon Some Gloomy Grove'   481

Far   527

Lily Bright and Shine-A   587

'Echo Then Shall Again Tell Her I Follow'   619

Old Tales and Balladry   665

Evening and Dream   703

The Garden   737

About and Roundabout (continued)   753

And so Farewell   909

Index: Titles and First Lines   911

Index of Notes   929

Index of Authors   933

'LIKE STARS UPON
SOME GLOOMY GROVE'

262. *Spring Quiet*

Gone were but the Winter,
    Come were but the Spring,
I would go to a covert
    Where the birds sing.

Where in the whitethorn
    Singeth a thrush,
And a robin sings
    In the holly-bush.

Full of fresh scents,
    Are the budding boughs
Arching high over
    A cool green house:

Full of sweet scents,
    And whispering air
Which sayeth softly:
    'We spread no snare;

'Here dwell in safety,
    Here dwell alone,
With a clear stream
    And a mossy stone.

'Here the sun shineth
    Most shadily;
Here is heard an echo
    Of the far sea,
    Though far off it be.'

CHRISTINA ROSSETTI

263. *A Widow Bird*

... A widow bird sat mourning for her love
    Upon a wintry bough;
The frozen wind crept on above,
    The freezing stream below.

There was no leaf upon the forest bare,
    No flower upon the ground
And little motion in the air
    Except the mill-wheel's sound.

PERCY BYSSHE SHELLEY

264. *Echo's Lament for Narcissus*

Slow, slow, fresh fount, keep time with my salt tears;
   Yet, slower yet; O faintly, gentle springs;
List to the heavy part the music bears;
   Woe weeps out her division when she sings.
       Droop herbs and flowers;
       Fall grief in showers,
       Our beauties are not ours;
       O, I could still,
Like melting snow upon some craggy hill,
       Drop, drop, drop, drop,
Since nature's pride is now a withered daffodil.

BEN JONSON

265. *This Life*

This Life, which seems so fair,
Is like a bubble blown up in the air
By sporting children's breath,
Who chase it everywhere,
And strive who can most motion it bequeath.
And though it sometimes seem of its own might
Like to an eye of gold to be fixed there,
And firm to hover in that empty height,
That only is because it is so light.
But in that pomp it doth not long appear;
For when 'tis most admirèd – in a thought,
Because it erst[1] was nought, it turns to nought.

WILLIAM DRUMMOND

266. *Sweet Content*

Art thou poor, yet hast thou golden slumbers?
O, sweet content!
Art thou rich, yet is thy mind perplexed?
O, punishment!
Dost thou laugh to see how fools are vexed
To add to golden numbers golden numbers?
O, sweet content! O, sweet, O sweet content!

Work apace, apace, apace, apace;
Honest labour bears a lovely face;
Then hey nonny, hey nonny, nonny!

1. Once

485

Canst drink the waters of the crispèd spring?
        O, sweet content!
Swimm'st thou in wealth, yet sink'st in thine own tears?
        O, punishment!
Then he that patiently want's burden bears,
No burden bears, but is a king, a king!
O, sweet content! O, sweet, O, sweet content!

  Work apace, apace, apace, apace;
  Honest labour bears a lovely face;
  Then hey nonny, hey nonny, nonny!

THOMAS DEKKER

267. *Oh, Sweet Content*

Oh, sweet content, that turns the labourer's sweat
  To tears of joy, and shines the roughest face;
How often have I sought you high and low,
  And found you still in some lone quiet place;

Here, in my room, when full of happy dreams,
  With no life heard beyond that merry sound
Of moths that on my lighted ceiling kiss
  Their shadows as they dance and dance around;

Or in a garden, on a summer's night,
  When I have seen the dark and solemn air
Blink with the blind bats' wings, and heaven's bright face
  Twitch with the stars that shine in thousands there.

WILLIAM H. DAVIES

268. *Rarely, Rarely, Comest Thou*

Rarely, rarely comest thou,
    Spirit of Delight!
Wherefore hast thou left me now
    Many a day and night?
Many a weary night and day
'Tis since thou art fled away.

How shall ever one like me
    Win thee back again?
With the joyous and the free
    Thou wilt scoff at pain.
Spirit false! thou hast forgot
All but those who need thee not.

As a lizard with the shade
    Of a trembling leaf,
Thou with sorrow art dismayed;
    Even the sighs of grief
Reproach thee, that thou art not near,
And reproach thou wilt not hear.

Let me set my mournful ditty
    To a merry measure;
Thou wilt never come for pity,
    Thou wilt come for pleasure;
Pity then will cut away,
Those cruel wings, and thou wilt stay.

I love all that thòu lovest,
    Spirit of Delight!
The fresh Earth in new leaves drest,
    And the starry night,
Autumn evening, and the morn
When the golden mists are born.

I love snow, and all the forms
    Of the radiant frost;
I love waves, and winds, and storms,
    Everything almost
Which is Nature's, and may be
Untainted by man's misery.

I love tranquil solitude
    And such society
As is quiet, wise, and good;
    Between thee and me
What difference? but thou dost possess
The things I seek, not love them less.

I love Love – though he has wings,
    And like light can flee,
But above all other things,
    Spirit, I love thee –
Thou art love and life! Oh, come,
Make once more my heart thy home!

PERCY BYSSHE SHELLEY

269. *Birthright*

Lord Rameses of Egypt sighed
Because a summer evening passed;
And little Ariadne cried
That summer fancy fell at last
To dust; and young Verona died
When beauty's hour was overcast.

Theirs was the bitterness we know
Because the clouds of hawthorn keep
So short a state, and kisses go

To tombs unfathomably deep,
While Rameses and Romeo
And little Ariadne sleep.

JOHN DRINKWATER

270. *O Sorrow!*

. . . 'O Sorrow,
  Why dost borrow
The natural hue of health, from vermeil lips? –
    To give maiden blushes
    To the white rose bushes?
Or is't thy dewy hand the daisy tips?

'O Sorrow,
  Why dost borrow
The lustrous passion from a falcon-eye? –
    To give the glow-worm light?
    Or, on a moonless night,
To tinge, on siren shores, the salt sea-spry?

'O Sorrow,
  Why dost borrow
The mellow ditties from a mourning tongue? –
    To give at evening pale
    Unto the nightingale,
That thou mayst listen the cold dews among?

'O Sorrow,
  Why dost borrow
Heart's lightness from the merriment of May? –
    A lover would not tread
    A cowslip on the head,

Though he should dance from eve till peep of day –
    Nor any drooping flower
    Held sacred for thy bower,
Wherever he may sport himself and play.'

    To Sorrow,
    I bade good-morrow,
And thought to leave her far away behind;
    But cheerly, cheerly,
    She loves me dearly;
She is so constant, to me, and so kind:
    I could deceive her
    And so leave her,
But oh! she is so constant and so kind . . .

    'Come then, Sorrow!
    Sweetest Sorrow!
Like an own babe I nurse thee on my breast:
    I thought to leave thee
    And deceive thee,
But now of all the world I love thee best.

    'There is not one,
    No, no, not one
But thee to comfort a poor lonely maid;
    Thou art her mother,
    And her brother,
Her playmate, and her wooer in the shade.' . . .

JOHN KEATS

271. *When the Lamp Is Shattered*

When the lamp is shattered,
The light in the dust lies dead –
When the cloud is scattered,
The rainbow's glory is shed.

When the lute is broken,
Sweet tones are remembered not;
    When the lips have spoken,
Loved accents are soon forgot.

    As music and splendour
Survive not the lamp and the lute,
    The heart's echoes render
No song when the spirit is mute:
    No song but sad dirges,
Like the wind through a ruined cell,
    Or the mournful surges
That ring the dead seaman's knell.

    When hearts have once mingled
Love first leaves the well-built nest;
    The weak one is singled
To endure what it once possessed.
    O Love, who bewailest
The frailty of all things here,
    Why choose you the frailest
For your cradle, your home, and your bier?

    Its passions will rock thee
As the storm rocks the ravens on high:
    Bright reason will mock thee,
Like the sun from a wintry sky.
    From thy nest every rafter
Will rot, and thine eagle home
    Leave thee naked to laughter,
When leaves fall and cold winds come.

PERCY BYSSHE SHELLEY

272. *Once*

He sees them pass
    As the light is graying
Each lad and lass
    In their beauty gaying
And a voice in his aching heart is saying:

'Once – once even I
    Was straight as these,
As clear of eye,
    And as apt to please
When I tuned my voice to balladries.

'Now my eyes are dim,
    Their old fires forsaking,
And each wasted limb
    As a branch is shaking,
And my grief-bowed heart will soon be breaking.

'– Ah, if One comes not
    Beckoning nigh
To that land where hums not
    One small fly,
These Strong and Fair shall be as I.'

ERIC N. BATTERHAM

273. *Upon the Image of Death*

Before my face the picture hangs
    That dailie should put me in minde
Of those cold qualms and bitter pangs
    That shortly I am like to finde:
        But yet, alas! full little I
        Do think hereon, that I must die.

I often look upon a face
　　Most uglie, grislie, bare, and thin;
I often view the hollow place
　　Where eyes and nose have sometime been;
　　　　I see the bones across that lie;
　　　　Yet little think, that I must die.

I read the label underneathe,
　　That telleth me whereto I must:
I see the sentence eke that saithe
　　'Remember, man, that thou art duste';
　　　　But yet, alas, but seldom I
　　　　Do think indeed, that I must die!

Continually at my bed's head
　　An hearse doth hang, which doth me tell
That I, ere morning, may be dead,
　　Though now I feel myself full well:
　　　　But yet, alas, for all this, I
　　　　Have little minde that I must die!

The gowne which I do use to weare,
　　The knife, wherewith I cut my meate,
And eke that old and ancient chair
　　Which is my only usual seate,
　　　　All these do tell me I must die;
　　　　And yet my life amende not I!

My ancestors are turned to clay,
　　And many of my mates are gone;
My youngers daily drop away; –
　　And can I think to 'scape alone?
　　　　No, no, I know that I must die;
　　　　And yet my life amende not I!

Not Solomon, for all his wit,
   Nor Samson, though he were so strong,
No king, nor ever person yet,
    Could 'scape, but Death laid him along!
      Wherefore I know that I must die;
      And yet my life amende not I!

Though all the east did quake to hear
   Of Alexander's dreadful name,
And all the west did likewise fear
    The sound of Julius Caesar's fame,
      Yet both by death in duste now lie;
      Who then can 'scape, but he must die?

If none can 'scape Death's dreadful darte,
   If rich and poor his beck obey,
If strong, if wise, if all do smarte,
    Then I to 'scape shall have no way.
      O grant me grace, O God, that I
      My life may mende, sith I must die!

                  ROBERT SOUTHWELL

274. *Adieu! Farewell Earth's Bliss!*

Adieu! farewell earth's bliss!
This world uncertain is:
Fond are life's lustful joys,
Death proves them all but toys.
None from his darts can fly:
I am sick, I must die –
   Lord, have mercy on us!

Rich men, trust not in wealth,
Gold cannot buy you health;
Physic himself must fade;
All things to end are made;

The plague full swift goes by:
I am sick, I must die –
   Lord, have mercy on us!

Beauty is but a flower
Which wrinkles will devour:
Brightness falls from the air;
Queens have died young and fair;
Dust hath closed Helen's eye:
I am sick, I must die –
   Lord, have mercy on us!

Strength stoops unto the grave;
Worms feed on Hector brave;
Swords may not fight with fate;
Earth still holds ope her gate;
Come! come! the bells do cry:
I am sick, I must die –
   Lord, have mercy on us!

Wit with his wantonness,
Tasteth death's bitterness;
Hell's executioner
Hath no ears for to hear
What vain art can reply.
I am sick, I must die –
   Lord, have mercy on us!

Haste, therefore, each degree
To welcome destiny!
Heaven is our heritage;
Earth but a player's stage.
Mount we unto the sky!
I am sick, I must die –
   Lord, have mercy on us!

THOMAS NASH

275. *Messages*

What shall I your true-love tell,
  Earth-forsaking maid?
What shall I your true-love tell,
  When life's spectre's laid?

'Tell him that, our side the grave,
  Maid may not conceive
Life should be so sad to have,
  That's so sad to leave!'

What shall I your true-love tell,
  When I come to him?
What shall I your true-love tell –
  Eyes growing dim!

'Tell him this, when you shall part
  From a maiden pined;
That I see him with my heart,
  Now my eyes are blind.'

What shall I your true-love tell?
  Speaking-while is scant.
What shall I your true-love tell,
  Death's white postulant?

'Tell him – love, with speech at strife,
  For last utterance saith:
I, who loved with all my life,
  Love with all my death.'

FRANCIS THOMPSON

276. *Doubts*

When she sleeps, her soul, I know,
Goes a wanderer on the air,
Wings where I may never go,
Leaves her lying, still and fair,
Waiting, empty, laid aside,
Like a dress upon a chair . . .
This I know, and yet I know
Doubts that will not be denied.

For if the soul be not in place,
What has laid trouble in her face?
And, sits there nothing ware and wise
Behind the curtains of her eyes,
What is it, in the self's eclipse,
Shadows, soft and passingly,
About the corners of her lips,
The smile that is essential she?

And if the spirit be not there,
Why is fragrance in the hair?

RUPERT BROOKE

277. *Hark*

Hark! now everything is still,
The screech-owl and the whistler shrill
Call upon our dame aloud,
And bid her quickly don her shroud.

Much you had of land and rent;
Your length in clay's now competent.
A long war disturbed your mind;
Here your perfect peace is signed.
Of what is't fools make such vain keeping? –
Sin their conception, their birth weeping,
Their life a general mist of error,
Their death a hideous storm of terror.
Strew your hair with powders sweet,
Don clean linen, bathe your feet,
And (the foul fiend more to check)
A crucifix let bless your neck:
'Tis now full tide 'tween night and day;
End your groan, and come away.

JOHN WEBSTER

278. *A Lyke-Wake Dirge*

This ae nighte, this ae nighte,
    Every nighte and alle,
Fire and sleet and candle-lighte,
    And Christe receive thy saule.

When thou from hence away art past,
    Every nighte and alle,
To Whinny-muir thou comest at last;
    And Christe receive thy saule.

If ever thou gavest hosen and shoon,
    Every night and alle,
Sit thee down and put them on;
    And Christe receive thy saule.

If hosen and shoon thou ne'er gav'st nane,
　　Every nighte and alle,
The whinnes sall prick thee to the bare bane;
　　And Christe receive thy saule.

From Whinny-muir that thou may'st pass,
　　Every nighte and alle,
To Brig o' Dread thou comest at last,
　　And Christe receive thy saule.

From Brig o' Dread that thou may'st pass,
　　Every nighte and alle,
To Purgatory fire thou com'st at last,
　　And Christe receive thy saule.

If ever thou gavest meat or drink,
　　Every nighte and alle,
The fire sall never make thee shrink;
　　And Christe receive thy saule.

If meat and drink thou ne'er gav'st nane,
　　Every nighte and alle,
The fire will gurn thee to the bare bane,
　　And Christe receive thy saule.

This ae nighte, this ae nighte,
　　Every nighte and alle,
Fire and sleet and candle-lighte,
　　And Christe receive thy saule.

279. *He Is the Lonely Greatness*

He is the lonely greatness of the world –
　　　　(His eyes are dim),
His power it is holds up the Cross
　　　　That holds up Him.

He takes the sorrow of the threefold hour –
        (His eyelids close),
Round Him and round, the wind – His Spirit – where
        It listeth blows.

And so the wounded greatness of the World
        In silence lies –
And death is shattered by the light from out
        Those darkened eyes.

           MADELEINE CARON ROCK

280. *O Sing unto My Roundelay*

O sing unto my roundelay,
  O drop the briny tear with me,
Dance no more at holyday
  Like a running river be!
    My love is dead,
      Gone to his death-bed,
        All under the willow-tree.

Black his cryne[1] as the winter night,
  White his rode[2] as the summer snow,
Red his face as the morning light,
  Cold he lies in the grave below:
    My love is dead,
      Gone to his death-bed,
        All under the willow-tree ...

See, the white moon shines on high;
  Winter is my true-love's shroud,
Whiter than the morning sky,
  Whiter than the evening cloud.
    My love is dead,
      Gone to his death-bed,
        All under the willow-tree ...

      1. Locks   2. Skin

With my hands I'll dent[3] the briars
  Round his holy corse to gre;[4]
Ouph[5] and fairy, light your fires,
  Here my body still shall be.
     My love is dead,
       Gone to his death-bed,
         All under the willow-tree . . .

THOMAS CHATTERTON

281. *Fear No More*

Feare no more the heate o' th' Sun,
Nor the fureous Winters rages,
Thou thy worldly task hast don,
Home art gon, and tane thy wages.
Golden Lads and Girles all must,
As Chimney-Sweepers, come to dust.

Feare no more the frowne o' th' Great,
Thou art past the Tirants stroake,
Care no more to cloath, and eate,
To thee the Reede is as the Oake:
The Scepter, Learning, Physicke must,
All follow this, and come to dust.

Feare no more the Lightning flash,
Nor the all-dreaded Thunder-stone,
Feare not Slander, Censure rash,
Thou hast finished joy and mone.
All Lovers young, all Lovers must,
Consigne to thee, and come to dust . . .

WILLIAM SHAKESPEARE

3. Set   5. Elf
4. Grow

282. *A Land Dirge*

Call for the robin-redbreast and the wren,
Since o'er shady groves they hover,
And with leaves and flowers do cover
The friendless bodies of unburied men.
Call unto his funeral dole
The ant, the field-mouse, and the mole,
To rear him hillocks that shall keep him warm,
And (when gay tombs are robbed) sustain no harm;
But keep the wolf far thence, that's foe to men,
For with his nails he'll dig them up again.

JOHN WEBSTER

283. *The Grave of Love*

I dug, beneath the cypress shade,
    What well might seem an elfin's grave;
And every pledge in earth I laid,
    That erst thy false affection gave.

I pressed them down the sod beneath;
    I placed one mossy stone above;
And twined the rose's fading wreath
    Around the sepulchre of love.

Frail as thy love, the flowers were dead
    Ere yet the evening sun was set:
But years shall see the cypress spread,
    Immutable as my regret.

THOMAS LOVE PEACOCK

284. *The Burial*

All the flowers of the spring
Meet to perfume our burying;
These have but their growing prime,
And man does flourish but his time.
Survey our progress from our birth –
We are set, we grow, we turn to earth,
Courts adieu, and all delights,
All bewitching appetites!
Sweetest breath and clearest eye,
Like perfumes go out and die;
And consequently this is done
As shadows wait upon the sun.
Vain the ambition of kings
Who seek by trophies and dead things
To leave a living name behind,
And weave but nets to catch the wind.

JOHN WEBSTER

285. *On the Tombs in Westminster Abbey*

Mortality, behold and fear!
What a change of flesh is here!
Think how many royal bones
Sleep within these heaps of stones;
Here they lie had realms and lands,
Who now want strength to stir their hands;
Where from their pulpits sealed with dust
They preach: 'In greatness is no trust.'
Here's an acre sown indeed
With the richest royallest seed

That the Earth did e'er suck in
Since the first man died for sin:
Here the bones of birth have cried:
'Though gods they were, as men they died!'
Here are sands, ignoble things,
Dropt from the ruined sides of Kings:
Here's a world of pomp and state
Buried in dust, once dead by fate.

FRANCIS BEAUMONT

286. *A Funerall Song*

(*Lamenting Syr Phillip Sidney*)

Come to me, grief, for ever;
Come to me, tears, day and night;
Come to me, plaint, ah, helpless;
Just grief, heart tears, plaint worthy.

Go from me dread to die now;
Go from me care to live more;
Go from me joys all on earth;
Sidney, O Sidney is dead.

He whom the court adornèd,
He whom the country courtesied,
He who made happy his friends,
He that did good to all men.

Sidney, the hope of land strange,
Sidney, the flower of England,
Sidney, the spirit heroic,
Sidney is dead, O dead.

Dead? no, no, but renownèd,
With the Anointed onèd;[1]
Honour on earth at his feet,
Bliss everlasting his seat.

Come to me, grief, for ever;
Come to me, tears, day and night;
Come to me, plaint, ah, helpless;
Just grief, heart tears, plaint worthy.

287. *On John Donne's Book of Poems*

I see in his last preached and printed Booke,
His Picture in a sheet. In Pauls I looke,
And see his Statue in a sheete of stone,
And sure his body in the grave hath one.
Those sheetes present him dead; these, if you buy,
You have him living to Eternity.

JOHN MARRIOT

288. *O, Lift One Thought*

Stop, Christian passer-by – Stop, child of God,
And read with gentle breast. Beneath this sod
A poet lies, or that which once seemed he.
O, lift one thought in prayer for S.T.C.;
That he who many a year with toil of breath
Found death in life, may here find life in death.
Mercy for praise – to be forgiven for fame
He asked, and hoped, through Christ. Do thou the same!

SAMUEL TAYLOR COLERIDGE

1. Made one

289. *Elegy*

To the Memory of an Unfortunate Lady

... Most souls, 'tis true, but peep out once an age,
Dull, sullen prisoners in the body's cage;
Dim lights of life, that burn a length of years,
Useless, unseen, as lamps in sepulchres;
Like eastern kings, a lazy state they keep,
And close confined to their own palace, sleep ...
Yet shall thy grave with rising flowers be dressed,
And the green turf lie lightly on thy breast:
There shall the morn her earliest tears bestow,
There the first roses of the year shall blow;
While angels with their silver wings o'ershade
The ground, now sacred by thy relics made.

So peaceful rests, without a stone, a name,
What once had beauty, titles, wealth and fame.
How loved, how honoured once, avails thee not
To whom related, or by whom begot;
A heap of dust alone remains of thee:
'Tis all thou art, and all the proud shall be!

Poets themselves must fall, like those they sung,
Deaf the praised ear, and mute the tuneful tongue.
Ev'n he whose soul now melts in mournful lays
Shall shortly want the generous tear he pays;
Then from his closing eyes thy form shall part,
And the last pang shall tear thee from his heart:
Life's idle business at one gasp be o'er,
The Muse forgot, and thou beloved no more!

ALEXANDER POPE

290. *Upon a Child That Died*

Here she lies, a pretty bud,
Lately made of flesh and blood:
Who, as soone, fell fast asleep,
As her little eyes did peep.
Give her strewings; but not stir
The earth, that lightly covers her.

ROBERT HERRICK

291. *The Turnstile*

Ah! sad wer we as we did peäce
The wold church road, wi' downcast feäce,
The while the bells, that mwoaned so deep
Above our child a-left asleep,
Wer now a-zingen all alive
Wi' tother bells to meäke the vive.
But up at woone peäce we come by,
'Twer hard to keep woone's two eyes dry;
On Steän-cliff road, 'ithin the drong,
Up where, as vo'k do pass along,
The turnèn stile, a-païnted white,
Do sheen by day an' show by night.

Vor always there, as we did goo
To church, thik stile did let us drough,
Wi' spreadén eärms that wheeled to guide
Us each in turn to tother zide.
An' vu'st ov all the traïn he took
My wife, wi' winsome gaït an' look;
An' then zent on my little maïd,
A-skippen onward, over-jäy'd
To reach ageän the pleäce o' pride,
Her comely mother's left han' zide.

An' then, a-wheelen roun', he took
On me, 'ithin his third white nook.
An' in the fourth, a-sheäken wild,
He zent us on our giddy child.
But eesterday he guided slow
My downcast Jenny, vull o' woe,
An' then my little maïd in black,
A-walken softly on her track;
An' after he'd a-turned ageän,
To let me goo along the leäne,
He had noo little bwoy to vill
His last white eärms, an' they stood still.

WILLIAM BARNES

292. *The Exequy*

... Sleep on, my Love, in thy cold bed
Never to be disquieted!
My last good-night! Thou wilt not wake
Till I thy fate shall overtake:
Till age, or grief, or sickness must
Marry my body to that dust
It so much loves; and fill the room
My heart keeps empty in that tomb.
Stay for me there: I will not fail
To meet thee in that hollow vale.
And think not much of my delay:
I am already on the way,
And follow thee with all the speed
Desire can make, or sorrows breed.
Each minute is a short degree
And every hour a step towards thee ...

HENRY KING

293. *I Found Her Out There*

I found her out there
On a slope few see,
That falls westwardly
To the salt-edged air,
Where the ocean breaks
On the purple strand,
And the hurricane shakes
The solid land.

I brought her here,
And have laid her to rest
In a noiseless nest
No sea beats near.
She will never be stirred
In her loamy cell
By the waves long heard
And loved so well.

So she does not sleep
By those haunted heights
The Atlantic smites
And the blind gales sweep,
Whence she often would gaze
At Dundagel's famed head,
While the dipping blaze
Dyed her face fire-red;

And would sigh at the tale
Of sunk Lyonnesse,
As a wind-tugged tress
Flapped her cheek like a flail;
Or listen at whiles
With a thought-bound brow
To the murmuring miles
She is far from now.

Yet her shade, maybe,
Will creep underground
Till it catch the sound
Of that western sea
As it swells and sobs
Where she once domiciled,
And joys in its throbs
With the heart of a child.

THOMAS HARDY

294. *I Never Shall Love the Snow Again*

I never shall love the snow again
  Since Maurice died:
With corniced drift it blocked the lane
And sheeted in a desolate plain
  The country side.

The trees with silvery rime bedight
  Their branches bare.
By day no sun appeared; by night
The hidden moon shed thievish light
  In the misty air.

We fed the birds that flew around
  In flocks to be fed:
No shelter in holly or brake they found.
The speckled thrush on the frozen ground
  Lay frozen and dead.

We skated on stream and pond; we cut
  The crinching snow
To Doric temple or Arctic hut;
We laughed and sang at nightfall, shut
  By the fireside glow.

Yet grudged we our keen delights before
     Maurice should come.
We said, In-door or out-of-door
We shall love life for a month or more,
     When he is home.

They brought him home; 'twas two days late
     For Christmas day:
Wrapped in white, in solemn state,
A flower in his hand, all still and straight
     Our Maurice lay.

And two days ere the year outgave
     We laid him low.
The best of us truly were not brave,
When we laid Maurice down in his grave
     Under the snow.

ROBERT BRIDGES

295. *The Comforters*

When I crept over the hill, broken with tears,
   When I crouched down in the grass, dumb in despair,
I heard the soft croon of the wind bend to my ears,
   I felt the light kiss of the wind touching my hair.

When I stood lone on the height my sorrow did speak,
   As I went down the hill, I cried and I cried,
The soft little hands of the rain stroking my cheek,
   The kind little feet of the rain ran by my side.

When I went to thy grave, broken with tears,
   When I crouched down in the grass, dumb in despair,
I heard the sweet croon of the wind soft in my ears,
   I felt the kind lips of the wind touching my hair.

When I stood lone by thy cross, sorrow did speak,
    When I went down the long hill, I cried and I cried,
The soft little hands of the rain stroked my pale cheek,
    The kind little feet of the rain ran by my side.

DORA SIGERSON SHORTER

296. *The Childless Father*

'Up, Timothy, up with your staff and away!
Not a soul in the village this morning will stay;
The hare has just started from Hamilton's grounds,
And Skiddaw is glad with the cry of the hounds.'

– Of coats and of jackets grey, scarlet, and green,
On the slopes of the pastures all colours were seen;
With their comely blue aprons, and caps white as snow,
The girls on the hills made a holiday show.

Fresh sprigs of green boxwood, not six months before,
Filled the funeral basin at Timothy's door;
A coffin through Timothy's threshold had passed;
One child did it bear, and that child was his last.

Now fast up the dell came the noise and the fray,
The horse and the horn, and the 'hark! hark away!'
Old Timothy took up his staff, and he shut,
With a leisurely motion, the door of his hut.

Perhaps to himself at that moment he said,
'The key I must take, for my Helen is dead.'
But of this in my ears not a word did he speak,
And he went to the chase with a tear on his cheek.

WILLIAM WORDSWORTH

297. *Lydia Is Gone This Many a Year*

Lydia is gone this many a year,
   Yet when the lilacs stir,
In the old gardens far or near,
   This house is full of her.

They climb the twisted chamber stair;
   Her picture haunts the room;
On the carved shelf beneath it there,
   They heap the purple bloom.

A ghost so long has Lydia been,
   Her cloak upon the wall,
Broidered, and gilt, and faded green,
   Seems not her cloak at all.

The book, the box on the mantle laid,
   The shells in a pale row,
Are those of some dim little maid,
   A thousand years ago.

And yet the house is full of her,
   She goes and comes again;
And longings thrill, and memories stir,
   Like lilacs in the rain.

Out in their yards the neighbours walk,
   Among the blossoms tall;
Of Anne, of Phyllis do they talk,
   Of Lydia not at all.

LIZETTE WOODWORTH REESE

298. *Remembrance*

Cold in the earth – and the deep snow piled above thee,
　Far, far removed, cold in the dreary grave!
Have I forgot, my only Love, to love thee,
　Severed at last by Time's all-severing wave?

Now – when alone – do my thoughts no longer hover
　Over the mountains, on that northern shore,
Resting their wings where heath and fern-leaves cover
　Thy noble heart for ever, ever more?

Cold in the earth – and fifteen wild Decembers,
　From those brown hills, have melted into spring:
Faithful, indeed, is the spirit that remembers
　After such years of change and suffering!

Sweet Love of youth, forgive, if I forget thee,
　While the world's tide is bearing me along;
Other desires and other hopes beset me,
　Hopes which obscure, but cannot do thee wrong!

No later light has lightened up my heaven,
　No second morn has ever shone for me;
All my life's bliss from thy dear life was given,
　All my life's bliss is in the grave with thee.

But, when the days of golden dreams had perished,
　And even Despair was powerless to destroy;
Then did I learn how existence could be cherished,
　Strengthened, and fed, without the aid of joy.

Then did I check the tears of useless passion –
　Weaned my young soul from yearning after thine;
Sternly denied its burning wish to hasten
　Down to that tomb already more than mine.

And, even yet, I dare not let it languish,
　　Dare not indulge in memory's rapturous pain;
Once drinking deep of that divinest anguish,
　　How could I seek the empty world again?

EMILY BRONTË

299. Song

When I am dead, my dearest,
　　Sing no sad songs for me;
Plant thou no roses at my head,
　　Nor shady cypress-tree:
Be the green grass above me
　　With showers and dewdrops wet;
And if thou wilt, remember,
　　And if thou wilt, forget.

I shall not see the shadows,
　　I shall not feel the rain;
I shall not hear the nightingale
　　Sing on, as if in pain:
And dreaming through the twilight
　　That doth not rise nor set,
Haply I may remember
　　And haply may forget.

CHRISTINA ROSSETTI

300. Where Shall the Lover Rest

Where shall the lover rest
　　Whom the fates sever
From his true maiden's breast
　　Parted for ever?

Where, through groves deep and high
   Sounds the far billow,
Where early violets die
   Under the willow.
     Eleu loro
   Soft shall be his pillow.

There through the summer day
   Cool streams are laving:
There, while the tempests sway,
   Scarce are boughs waving;
There thy rest shalt thou take,
   Parted for ever,
Never again to wake
   Never, O never!
     Eleu loro
   Never, O never!

SIR WALTER SCOTT

301. *Remember*

Remember me when I am gone away,
   Gone far away into the silent land;
   When you can no more hold me by the hand,
Nor I half turn to go yet turning stay.
Remember me when no more day by day
   You tell me of our future that you planned:
   Only remember me; you understand
It will be late to counsel then or pray.

Yet if you should forget me for a while
   And afterwards remember, do not grieve:
   For if the darkness and corruption leave
A vestige of the thoughts that once I had,

Better by far you should forget and smile
Than that you should remember and be sad.

CHRISTINA ROSSETTI

302. *Readen ov a Head-stwone*

As I wer readen ov a stwone,
In Grenly church-yard, all alwone,
A little maïd ran up, wi' pride
To zee me there; an' pushed azide
A bunch o' bennets, that did hide
   A verse her father, as she zaïd,
   Put up above her mother's head
      To tell how much he loved her.

The verse wer short, but very good,
I stood an' larn'd en where I stood:
'Mid[1] God, dear Meäry, gi'e me greäce
'To vind, lik' thee, a better pleäce,
'Where I, oonce mwore, mid zee thy feäce;
   'An' bring thy children up, to know
   'His word, that they mid come an' show
      'Thy soul how much I loved thee.'

'Where's father, then,' I zaid, 'my child?'
'Dead, too,' she answered wi' a smile;
'An I an' brother Jem do bide
'At Betty White's, o'tother zide
   'O' road.' 'Mid He, my chile,' I cried,
   'That's father to the fatherless,
   'Become thy father now, an' bless
      'An' keep, an' leäd, an' love thee.'

1. May

– Though she've a-lost, I thought, so much,
Still He don't let the thoughts o't touch
Her litsome heart, by day or night;
An' zoo, if we could teäke it right,
Do show He'll meäke his burdens light
    To weaker souls; an' that his smile,
      Is sweet upon a harmless chile,
        When they be dead that loved it.

WILLIAM BARNES

303. *Golden Slumbers*

Golden slumbers kiss your eyes,
Smiles awake you when you rise.
Sleep, pretty wantons, do not cry,
And I will sing a lullaby.
Rock them, rock them, lullaby.

Care is heavy, therefore sleep you;
You are care, and care must keep you.
Sleep, pretty wantons, do not cry,
And I will sing a lullaby:
Rock them, rock them, lullaby.

THOMAS DEKKER

304. *Mater Dolorosa*

    I'd a dream to-night
      As I fell asleep,
    O! the touching sight
      Makes me still to weep:

Of my little lad,
Gone to leave me sad,
Ay, the child I had,
   But was not to keep.

As in heaven high,
   I my child did seek,
There in train came by
   Children fair and meek,
Each in lily white,
With a lamp alight;
Each was clear to sight,
   But they did not speak.

Then, a little sad,
   Came my child in turn,
But the lamp he had
   O it did not burn!
He, to clear my doubt,
Said, half-turned about,
'Your tears put it out;
   Mother, never mourn.'

WILLIAM BARNES

305. *Weep You No More*

Weep you no more, sad fountains!
   What need you flow so fast?
Look how the snowy mountains
   Heaven's sun doth gently waste!
But my sun's heavenly eyes
   View not your weeping,
   That now lies sleeping
Softly, now softly lies
         Sleeping.

Sleep is a reconciling,
   A rest that peace begets:
Doth not the sun rise smiling
   When fair at even he sets?
Rest you then, rest, sad eyes!
   Melt not in weeping,
    While she lies sleeping
Softly, now softly lies
           Sleeping.

306. *Faery Song*

Shed no tear – O shed no tear!
The flower will bloom another year.
Weep no more – O weep no more!
Young buds sleep in the root's white core.
Dry your eyes – O dry your eyes!
For I was taught in Paradise
To ease my breast of melodies –
           Shed no tear.

Overhead – look overhead
'Mong the blossoms white and red, –
Look up, look up – I flutter now
On this flush pomegranate bough –
See me – 'tis this silvery bill
Ever cures the good man's ill –
Shed no tear – O shed no tear!
The flower will bloom another year.
Adieu – Adieu – I fly, adieu,
I vanish in the heaven's blue –
           Adieu, Adieu!

JOHN KEATS

307. *The World of Light*

They are all gone into the world of light!
   And I alone sit lingering here;
Their very memory is fair and bright,
      And my sad thoughts doth clear.

It glows and glitters in my cloudy breast
   Like stars upon some gloomy grove,
Or those faint beams in which this hill is drest
      After the Sun's remove.

I see them walking in an Air of glory,
   Whose light doth trample on my days;
My days, which are at best but dull and hoary,
      Mere glimmering and decays.

O holy hope! and high humility,
   High as the Heavens above!
These are your walks, and you have showed them me,
      To kindle my cold love.

Dear, beauteous Death! the Jewel of the Just!
   Shining nowhere but in the dark;
What mysteries do lie beyond thy dust,
      Could man outlook that mark!

He that hath found some fledge bird's nest may know
   At first sight if the bird be flown;
But what fair Well or Grove he sings in now,
      That is to him unknown.

And yet, as Angels in some brighter dreams
   Call to the soul, when man doth sleep,
So some strange thoughts transcend our wonted themes,
      And into glory peep . . .

HENRY VAUGHAN

308. *Silent Is the House*

Silent is the house: all are laid asleep:
One alone looks out o'er the snow-wreaths deep,
Watching every cloud, dreading every breeze
That whirls the wildering drift, and bends the groaning trees.

Cheerful is the hearth, soft the matted floor;
Not one shivering gust creeps through pane or door;
The little lamp burns straight, its rays shoot strong and far:
I trim it well, to be the wanderer's guiding-star.

Frown, my haughty sire; chide, my angry dame;
Set your slaves to spy; threaten me with shame!
But neither sire, nor dame, nor prying serf shall know,
What angel nightly tracks that waste of frozen snow.

What I love shall come like visitant of air,
Safe in secret power from lurking human snare;
What loves me, no word of mine shall e'er betray,
Though for faith unstained my life must forfeit pay.

Burn, then, little lamp; glimmer straight and clear –
Hush! a rustling wing stirs, methinks, the air:
He for whom I wait, thus ever comes to me;
Strange Power! I trust thy might; trust thou my constancy.

EMILY BRONTË

309. *The Mistress of Vision*

... Secret was the garden;
    Set i' the pathless awe
    Where no star its breath can draw.
    Life, that is its warden,
Sits behind the fosse of death. Mine eyes saw not, and I saw.

It was a mazeful wonder;
Thrice three times it was enwalled
With an emerald –
Sealèd so asunder.
All its birds in middle air hung a-dream, their music thralled.

The Lady of fair weeping,
At the garden's core,
Sang a song of sweet and sore
And the after-sleeping;
In the land of Luthany, and the tracts of Elenore.

With sweet-pangèd singing,
Sang she through a dream-night's day;
That the bowers might stay,
Birds bate their winging,
Nor the wall of emerald float in wreathèd haze away . . .

Her song said that no springing
Paradise but evermore
Hangeth on a singing
That has chords of weeping,
And that sings the after-sleeping
To souls which wake too sore.
'But woe the singer, woe!' she said; 'beyond the dead his singing-
lore,

All its art of sweet and sore
He learns, in Elenore!'
Where is the land of Luthany,
Where is the tract of Elenore?
I am bound therefor.

'Pierce thy heart to find the key;
With thee take
Only what none else would keep;
Learn to dream when thou dost wake,
Learn to wake when thou dost sleep.

Learn to water joy with tears,
Learn from fears to vanquish fears;
To hope, for thou dar'st not despair,
Exult, for that thou dar'st not grieve;
Plough thou the rock until it bear;
Know, for thou else couldst not believe;
Lose, that the lost thou may'st receive;
Die, for none other way canst live.
When earth and heaven lay down their veil,
And that apocalypse turns thee pale;
When thy seeing blindeth thee
To what thy fellow-mortals see;
When their sight to thee is sightless;
Their living, death; their light, most lightless;
Search no more —
Pass the gates of Luthany, tread the region Elenore.'

Where is the land of Luthany,
And where the region Elenore?
I do faint therefor.
'When to the new eyes of thee
All things by immortal power,
Near or far,
Hiddenly
To each other linkèd are,
That thou canst not stir a flower
Without troubling of a star;
When thy song is shield and mirror
To the fair snake-curlèd Pain,
Where thou dar'st affront her terror
That on her thou may'st attain
Perséan conquest; seek no more,
O seek no more!
Pass the gates of Luthany, tread the region Elenore.'

So sang she, so wept she,
Through a dream-night's day;

And with her magic singing kept she –
Mystical in music –
The garden of enchanting
In visionary May;
Songless from my spirits' haunting,
Thrice-threefold walled with emerald from our mortal mornings
grey . . .

FRANCIS THOMPSON

FAR

310. *Tom O' Bedlam*

The moon's my constant mistress,
   And the lovely owl my marrow;
     The flaming drake,
     And the night-crow, make
Me music to my sorrow.

I know more than Apollo;
   For oft, when he lies sleeping,
     I behold the stars
     At mortal wars,
And the rounded welkin weeping.

The moon embraces her shepherd,
   And the Queen of Love her warrior;
     While the first does horn
     The stars of the morn,
And the next the heavenly farrier.

With a heart of furious fancies,
   Whereof I am commander:
     With a burning spear,
     And a horse of air,
To the wilderness I wander;

With a Knight of ghosts and shadows,
   I summoned am to Tourney:
     Ten leagues beyond
     The wide world's end;
Methinks it is no journey.

311. *The Night-Piece*

Her Eyes the Glow-worme lend thee,
The Shooting Starres attend thee:
    And the Elves also,
    Whose little eyes glow,
Like the sparks of fire, befriend thee.

No *will-o'-th'-Wispe* mis-light thee;
Nor Snake, or Slow-worme bite thee:
    But on, on thy way
    Not making a stay,
Since Ghost ther's none to affright thee.

Let not the darke thee cumber;
What though the Moon does slumber?
    The Starres of the night
    Will lend thee their light,
Like Tapers cleare without number ...

ROBERT HERRICK

312. *My Plaid Awa'*

'My plaid awa', my plaid awa',
And ore the hill and far awa',
And far awa' to Norrowa,
My plaid shall not be blown awa'.'

The elphin knight sits on yon hill,
  Ba, ba, lilli ba,
He blowes it east, he blowes it west,
He blowes it where he lyketh best ...
'My plaid awa', my plaid awa',
And ore the hill and far awa'.'

313. *Buckee Bene*

Buckee, Buckee, biddy Bene,
Is the way now fair and clean?
Is the goosey gone to nest?
And the foxy gone to rest?
Shall I come away?

314. *What's in There?*

Faht's in there?
Gold and money.
Fahr's[1] my share o't?
The moosie ran awa' wi't
Fahr's the moosie?
In her hoosie.
Fahr's her hoosie?
In the wood.
Fahr's the wood?
The fire burnt it.
Fahr's the fire?
The water quenched it.
Fahr's the water?
The broon bull drank it.
Fahr's the broon bull?
Back a Burnie's hill.
Fahr's Burnie's hill?
A' claid wi' snaw.
Fahr's the snaw?
The sun meltit it.
Fahr's the sun?
Heigh, heigh up i' the air!

1. Where's

315. *The Wee Wee Man*

As I was wa'king all alone,
    Between a water and a wa',
And there I spy'd a Wee Wee Man,
    And he was the least that ere I saw.

His legs were scarce a shathmont's length
    And thick and timber was his thigh;
Between his brows there was a span,
    And between his shoulders there was three.

He took up a meikle stane,
    And he flang't as far as I could see;
Though I had been a Wallace wight,
    I couldna' liften't to my knee.

'O Wee Wee Man, but thou be strang!
    O tell me where thy dwelling be?'
'My dwelling's down at yon bonny bower;
    O will you go with me and see?'

On we lap, and awa' we rade,
    Till we came to yon bonny green;
We lighted down for to bait our horse,
    And out there came a lady fine.

Four and twenty at her back,
    And they were a' clad out in green;
Though the King of Scotland had been there,
    The warst o' them might hae been his queen.

On we lap, and awa' we rade,
    Till we came to yon bonny ha',
Whare the roof was o' the beaten gould,
    And the floor was o' the cristal a'.

When we came to the stair-foot,
   Ladies were dancing, jimp and sma',
But in the twinkling of an eye,
   My Wee Wee Man was clean awa'.

316. *I Saw a Peacock*

I saw a peacock with a fiery tail
I saw a blazing comet drop down hail
I saw a cloud wrappèd with ivy round
I saw an oak creep on along the ground
I saw a pismire swallow up a whale
I saw the sea brim full of ale
I saw a Venice glass five fathom deep
I saw a well full of men's tears that weep
I saw red eyes all of a flaming fire
I saw a house bigger than the moon and higher
I saw the sun at twelve o'clock at night
I saw the Man that saw this wondrous sight.

317. *Giraffe and Tree*

Upon a dark ball spun in Time
   Stands a Giraffe beside a Tree:
Of what immortal stuff can that
   The fading picture be?

So, thought I, standing beside my love
   Whose hair, a small black flag,
Broke on the universal air
   With proud and lovely brag:

It waved among the silent hills,
  A wind of shining ebony
In Time's bright glass, where mirrored clear
  Stood the Giraffe beside a Tree.

WALTER J. TURNER

318. *The Water Lady*

Alas, the moon should ever beam
To show what man should never see!
I saw a maiden on a stream,
  And fair was she!

I stayed awhile, to see her throw
Her tresses back, that all beset
The fair horizon of her brow
  With clouds of jet.

I stayed a little while to view
Her cheek, that wore in place of red
The bloom of water, tender blue,
  Daintily spread.

I stayed to watch, a little space,
Her parted lips if she would sing;
The waters closed above her face
  With many a ring.

And still I stayed a little more,
Alas! she never comes again;
I throw my flowers from the shore,
  And watch in vain.

I know my life will fade away,
I know that I must vainly pine,
For I am made of mortal clay,
But she's divine!

THOMAS HOOD

319. *The Song of Wandering Aengus*

I went out to the hazel wood,
Because a fire was in my head,
And cut and peeled a hazel wand,
And hooked a berry to a thread;
And when white moths were on the wing,
And moth-like stars were flickering out,
I dropped the berry in a stream
And caught a little silver trout.

When I had laid it on the floor
I went to blow the fire a-flame,
But something rustled on the floor,
And someone called me by my name:
It had become a glimmering girl
With apple blossom in her hair
Who called me by my name and ran
And faded through the brightening air.

Though I am old with wandering
Through hollow lands and hilly lands,
I will find out where she has gone,
And kiss her lips and take her hands;
And walk among long dappled grass,
And pluck till time and times are done
The silver apples of the moon,
The golden apples of the sun.

WILLIAM BUTLER YEATS

320. *The Way Through the Woods*

They shut the road through the woods
Seventy years ago.
Weather and rain have undone it again,
And now you would never know
There was once a road through the woods
Before they planted the trees.
It is underneath the coppice and heath,
And the thin anemones.
Only the keeper sees
That, where the ring-dove broods,
And the badgers roll at ease,
There was once a road through the woods.

Yet, if you enter the woods
Of a summer evening late,
When the night-air cools on the trout-ringed pools
Where the otter whistles his mate
(They fear not men in the woods,
Because they see so few),
You will hear the beat of a horse's feet,
And the swish of a skirt in the dew,
Steadily cantering through
The misty solitudes,
As though they perfectly knew
The old lost road through the woods . . .
But there is no road through the woods!

RUDYARD KIPLING

321. *The Fallow Deer at the Lonely House*

One without looks in to-night
   Through the curtain-chink
From the sheet of glistening white;
One without looks in to-night
    As we sit and think
    By the fender-brink.

We do not discern those eyes
   Watching in the snow;
Lit by lamps of rosy dyes
We do not discern those eyes
    Wondering, aglow,
    Fourfooted, tiptoe.

THOMAS HARDY

322. *Deer*

Shy in their herding dwell the fallow deer.
They are spirits of wild sense. Nobody near
Comes upon their pastures. There a life they live,
Of sufficient beauty, phantom, fugitive,
Treading as in jungles free leopards do,
Printless as eyelight, instant as dew.
The great kine are patient, and home-coming sheep
Know our bidding. The fallow deer keep
Delicate and far their counsels wild,
Never to be folded reconciled
To the spoiling hand as the poor flocks are;
Lightfoot, and swift, and unfamiliar,
These you may not hinder, unconfined
Beautiful flocks of the mind.

JOHN DRINKWATER

323. *The Two Swans*

(A FAIRY TALE)

Immortal Imogen, crowned queen above
The lilies of thy sex, vouchsafe to hear
A fairy dream in honour of true love –
True above ills, and frailty, and all fear –
Perchance a shadow of his own career
Whose youth was darkly prisoned and long twined
By serpent-sorrow, till white Love drew near,
And sweetly sang him free, and round his mind
A bright horizon threw, wherein no grief may wind.

I saw a tower builded on a lake,
Mocked by its inverse shadow, dark and deep –
That seemed a still intenser night to make,
Wherein the quiet waters sunk to sleep, –
And, whatsoe'er was prisoned in that keep,
A monstrous Snake was warden: round and round
In sable ringlets I beheld him creep,
Blackest amid black shadows, to the ground,
Whilst his enormous head the topmost turret crowned:

From whence he shot fierce light against the stars,
Making the pale moon paler with affright;
And with his ruby eye out-threatened Mars –
That blazed in the mid-heavens, hot and bright –
Nor slept, nor winked, but with a steadfast spite
Watched their wan looks and tremblings in the skies;
And that he might not slumber in the night,
The curtain-lids were plucked from his large eyes,
So he might never drowse, but watch his secret prize.

Prince or princess in dismal durance pent,
Victims of old Enchantment's love or hate,

Their lives must all in painful sighs be spent,
Watching the lonely waters soon and late,
And clouds that pass and leave them to their fate,
Or company their grief with heavy tears:
Meanwhile that Hope can spy no golden gate
For sweet escapement, but in darksome fears
They weep and pine away as if immortal years.

No gentle bird with gold upon its wing
Will perch upon the grate – the gentle bird
Is safe in leafy dell, and will not bring
Freedom's sweet keynote and commission-word
Learned of a fairy's lips, for pity stirred –
Lest while he trembling sings, untimely guest!
Watched by that cruel Snake and darkly heard,
He leave a widow on her lonely nest,
To press in silent grief the darlings of her breast.

No gallant knight, adventurous, in his bark,
Will seek the fruitful perils of the place,
To rouse with dipping oar the waters dark
That bear that serpent-image on their face.
And Love, brave Love, though he attempt the base,
Nerved to his loyal death, he may not win
His captive lady from the strict embrace
Of that foul Serpent, clasping her within
His sable folds – like Eve enthralled by the old Sin.

But there is none – no knight in panoply,
Nor Love, intrenched in his strong steely coat:
No little speck – no sail – no helper nigh,
No sign – no whispering – no plash of boat:
The distant shores show dimly and remote,
Made of a deeper mist, – serene and grey, –
And slow and mute the cloudy shadows float
Over the gloomy wave, and pass away,
Chased by the silver beams that on their marges play.

And bright and silvery the willows sleep
Over the shady verge – no mad winds tease
Their hoary heads; but quietly they weep
Their sprinkling leaves – half fountains and half trees;
There lilies be – and fairer than all these,
A solitary Swan her breast of snow
Launches against the wave that seems to freeze
Into a chaste reflection, still below,
Twin-shadow of herself wherever she may go.

And forth she paddles in the very noon
Of solemn midnight, like an elfin thing
Charmed into being by the argent moon –
Whose silver light for love of her fair wing
Goes with her in the shade, still worshipping
Her dainty plumage: all around her grew
A radiant circlet, like a fairy ring;
And all behind, a tiny little clue
Of light, to guide her back across the waters blue.

And sure she is no meaner than a fay
Redeemed from sleepy death, for beauty's sake,
By old ordainment: silent as she lay,
Touched by a moonlight wand I saw her wake,
And cut her leafy slough and so forsake
The verdant prison of her lily peers,
That slept amidst the stars upon the lake –
A breathing shape – restored to human fears,
And new-born love and grief – self-conscious of her tears.

And now she clasps her wings around her heart,
And near that lonely isle begins to glide,
Pale as her fears, and oft-times with a start
Turns her impatient head from side to side
In universal terrors – all too wide
To watch; and often to that marble keep
Upturns her pearly eyes, as if she spied

Some foe, and crouches in the shadows steep
That in the gloomy wave go diving fathoms deep.

And well she may, to spy that fearful thing
All down the dusky walls in circlets wound;
Alas! for what rare prize, with many a ring
Girding the marble casket round and round?
His folded tail, lost in the gloom profound,
Terribly darkeneth the rocky base;
But on the top his monstrous head is crowned
With prickly spears, and on his doubtful face
Gleam his unwearied eyes, red watchers of the place.

Alas! of the hot fires that nightly fall,
No one will scorch him in those orbs of spite,
So he may never see beneath the wall
That timid little creature, all too bright,
That stretches her fair neck, slender and white,
Invoking the pale moon, and vainly tries
Her throbbing throat, as if to charm the night
With song – but, hush – it perishes in sighs,
And there will be no dirge sad-swelling, though she dies!

She droops – she sinks – she leans upon the lake,
Fainting again into a lifeless flower;
But soon the chilly springs anoint and wake
Her spirit from its death, and with new power
She sheds her stifled sorrows in a shower
Of tender song, timed to her falling tears –
That wins the shady summit of that tower,
And, trembling all the sweeter for its fears,
Fills with imploring moan that cruel monster's ears.

And, lo! the scaly beast is all deprest,
Subdued like Argus by the might of sound –
What time Apollo his sweet lute addrest
To magic converse with the air, and bound
The many monster eyes, all slumber-drowned:

So on the turret-top that watchful Snake
Pillows his giant head, and lists profound,
As if his wrathful spite would never wake,
Charmed into sudden sleep for Love and Beauty's sake!

His prickly crest lies prone upon his crown,
And thirsty lip from lip disparted flies,
To drink that dainty flood of music down –
His scaly throat is big with pent-up sighs –
And whilst his hollow ear entrancèd lies,
His looks for envy of the charmèd sense
Are fain to listen, till his steadfast eyes,
Stung into pain by their own impotence,
Distil enormous tears into the lake immense.

Oh, tuneful Swan! oh, melancholy bird!
Sweet was that midnight miracle of song,
Rich with ripe sorrow, needful of no word
To tell of pain, and love, and love's deep wrong –
Hinting a piteous tale – perchance how long
Thy unknown tears were mingled with the lake,
What time disguised thy leafy mates among –
And no eye knew what human love and ache
Dwelt in those dewy leaves, and heart so nigh to break.

Therefore no poet will ungently touch
The water-lily, on whose eyelids dew
Trembles like tears; but ever hold it such
As human pain may wander through and through,
Turning the pale leaf paler in its hue –
Wherein life dwells, transfigured, not entombed,
By magic spells. Alas! who ever knew
Sorrow in all its shades, leafy and plumed,
Or in gross husks of brutes eternally inhumed?

And now the wingèd song has scaled the height
Of that dark dwelling, builded for despair,
And soon a little casement flashing bright
Widens self-opened into the cool air –

That music like a bird may enter there
And soothe the captive in his stony cage;
For there is nought of grief, or painful care,
But plaintive song may happily engage
From sense of its own ill, and tenderly assuage.

And forth into the light, small and remote,
A creature, like the fair son of a king,
Draws to the lattice in his jewelled coat
Against the silver moonlight glistening,
And leans upon his white hand listening
To that sweet music that with tenderer tone
Salutes him, wondering what kindly thing
Is come to soothe him with so tuneful moan,
Singing beneath the walls as if for him alone!

And while he listens, the mysterious song,
Woven with timid particles of speech,
Twines into passionate words that grieve along
The melancholy notes, and softly teach
The secrets of true love, – that trembling reach
His earnest ear, and through the shadows dun
He missions like replies and each to each
Their silver voices mingle into one,
Like blended streams that make one music as they run.

'Ah, Love! my hope is swooning in my heart, – '
'Ay, sweet! my cage is strong and hung full high – '
'Alas! our lips are held so far apart,
Thy words come faint, – they have so far to fly! – '
'If I may only shun that serpent-eye! – '
'Ah me! that serpent-eye doth never sleep; – '
'Then nearer thee, Love's martyr, I will die! – '
'Alas, alas! that word has made me weep!
For pity's sake remain safe in thy marble keep!'

'My marble keep! it is my marble tomb – '
'Nay, sweet! but thou hast there thy living breath – '
'Aye to expend in sighs for this hard doom; – '
'But I will come to thee and sing beneath,
And nightly so beguile this serpent wreath; – '
'Nay, I will find a path from these despairs.'
'Ah! needs then thou must tread the back of death,
Making his stony ribs thy stony stairs. –
Behold his ruby eye, how fearfully it glares!'

Full sudden at these words, the princely youth
Leaps on the scaly back that slumbers, still
Unconscious of his foot, yet not for ruth,
But numbed to dulness by the fairy skill
Of that sweet music (all more wild and shrill
For intense fear) that charmed him as he lay –
Meanwhile the lover nerves his desperate will,
Held some short throbs by natural dismay,
Then, down the serpent-tracks begins his darksome way.

Now dimly seen – now toiling out of sight,
Eclipsed and covered by the envious wall;
Now fair and spangled in the sudden light,
And clinging with wide arms for fear of fall:
Now dark and sheltered by a kindly pall
Of dusky shadow from his wakeful foe;
Slowly he winds adown – dimly and small,
Watched by the gentle Swan that sings below,
Her hope increasing, still, the larger he doth grow.

But nine times nine the Serpent folds embrace
The marble walls about – which he must tread
Before his anxious foot may touch the base:
Long is the dreary path, and must be sped!
But Love, that holds the mastery of dread,
Braces his spirit, and with constant toil
He wins his way, and now, with arms outspread,

Impatient plunges from the last long coil:
So may all gentle Love ungentle Malice foil!

The song is hushed, the charm is all complete,
And two fair Swans are swimming on the lake:
But scarce their tender bills have time to meet,
When fiercely drops adown that cruel Snake –
His steely scales a fearful rustling make,
Like autumn leaves that tremble and foretell
The sable storm; – the plumy lovers quake –
And feel the troubled waters pant and swell,
Heaved by the giant bulk of their pursuer fell.

His jaws, wide yawning like the gates of Death,
His horrible pursuit – his red eyes glare
The waters into blood – his eager breath
Grows hot upon their plumes: now, minstrel fair!
She drops her ring into the waves, and there
It widens all around, a fairy ring
Wrought of the silver light – the fearful pair
Swim in the very midst, and pant and cling
The closer for their fears, and tremble wing to wing.

Bending their course over the pale grey lake,
Against the pallid East, wherein light played
In tender flushes, still the baffled Snake
Circled them round continually, and bayed
Hoarsely and loud, forbidden to invade
The sanctuary ring: his sable mail
Rolled darkly through the flood, and writhed and made
A shining track over the waters pale,
Lashed into boiling foam by his enormous tail,

And so they sailed into the distance dim,
Into the very distance – small and white,
Like snowy blossoms of the spring that swim
Over the brooklets – followed by the spite

Of that huge Serpent, that with wild affright
Worried them on their course, and sore annoy,
Till on the grassy marge I saw them 'light,
And change, anon, a gentle girl and boy,
Locked in embrace of sweet unutterable joy!

Then came the Morn, and with her pearly showers
Wept on them, like a mother, in whose eyes
Tears are no grief; and from his rosy bowers
The Oriental sun began to rise,
Chasing the darksome shadows from the skies;
Wherewith that sable Serpent far away
Fled, like a part of night – delicious sighs
From waking blossoms purified the day,
And little birds were singing sweetly from each spray.

THOMAS HOOD

324. *The Earl of Mar's Daughter*

It was intill a pleasant time,
    Upon a simmer's day,
The noble Earl of Mar's daughter
    Went forth to sport and play.

As thus she did amuse hersell,
    Below a green aik tree,
There she saw a sprightly doo[1]
    Set on a tower saw hie,

'O Cow-me-doo, my love sae true,
    If ye'll come down to me,
Ye'se hae a cage o' guid red gowd
    Instead o' simple tree:

1. Dove

'I'll put gowd hingers[2] roun' your cage,
  And siller roun' your wa';
I'll gar[3] ye shine as fair a bird
  As ony o' them a'.'

But she hadnae these words well spoke,
  Nor yet these words well said,
Till Cow-me-doo flew frae the tower
  And lighted on her head.

Then she has brought this pretty bird
  Hame to her bowers and ha',
And made him shine as fair a bird
  As ony o' them a'.

When day was gane, and night was come,
  About the evening tide
This lady spied a sprightly youth
  Stand straight up by her side.

'From whence came ye, young man?' she said;
  'That does surprise me sair;
My door was bolted right secure,
  What way hae ye come here?'

'O had[4] your tongue, ye lady fair,
  Lat a' folly be;
Mind ye not on your turtle-doo
  Last day ye brought wi' thee?'

'O tell me mair, young man,' she said,
  'This does surprise me now;
What country hae ye come frae?
  What pedigree are you?'

2. Trappings
3. Make   4. Hold

547

'My mither lives on foreign isles,
   She has nae mair but me;
She is a queen o' wealth and state,
   And birth and high degree.

'Likewise well skilled in magic spells,
   As ye may plainly see,
And she transformed me to yon shape,
   To charm such maids as thee.

'I am a doo the live-lang day,
   A sprightly youth at night;
This aye gars me appear mair fair
   In a fair maiden's sight.

'And it was but this verra day
   That I came ower the sea;
Your lovely face did me enchant;
   I'll live and dee wi' thee.'

'O Cow-me-doo, my luve sae true,
   Nae mair frae me ye'se gae';
'That's never my intent, my luve,
   As ye said, it shall be sae . . .'

325. *The Broomfield Hill*

Brome, brome on hill,
The gentle brome on hill, hill,
Brome, brome on Hive hill,
The gentle brome on Hive hill,
The brome stands on Hive hill-a . . .

'O where were ye, my milk-white steed,
   That I hae coft[1] sae dear,
That wadna' watch and waken me
   When there was maiden here?'

1. Bought

'I stampèd wi' my foot, master,
 And gard my bridle ring,
But na kin thing wald waken ye,
 Till she was past and gane.'

'And wae betide ye, my gay goss-hawk,
 That I did love sae dear,
That wadna' watch and waken me
 When there was maiden here.'

'I clappèd wi' my wings, master,
 And aye my bells I rang,
And aye cryed, Waken, waken, master,
 Before the ladye gang.'

'But haste and haste, my gude white steed,
 To come the maiden till,
Or a' the birds of gude green wood
 Of your flesh shall have their fill.'

'Ye need no burst your gude white steed
 Wi' racing o'er the howm;[2]
Nae bird flies faster through the wood,
 Than she fled through the broom.'

326. *The Changeling*

Toll no bell for me, dear Father, dear Mother,
 Waste no sighs;
There are my sisters, there is my little brother
 Who plays in the place called Paradise,
Your children all, but children for ever;
 But I, so wild,
Your disgrace, with the queer brown face, was never,
 Never, I know, but half your child!

2. The green margin of a river

In the garden at play, all day, last summer,
    Far and away I heard
The sweet 'tweet-tweet' of a strange new-comer,
    The dearest, clearest call of a bird.
It lived down there in the deep green hollow,
    My own old home, and the fairies say
The word of a bird is a thing to follow,
    So I was away a night and a day.

One evening, too, by the nursery fire,
    We snuggled close and sat round so still,
When suddenly as the wind blew higher,
    Something scratched on the window-sill,
A pinched brown face peered in – I shivered;
    No one listened or seemed to see;
The arms of it waved and the wings of it quivered,
    Whoo – I knew it had come for me!
    Some are as bad as bad can be!
All night long they danced in the rain,
Round and round in a dripping chain,
Threw their caps at the window-pane,
    Tried to make me scream and shout
    And fling the bedclothes all about:
I meant to stay in bed that night,
And if only you had left a light
    They would never have got me out!

    Sometimes I wouldn't speak, you see,
    Or answer when you spoke to me,
Because in the long, still dusks of Spring
You can hear the whole world whispering;
    The shy green grasses making love,
    The feathers grow on the dear grey dove,
    The tiny heart of the redstart beat,
    The patter of the squirrel's feet,
The pebbles pushing in the silver streams,
The rushes talking in their dreams,

The swish-swish of the bat's black wings,
The wild-wood bluebell's sweet ting-tings,
    Humming and hammering at your ear,
    Everything there is to hear
In the heart of hidden things.
    But not in the midst of the nursery riot,
    That's why I wanted to be quiet,
        Couldn't do my sums, or sing,
        Or settle down to anything.
    And when, for that, I was sent upstairs
    I *did* kneel down to say my prayers;
But the King who sits on your high church steeple
Has nothing to do with us fairy people!

'Times I pleased you, dear Father, dear Mother,
    Learned all my lessons and liked to play,
And dearly I loved the little pale brother
    Whom some other bird must have called away.
Why did they bring me here to make me
    Not quite bad and not quite good,
Why, unless They're wicked, do They want, in spite, to take me
        Back to Their wet, wild wood?
Now, every night I shall see the windows shining,
    The gold lamp's glow, and the fire's red gleam,
While the best of us are twining twigs and the rest of us are whining
        In the hollow by the stream.
Black and chill are Their nights on the wold;
    And They live so long and They feel no pain:
I shall grow up, but never grow old,
I shall always, always be very cold,
        I shall never come back again!

CHARLOTTE MEW

327. *The Host of the Air*

O'Driscoll drove with a song
The wild duck and the drake
From the tall and the tufted reeds
Of the drear Hart Lake.

And he saw how the reeds grew dark
At the coming of night tide,
And dreamed of the long dim hair
Of Bridget his bride.

He heard while he sang and dreamed
A piper piping away,
And never was piping so sad,
And never was piping so gay.

And he saw young men and young girls
Who danced on a level place
And Bridget his bride among them,
With a sad and a gay face.

The dancers crowded about him,
And many a sweet thing said,
And a young man brought him red wine
And a young girl white bread.

But Bridget drew him by the sleeve,
Away from the merry bands,
To old men playing at cards
With a twinkling of ancient hands.

The bread and the wine had a doom,
For these were the host of the air;
He sat and played in a dream
Of her long dim hair.

He played with the merry old men
And thought not of evil chance,
Until one bore Bridget his bride
Away from the merry dance.

He bore her away in his arms,
The handsomest young man there,
And his neck and his breast and his arms
Were drowned in her long dim hair.

O'Driscoll scattered the cards
And out of his dream awoke:
Old men and young men and young girls
Were gone like a drifting smoke;

But he heard high up in the air
A piper piping away,
And never was piping so sad,
And never was piping so gay.

WILLIAM BUTLER YEATS

328. *The Love-Talker*

I met the Love-Talker one eve in the glen,
He was handsomer than any of our handsome young men,
His eyes were blacker than the sloe, his voice sweeter far
Then the crooning of old Kevin's pipes beyond in Coolnagar.

I was bound for the milking with a heart fair and free –
My grief! my grief! that bitter hour drained the life from me;
I thought him human lover, though his lips on mine were cold,
And the breath of death blew keen on me within his hold.

I know not what way he came, no shadow fell behind,
But all the sighing rushes swayed beneath a faery wind,

The thrush ceased its singing, a mist crept about,
We two clung together – with the world shut out.

Beyond the ghostly mist I could hear my cattle low,
The little cow from Ballina, clean as driven snow,
The dun cow from Kerry, the roan from Inisheer,
Oh, pitiful their calling – and his whispers in my ear!

His eyes were a fire; his words were a snare;
I cried my mother's name, but no help was there;
I made the blessed Sign; then he gave a dreary moan,
A wisp of cloud went floating by, and I stood alone.

Running ever through my head, is an old-time rune –
'Who meets the Love-Talker must weave her shroud soon.'
My mother's face is furrowed with the salt tears that fall,
But the kind eyes of my father are the saddest sight of all.

I have spun the fleecy lint, and now my wheel is still,
The linen length is woven for my shroud fine and chill,
I shall stretch me on the bed where a happy maid I lay –
Pray for the soul of Mairé Og at dawning of the day!

ETHNA CARBERY

329. *Mariana*

With blackest moss the flower-plots
    Were thickly crusted, one and all:
The rusted nails fell from the knots
    That held the pear to the garden-wall.
The broken sheds looked sad and strange:
    Unlifted was the clinking latch;
    Weeded and worn the ancient thatch
Upon the lonely moated grange.

> *She only said, 'My life is dreary,*
> *He cometh not,' she said;*
> *She said, 'I am aweary, aweary,*
> *I would that I were dead!'*

Her tears fell with the dews at even;
  Her tears fell ere the dews were dried;
She could not look on the sweet heaven,
  Either at morn or eventide.
After the flitting of the bats,
  When thickest dark did trance the sky,
  She drew her casement-curtain by,
And glanced athwart the glooming flats.
> *She only said, 'The night is dreary,*
> *He cometh not,' she said;*
> *She said, 'I am aweary, aweary,*
> *I would that I were dead!'*

Upon the middle of the night,
  Waking she heard the night-foul crow:
The cock sung out an hour ere light:
  From the dark fen the oxen's low
Came to her: without hope of change,
  In sleep she seemed to walk forlorn,
  Till cold winds woke the grey-eyed morn
About the lonely moated grange.
> *She only said, 'The day is dreary,*
> *He cometh not,' she said;*
> *She said, 'I am aweary, aweary,*
> *I would that I were dead!'*

About a stone-cast from the wall
  A sluice with blackened water slept,
And o'er it many, round and small,
  The clustered marish-mosses crept.
Hard by a poplar shook alway,
  All silver-green with gnarled bark:

For leagues no other tree did mark
The level waste, the rounding grey.
　　She only said, 'My life is dreary,
　　　He cometh not,' she said;
　　She said, 'I am aweary, aweary,
　　　I would that I were dead!'

And ever when the moon was low,
　　And the shrill winds were up and away,
In the white curtain, to and fro,
　　She saw the gusty shadow sway.
But when the moon was very low,
　　And wild winds bound within their cell,
　　The shadow of the poplar fell
Upon her bed, across her brow.
　　She only said, 'The night is dreary,
　　　He cometh not,' she said;
　　She said, 'I am aweary, aweary,
　　　I would that I were dead!'

All day within the dreamy house,
　　The doors upon their hinges creaked;
The blue fly sung in the pane; the mouse
　　Behind the mouldering wainscot shrieked,
Or from the crevice peered about.
　　Old faces glimmered thro' the doors,
　　Old footsteps trod the upper floors,
Old voices called her from without.
　　She only said, 'My life is dreary,
　　　He cometh not,' she said;
　　She said, 'I am aweary, aweary,
　　　I would that I were dead!'

The sparrow's chirrup on the roof,
　　The slow clock ticking, and the sound
Which to the wooing wind aloof
　　The poplar made, did all confound

Her sense; but most she loathed the hour
  When the thick-moted sunbeam lay
Athwart the chambers, and the day
Was sloping toward his western bower.
      Then, said she, 'I am very dreary,
        He will not come,' she said;
      She wept, 'I am aweary, aweary,
        Oh God, that I were dead!'

ALFRED, LORD TENNYSON

330. *Keith of Ravelston*

The murmur of the mourning ghost
  That keeps the shadowy kine,
'Oh, Keith of Ravelston,
  The sorrows of thy line!'

Ravelston, Ravelston,
  The merry path that leads
Down the golden morning hill,
  And thro' the silver meads;

Ravelston, Ravelston,
  The stile beneath the tree,
The maid that kept her mother's kine
  The song that sang she!

She sang her song, she kept her kine,
  She sat beneath the thorn
When Andrew Keith of Ravelston
  Rode thro' the Monday morn.

His henchmen sing, his hawk-bells ring,
  His belted jewels shine!
Oh, Keith of Ravelston,
  The sorrows of thy line!

Year after year, where Andrew came,
    Comes evening down the glade,
And still there sits a moonshine ghost
    Where sat the sunshine maid.

Her misty hair is faint and fair,
    She keeps the shadowy kine;
Oh, Keith of Ravelston,
    The sorrows of thy line!

I lay my hand upon the stile,
    The stile is lone and cold,
The burnie that goes babbling by
    Says naught that can be told.

Yet, stranger! here, from year to year,
    She keeps her shadowy kine;
Oh, Keith of Ravelston,
    The sorrows of thy line!

Step out three steps, where Andrew stood –
    Why blanch thy cheeks for fear
The ancient stile is not alone,
    'Tis not the burn I hear!

She makes her immemorial moan,
    She keeps her shadowy kine;
Oh, Keith of Ravelston,
    The sorrows of thy line!

SYDNEY DOBELL

331. *Unwelcome*

We were young, we were merry, we were very very wise,
    And the door stood open at our feast,
When there passed us a woman with the West in her eyes,
    And a man with his back to the East.

O, still grew the hearts that were beating so fast,
    The loudest voice was still.
The jest died away on our lips as they passed,
    And the rays of July struck chill.

The cups of red wine turned pale on the board,
    The white bread black as soot.
The hound forgot the hand of her lord,
    She fell down at his foot.

Low let me lie, where the dead dog lies,
    Ere I sit me down again at a feast,
When there passes a woman with the West in her eyes,
    And a man with his back to the East.

MARY COLERIDGE

332. *On Yes Tor*

Beneath our feet, the shuddering bogs
    Made earthquakes of their own,
For greenish-grizzled furtive frogs
    And lizards lithe and brown;

And high to east and south and west,
    Girt round the feet with gorse,
Lay, summering, breast by giant breast,
    The titan brood of tors;

Golden and phantom-pale they lay,
    Calm in the cloudless light,
Like gods that, slumbering, still survey
    The obsequious infinite.

Plod, plod, through herbage thin or dense;
    Past chattering rills of quartz;
Across brown bramble-coverts, whence
    The shy black ouzel darts;

Through empty leagues of broad, bare lands,
   Beneath the empty skies,
Clutched in the grip of those vast hands,
   Cowed by those golden eyes,

We fled beneath their scornful stare,
   Like terror-hunted dogs,
More timid than the lizards were,
   And shyer than the frogs.

EDMUND GOSSE

333. *The Witches' Song*

'I have beene all day looking after
A raven feeding upon a quarter;
And, soone as she turned her back to the south,
I snatched this morsell out of her mouth.' . . .

'I last night lay all alone
O' the ground, to heare the madrake grone;
And pluckt him up, though he grew full low:
And, as I had done, the cocke did crow.' . . .

'And I ha' been plucking (plants among)
Hemlock, henbane, adders-tongue,
Night-shade, moon-wort, libbards-bane;
And twise by the dogges was like to be tane.' . . .

'Yes: I have brought, to helpe your vows,
Hornèd poppie, cypresse boughes.
The fig-tree wild, that grows on tombes,
And juice that from the larch-tree comes,
The basiliske's bloud, and the viper's skin;
And now our orgies let's begin.'

BEN JONSON

334. *The Raven*

Once upon a midnight dreary, while I pondered, weak and weary,
Over many a quaint and curious volume of forgotten lore, –
While I nodded, nearly napping, suddenly there came a tapping,
As of some one gently rapping, rapping at my chamber door.
' 'Tis some visitor,' I muttered, 'tapping at my chamber door;
   Only this and nothing more.'

Ah, distinctly I remember it was in the bleak December,
And each separate dying ember wrought its ghost upon the floor.
Eagerly I wished the morrow; – vainly I had sought to borrow
From my books surcease of sorrow – sorrow for the lost Lenore,
For the rare and radiant maiden whom the angels name Lenore:
   Nameless here for evermore.

And the silken sad uncertain rustling of each purple curtain
Thrilled me – filled me with fantastic terrors never felt before;
So that now, to still the beating of my heart, I stood repeating,
' 'Tis some visitor entreating entrance at my chamber door –
Some late visitor entreating entrance at my chamber door;
   This it is and nothing more.'

Presently my soul grew stronger; hesitating then no longer,
'Sir,' said I, 'or Madam, truly your forgiveness I implore;
But the fact is I was napping, and so gently you came rapping,
And so faintly you came tapping, tapping at my chamber door,
That I scarce was sure I heard you' – here I opened wide the door:
   Darkness there and nothing more.

Deep into that darkness peering, long I stood there wondering,
   fearing,
Doubting, dreaming, dreams no mortals ever dared to dream
   before;
But the silence was unbroken, and the stillness gave no token,

And the only word there spoken was the whispered word,
    'Lenore?'
This I whispered, and an echo murmured back the word, 'Lenore':
  Merely this and nothing more.

Back into the chamber turning, all my soul within me burning,
Soon again I heard a tapping somewhat louder than before.
'Surely,' said I, 'surely that is something at my window lattice;
Let me see, then, what thereat is, and this mystery explore:
Let my heart be still a moment and this mystery explore;
    'Tis the wind and nothing more.'

Open here I flung the shutter, when, with many a flirt and flutter,
In there stepped a stately Raven of the saintly days of yore.
Not the least obeisance made he; not a minute stopped or stayed he;
But, with mien of lord or lady, perched above my chamber door,
Perched upon a bust of Pallas just above my chamber door:
    Perched, and sat, and nothing more.

Then this ebony bird beguiling my sad fancy into smiling
By the grave and stern decorum of the countenance it wore, –
'Though thy crest be shorn and shaven, thou,' I said, 'art sure no
    craven,
Ghastly grim and ancient Raven wandering from the Nightly shore:
Tell me what thy lordly name is on the Night's Plutonian shore!'
    Quoth the Raven, 'Nevermore.'

Much I marvelled this ungainly fowl to hear discourse so plainly,
Though its answer little meaning – little relevancy bore;
For we cannot help agreeing that no living human being
Ever yet was blessed with seeing bird above his chamber door –
Bird or beast upon the sculptured bust above his chamber door,
    With such name as 'Nevermore.'

But the Raven, sitting lonely on the placid bust, spoke only
That one word, as if his soul in that one word he did outpour.
Nothing further then he uttered, not a feather then he fluttered,

Till I scarcely more than muttered, – 'Other friends have flown,
    before;
On the morrow *he* will leave me, as my Hopes have flown before.'
    Then the bird said, 'Nevermore.'

Startled at the stillness broken by reply so aptly spoken,
'Doubtless,' said I, 'what it utters is its only stock and store,
Caught from some unhappy master whom unmerciful Disaster
Followed fast and followed faster till his songs one burden bore:
Till the dirges of his Hope that melancholy burden bore
    Of "Never – nevermore." '

But the Raven still beguiling all my sad soul into smiling,
Straight I wheeled a cushioned seat in front of bird and bust and
    door;
Then, upon the velvet sinking, I betook myself to linking
Fancy unto fancy, thinking what this ominous bird of yore,
What this grim, ungainly, ghastly, gaunt, and ominous bird of yore
    Meant in croaking 'Nevermore.'

This I sat engaged in guessing, but no syllable expressing
To the fowl whose fiery eyes now burned into my bosom's core;
This and more I sat divining, with my head at ease reclining
On the cushion's velvet lining that the lamplight gloated o'er,
But whose velvet violet lining with the lamplight gloating o'er
    She shall press, ah, nevermore!

Then, methought, the air grew denser, perfumed from an unseen
    censer
Swung by seraphim whose foot-falls tinkled on the tufted floor.
'Wretch,' I cried, 'thy God hath lent thee – by these angels he hath
    sent thee
Respite – respite and nepenthe from thy memories of Lenore!
Quaff, oh quaff this kind nepenthe, and forget this lost Lenore!'
    Quoth the Raven, 'Nevermore.'

'Prophet!' said I, 'thing of evil! prophet still, if bird or devil!
Whether Tempter sent or whether tempest tossed thee here ashore,

Desolate, yet all undaunted, on this desert land enchanted,
On this home by Horror haunted – tell me truly, I implore:
Is there – *is* there balm in Gilead? – tell me – tell me, I implore!'
   Quoth the Raven, 'Nevermore.'

'Prophet!' said I, 'thing of evil – prophet still, if bird or devil!
By that Heaven that bends above us, by that God we both adore,
Tell this soul with sorrow laden if, within distant Aidenn,
It shall clasp a sainted maiden whom the angels name Lenore:
Clasp a rare and radiant maiden whom the angels name Lenore!'
   Quoth the Raven, 'Nevermore.'

'Be that word our sign of parting, bird or fiend!' I shrieked, up-
    starting
'Get thee back into the tempest and the Night's Plutonian shore!
Leave no black plume as a token of that lie thy soul hath spoken!
Leave my loneliness unbroken! quit the bust above my door!
Take thy beak from out my heart, and take thy form from off my
    door!'
   Quoth the Raven, 'Nevermore.'

And the Raven, never flitting, still is sitting, still is sitting
On the pallid bust of Pallas just above my chamber door;
And his eyes have all the seeming of a demon's that is dreaming,
And the lamp-light o'er him streaming throws his shadow on the
    floor;
And my soul from out that shadow that lies floating on the floor
   Shall be lifted – nevermore!

                 EDGAR ALLAN POE

335. *The Witches' Ballad*

O, I hae come from far away,
   From a warm land far away,
A southern land across the sea,
With sailor-lads about the mast,
Merry and canny, and kind to me.

And I hae been to yon town
　　To try my luck in yon town;
Nort, and Mysie, Elspie too.
Right braw we were to pass the gate,
Wi' gowden-clasps on girdles blue.

Mysie smiled wi' miminy mouth,
　　Innocent mouth, miminy mouth;
Elspie wore a scarlet gown.
Nort's grey eyes were unco' gleg.[1]
My Castile comb was like a crown.

We walk'd abreast all up the street,
　　Into the market up the street;
Our hair with marigolds was wound,
Our bodices with love-knots laced,
Our merchandise with tansy bound.

Nort had chickens, I had cocks;
　　Gamesome cocks, loud-crowing cocks;
Mysie ducks, and Elspie drakes, –
For a wee groat or a pound
We lost nae time wi' gives and takes.

– Lost nae time for well we knew,
　　In our sleeves full well we knew,
When the gloaming came that night,
Duck nor drake, nor hen nor cock
Would be found by candle-light.

And when our chaffering all was done,
　　All was paid for, sold and done,
We drew a glove on ilka hand,
We sweetly curtsied, each to each.
And deftly danced a saraband.

　　　　　1. Wild and lively

The market-lassies looked and laughed,
    Left their gear, and looked and laughed;
They made as they would join the game,
But soon their mithers, wild and wud,[2]
With whack and screech they stopped the same.

Sae loud the tongues o' randies[3] grew,
    The flytin'[4] and the skirlin' grew,
At all the windows in the place,
Wi' spoons or knives, wi' needle or awl,
Was thrust out every hand and face.

And down each stair they thronged anon,
    Gentle, semple, thronged anon;
Souter[5] and tailor, frowsy Nan,
The ancient widow young again,
Simpering behind her fan.

Without a choice, against their will,
    Doited,[6] dazed, against their will,
    The market lassie and her mither,
The farmer and his husbandman,
Hand in hand dance a' thegither.

Slow at first, but faster soon,
    Still increasing, wild and fast,
Hoods and mantles, hats and hose,
Blindly doffed and cast away,
Left them naked, heads and toes.

They would have torn us limb from limb,
    Dainty limb from dainty limb;
But never one of them could win
Across the line that I had drawn
With bleeding thumb a-widdershin.

2. Furious   5. Cobbler
3. Carousers   6. Spellbound
4. Brawling

But there was Jeff the provost's son,
   Jeff the provost's only son;
There was Father Auld himsel',
The Lombard frae the hostelry,
And the lawyer Peter Fell.

All goodly men we singled out,
   Waled[7] them well, and singled out,
And drew them by the left hand in;
Mysie the priest, and Elspie won
The Lombard, Nort the lawyer carle,
I mysel' the provost's son.

Then, with cantrip[8] kisses seven,
   Three times round with kisses seven,
Warped and woven there spun we
Arms and legs and flaming hair,
Like a whirlwind on the sea.

Like a wind that sucks the sea,
   Over and in and on the sea,
Good sooth it was a mad delight;
And every man of all the four
Shut his eyes and laughed outright.

Laughed as long as they had breath,
   Laughed while they had sense or breath;
And close about us coiled a mist
Of gnats and midges, wasps and flies,
Like the whirlwind shaft it rist.

Drawn up I was right off my feet,
   Into the mist and off my feet;
And, dancing on each chimney-top,
I saw a thousand darling imps
Keeping time with skip and hop.

      7. Chose   8. Witching

And on the provost's brave ridge-tile,
  On the provost's grand ridge-tile,
The Blackamoor first to master me
I saw, I saw that winsome smile,
The mouth that did my heart beguile,
And spoke the great Word over me,
In the land beyond the sea.

I called his name, I called aloud,
  Alas! I called on him aloud;
And then he filled his hand with stour,[9]
And threw it towards me in the air;
My mouse flew out, I lost my pow'r!

My lusty strength, my power were gone;
  Power was gone, and all was gone.
He will not let me love him more!
Of bell and whip and horse's tail
He cares not if I find a store.

But I am proud if he is fierce!
  I am as proud as he is fierce;
I'll turn about and backward go,
If I meet again that Blackamoor,
And he'll help us then, for he shall know
I seek another paramour.

And we'll gang once more to yon town,
  Wi' better luck to yon town;
We'll walk in silk and cramoisie,
And I shall wed the provost's son
My lady of the town I'll be!

For I was born a crowned king's child,
  Born and nursed a king's child,
King o' the land ayont the sea,
Where the Blackamoor kissed me first,
And taught me art and glamourie.

9. Dust: reek

Each one in her wame shall hide
    Her hairy mouse, her wary mouse,
Fed on madwort and agramie, —
Wear amber beads between her breasts,
And blind-worm's skin about her knee.

The Lombard shall be Elspie's man,
    Elspie's gowden husband-man;
Nort shall take the lawyer's hand;
The priest shall swear another vow;
We'll dance again the saraband!

WILLIAM BELL SCOTT

336. *Annan Water*

Annan Water's wading deep,
    'And my Love Annie's wondrous bonny;
And I am loath she should wet her feet,
    Because I love her best of ony.'

He's loupen on his bonny gray,
    He rode the right gate[1] and the read;[2]
For all the storm he wadna stay,
    For seeking of his bonny lady.

And he has ridden o'er field and fell,
    Through moor, and moss, and many a mire;
His spurs of steel were sair to bide,
    And from her four feet flew the fire.

'My bonny gray, now play your part!
    If ye be the steed that wins my dearie,
With corn and hay ye'll be fed for aye,
    And never spur shall make you wearie.'

1. Road   2. Nearest

The gray was a mare, and a right gude mare;
    But when she wan the Annan Water,
She should not have ridden the ford that night
    Had a thousand marks been wadded at her.

'O boatman, boatman, put off your boat,
    Put off your boat for golden money!'
But for all the gold in fair Scotland,
    He dared not take him through to Annie.

'O I was sworn so late yestreen,
    Not by a single oath, but mony!
I'll cross the drumly stream to-night,
    Or never could I face my honey.'

The side was steep, and the bottom deep,
    From bank to brae the water pouring;
The bonny gray mare she swat for fear,
    For she heard the Water-Kelpy roaring.

He spurred her forth into the flood,
    I wot she swam both strong and steady;
But the stream was broad, and her strength did fail,
    And he never saw his bonny lady!

337. *Song*

Ah! County Guy, the hour is nigh:
    The sun has left the lea,
The orange flower perfumes the bower,
    The breeze is on the sea,
The lark, his lay who thrilled all day,
    Sits hushed his partner nigh:
Breeze, bird, and flower, confess the hour,
    But where is County Guy? –

The village maid steals through the shade,
　　Her shepherd's suit to hear;
To beauty shy, by lattice high,
　　Sings high-born Cavalier;
The star of Love, all stars above,
　　Now reigns o'er earth and sky,
And high and low the influence know —
　　But where is County Guy?

SIR WALTER SCOTT

338. *Deadman's Dirge*

Prayer unsaid, and Mass unsung,
Deadman's dirge must still be rung:
　　Dingle-dong, the dead-bells sound!
　　Mermen chant his dirge around!

Wash him bloodless, smooth him fair,
Stretch his limbs, and sleek his hair:
　　Dingle-dong, the dead-bells go!
　　Mermen swing them to and fro!

In the wormless sand shall he
Feast for no foul glutton be:
　　Dingle-dong, the dead-bells chime!
　　Mermen keep the tone and time!

We must with a tombstone brave
Shut the shark out from his grave:
　　Dingle-dong, the dead-bells toll!
　　Mermen dirgers ring his knoll!

Such a slab will we lay o'er him,
All the dead shall rise before him:
　　Dingle-dong, the dead-bells boom!
　　Mermen lay him in his tomb!

GEORGE DARLEY

339. *Boats at Night*

How lovely is the sound of oars at night
    And unknown voices, borne through windless air,
From shadowy vessels floating out of sight
    Beyond the harbour lantern's broken glare
To those piled rocks that make on the dark wave
    Only a darker stain. The splashing oars
Slide softly on as in an echoing cave
    And with the whisper of the unseen shores
Mingle their music, till the bell of night
    Murmurs reverberations low and deep
That droop towards the land in swooning flight
    Like whispers from the lazy lips of sleep.
The oars grow faint. Below the cloud-dim hill
The shadows fade and now the bay is still.

EDWARD SHANKS

340. *A Voice Sings*

Hear, sweet spirit, hear the spell,
Lest a blacker charm compel!
So shall the midnight breezes swell
With thy deep long-lingering knell.

And at evening evermore,
In a chapel on the shore,
Shall the chaunters, sad and saintly,
Yellow tapers burning faintly,
Doleful masses chaunt for thee,
    Miserere Domine!

Hark, the cadence dies away
   On the quiet moonlight sea:
The boatmen rest their oars; and say,
   Miserere Domine!

SAMUEL TAYLOR COLERIDGE

341. *The Wandering Spectre*

Wae's me, wae's me,
The acorn's not yet
Fallen from the tree
That's to grow the wood,
That's to make the cradle,
That's to rock the bairn,
That's to grow a man,
That's to lay me.

342. *Lucifer in Starlight*

On a starred night Prince Lucifer uprose.
Tired of his dark dominion swung the fiend
Above the rolling ball in cloud part screened,
Where sinners hugged their spectre of repose.
Poor prey to his hot fit of pride were those.
And now upon his western wing he leaned,
Now his huge bulk o'er Afric's sands careened,
Now the black planet shadowed Arctic snows.
Soaring through wider zones that pricked his scars
With memory of the old revolt from Awe,
He reached a middle height, and at the stars,
Which are the brain of heaven, he looked, and sank.
Around the ancient track marched rank on rank,
The army of unalterable law.

GEORGE MEREDITH

343. *There Was a Knight*

There was a knicht riding frae the east
  Jennifer gentle an' rosemaree.
Who had been wooing at monie a place,
  As the doo[1] flies owre the mulberry tree.

He cam' unto a widow's door,
And speird[2] whare her three dochters were.

'The auldest ane's to a washing gane,
The second's to a baking gane.

'The youngest ane's to a wedding gane,
And it will be nicht or[3] she be hame.'

He sat him doun upon a stane,
Till thir three lasses cam' tripping hame.

The auldest ane she let him in,
And pinned the door wi' a siller pin.

The second ane she made his bed,
And laid saft pillows unto his head.

The youngest ane was bauld[4] and bricht,
And she tarried for words wi' this unco knicht. —

'Gin ye will answer me questions ten,
The morn ye sall me made my ain:

'O what is higher nor[5] the tree?
And what is deeper nor the sea?

1. Dove   4. Bold
2. Asked   5. Than
3. Ere

'Or what is heavier nor the lead?
And what is better nor the bread?

'Or what is whiter nor the milk?
Or what is safter nor the silk?

'Or what is sharper nor a thorn?
Or what is louder nor a horn?

'Or what is greener nor the grass?
Or what is waur[6] nor a woman was?'

'O heaven is higher nor the tree.
And hell is deeper nor the sea.

'O sin is heavier nor the lead,
The blessing's better nor the bread.

'The snaw is whiter nor the milk,
And the down is safter nor the silk.

'Hunger is sharper nor a thorn,
And shame is louder nor a horn.

'The pies are greener nor the grass,
And Clootie's waur nor a woman was.'

As sure as she the fiend did name,
   Jennifer gentle an' rosemaree,
He flew awa' in a blazing flame,
   As the doo flies owre the mulberry tree.

6. Worse

344. *The False Knight Upon the Road*

'O whare are ye gaun?'
  Quo' the fause knicht upon the road:
'I'm gaun to the scule.'
  Quo' the wee boy, and still he stude.

'What is that upon your back?'
  Quo' the fause knicht upon the road:
'Atweel[1] it is my bukes.'
  Quo' the wee boy, and still he stude.

'What's that ye've got in your arm?'
  Quo' the fause knicht upon the road:
'Atweel it is my peit.'[2]
  Quo' the wee boy, and still he stude.

'Wha's aucht[3] they sheep?'
  Quo' the fause knicht upon the road:
'They're mine and my mither's.'
  Quo' the wee boy, and still he stude.

'How monie o' them are mine?'
  Quo' the fause knicht upon the road:
'A' they that hae blue tails.'
  Quo' the wee boy, and still he stude.

'I wiss ye were on yon tree:'
  Quo' the fause knicht upon the road:
'And a gude ladder under me.'
  Quo' the wee boy, and still he stude.

'And the ladder for to break:'
  Quo' the fause knicht upon the road:

1. Why, sure   3. Who owns
2. Peat for school fire

'And *you* for to fa' down.'
  Quo' the wee boy, and still he stude.

'I wiss ye were in yon sie:'
  Quo' the fause knicht upon the road:
'And a gude bottom⁴ under me.'
  Quo' the wee boy, and still he stude.

'And the bottom for to break:'
  Quo' the fause knicht upon the road:
'And *ye* to be drowned.'
  Quo' the wee boy, and still he stude.

345. *Christabel*

'Tis the middle of night by the castle clock,
And the owls have awakened the crowing cock;
Tu-whit!———Tu-whoo!
And hark, again! the crowing cock,
How drowsily it crew.

Sir Leoline, the Baron rich,
Hath a toothless mastiff bitch;
From her kennel beneath the rock
She maketh answer to the clock,
Four for the quarters, and twelve for the hour;
Ever and aye, by shine and shower,
Sixteen short howls, not over loud;
Some say, she sees my lady's shroud.

Is the night chilly and dark?
The night is chilly, but not dark.
The thin gray cloud is spread on high,
It covers but not hides the sky.

4. Vessel, ship

The moon is behind, and at the full;
And yet she looks both small and dull.
The night is chill, the cloud is gray:
'Tis a month before the month of May,
And the Spring comes slowly up this way.

The lovely lady, Christabel,
Whom her father loves so well,
What makes her in the wood so late,
A furlong from the castle gate?
She had dreams all yesternight
Of her own betrothèd knight;
And she in the midnight wood will pray
For the weal of her lover that's far away.
She stole along, she nothing spoke,
The sighs she heaved were soft and low,
And naught was green upon the oak
But moss and rarest mistletoe:
She kneels beneath the huge oak tree,
And in silence prayeth she.

The lady sprang up suddenly,
The lovely lady, Christabel!
It moaned as near, as near can be,
But what it is she cannot tell. –
On the other side it seems to be,
Of the huge, broad-breasted, old oak tree.

The night is chill; the forest bare;
Is it the wind that moaneth bleak?
There is not wind enough in the air
To move away the ringlet curl
From the lovely lady's cheek –
There is not wind enough to twirl
The one red leaf, the last of its clan,
That dances as often as dance it can,
Hanging so light, and hanging so high,
On the topmost twig looks up at the sky.

Hush, beating heart of Christabel!
Jesu, Maria, shield her well!
She folded her arms beneath her cloak,
And stole to the other side of the oak.
    What sees she there?

There she sees a damsel bright,
Drest in a silken robe of white,
That shadowy in the moonlight shone:
The neck that made that white robe wan –
Her stately neck, and arms were bare;
Her blue-veined feet unsandaled were,
And wildly glittered here and there
The gems entangled in her hair . . .

SAMUEL TAYLOR COLERIDGE

346. *The Fruit Plucker*

Encinctured with a twine of leaves,
That leafy twine his only dress,
A lovely Boy was plucking fruits,
By moonlight, in a wilderness.
The moon was bright, the air was free,

And fruits and flowers together grew
On many a shrub and many a tree:
And all put on a gentle hue,
Hanging in the shadowy air
Like a picture rich and rare.

It was a climate where, they say,
The night is more beloved than day.
But who that beauteous Boy beguiled,
That beauteous Boy to linger here?

Alone, by night, a little child,
In place so silent and so wild –
Has he no friend, no loving mother near?

SAMUEL TAYLOR COLERIDGE

347. *The Haunted Palace*

In the greenest of our valleys
    By good angels tenanted,
Once a fair and stately palace –
    Radiant palace – reared its head.
In the monarch's Thought's dominion
        It stood there!
Never seraph spread a pinion
    Over fabric half so fair.

Banners yellow, glorious, golden,
    On its roof did float and flow,
(This – all this – was in the olden
        Time long ago),
And every gentle air that dallied
        In that sweet day,
Along the ramparts plumed and pallid
    A wingèd odour went away.

Wanderers, in that happy valley,
    Through two luminous windows saw
Spirits moving musically,
    To a lute's well-tunèd law,
Round about a throne, where sitting
        (Porphyrogene),
In state his glory well befitting,
    The ruler of the realm was seen.

And all with pearl and ruby glowing
    Was the fair palace door,

Through which came flowing, flowing, flowing,
   And sparkling evermore,
A troop of Echoes, whose sweet duty
     Was but to sing,
In voices of surpassing beauty,
   The wit and wisdom of their king.

But evil things, in robes of sorrow,
   Assailed the monarch's high estate.
(Ah, let us mourn, for never morrow
   Shall dawn upon him desolate!)
And round about his home, the glory,
     That blushed and bloomed,
Is but a dim-remembered story
   Of the old time entombed.

And travellers, now, within that valley,
   Through the red-litten windows see
Vast forms, that move fantastically
   To a discordant melody;
While, like a ghastly rapid river,
     Through the pale door
A hideous throng rush out for ever,
   And laugh – but smile no more.

EDGAR ALLAN POE

348. *The House of Richesse*

NEIGHBOURING THE GATE OF HELL INTO WHICH
MAMMON LED THE ELFIN KNIGHT

... That houses forme within was rude and strong,
Like an huge cave, hewne out of rocky clift,
From whose rough vaut the ragged breaches hong,
Embost with massy gold of glorious gift,

And with rich metall loaded every rift,
　　That heavy ruine they did seeme to threat;
　　And over them *Arachne* high did lift
　　Her cunning web, and spred her subtile net,
Enwrappèd in fowle smoke and clouds more blacke then jet.

Both roofe, and floore, and wals were all of gold,
　　But overgrowne with dust and old decay,
　　And hid in darkenesse, that none could behold
　　The hew thereof: for vew of chearefull day
　　Did never in that house it selfe display,
　　But a faint shadow of uncertain light;
　　Such as a lamp, whose life does fade away:
　　Or as the Noone cloathèd with clowdy night,
Does shew to him that walkes in feare and sad affright.

In all that rowme was nothing to be seene,
　　But huge great yron chests and coffers strong,
　　All bard with double bends,[1] that none could weene
　　Them to efforce by violence or wrong;
　　On every side they placèd were along.
　　But all the ground which sculs was scatterèd,
　　And dead mens bones, which round about were flong,
　　Whose lives, it seemèd, whilome there were shed,
And their vile carcases now left unburièd . . .

　　　　　　　　　　　　　　EDMUND SPENSER

349. *The Old City*

Thou hast come from the old city,
From the gate and the tower,
From King and priest and serving man
And burnished bower,

1. Bands

From beggar's whine and barking dogs,
From Prison sealed —
Thou hast come from the old city
Into the field.

The gables in the old city
Are stooping awry,
They gloom upon the muddy lanes
And smother the sky
And nightly through those mouldy lanes,
Moping and slow,
They who builded the old city
The cold ghosts go.

There is plague in the old city,
And the priests are sped
To graveyard and vault
To bury the dead;
Brittle bones and dusty breath
To death must yield —
Fly, fly, from the old city
Into the field!

RUTH MANNING-SANDERS

350. *The Two Spirits*

First Spirit.　O Thou, who plumed with strong desire
　　　　Wouldst float above the earth, beware!
　　　A Shadow tracks thy flight of fire —
　　　　　Night is coming!
　　　Bright are the regions of the air,
　　And among the winds and beams
　　　It were delight to wander there —
　　　　　Night is coming!

Second Spirit.   The deathless stars are bright above;
     If I would cross the shade of night,
Within my heart is the lamp of love,
     And that is day!
    And the moon will smile with gentle light
On my golden plumes where'er they move;
     The meteors will linger round my flight;
     And make night day.

First Spirit.   But if the whirlwinds of darkness waken
     Hail, and lightning, and stormy rain;
See, the bounds of the air are shaken –
     Night is coming!
    The red swift clouds of the hurricane
Yon declining sun have overtaken,
     The clash of the hail sweeps over the plain –
     Night is coming!

Second Spirit.   I see the light, and I hear the sound;
     I'll sail on the flood of the tempests dark,
With the calm within and the light around
     Which makes night day:
    And thou, when the gloom is deep and stark,
Look from thy dull earth, slumber-bound,
     My moon-like flight thou then may'st mark
     On high, far away.

*

Some say there is a precipice
    Where one vast pine is frozen to ruin
O'er piles of snow and chasms of ice
     'Mid Alpine mountains;
    And that the languid storm pursuing
That wingèd shape, for ever flies
    Round those hoar branches, aye renewing
     Its aëry fountains.

Some say, when nights are dry and clear,
  And the death-dews sleep on the morass,
Sweet whispers are heard by the traveller,
    Which make night day;
  And a silver shape, like his early love, doth pass
Up-borne by her wild and glittering hair,
  And when he awakes on the fragrant grass,
    He finds night day.

PERCY BYSSHE SHELLEY

LILY BRIGHT AND SHINE-A

351. *Silly Sweetheart*

Silly Sweetheart, say not nay,
     Come away:
All I tell is sweet and merry;
Soon rings evensong, and soon
Where was blossom hangs a berry;
Where was darkness shines a moon.
Prythee, Sweetheart, then I say,
     Come, come away!

     O away,
     Come away:
Maids there are with cheeks like roses,
Thine are roses in the snow.
Fie, the lass whose dainty nose is
Tilted not as one I know.
Nought heeds she, Alackaday!
     My, 'Come, come away!'

     O away,
     Come away:
Honeycomb by bees made sweet is;
Dew on apple, bloom on plum;
Hearken, my heart's lightest beat is
Drumming, drumming; haste and come
     Say not nay, then;
     Make no stay, then;
Dance thy dainty foot and straying
     Come, come away!

352. *Here Comes a Lusty Wooer*

'Here comes a lusty wooer,
My a dildin, my a daldin;
Here comes a lusty wooer,
Lily bright and shine-a.'

'Pray who do you woo?
My a dildin, my a daldin;
Pray who do you woo?
Lily bright and shine-a.'

'Woo! Your fairest daughter!
My a dildin, my a daldin;
Woo! your fairest daughter!
Lily bright and shine-a.'

'There! there! she is for you,
My a dildin, my a daldin;
There! there! she is for you,
Lily bright and shine-a.'

353. *Three Knights from Spain*

We are three Brethren come from Spain,
All in French garlands;
We are come to court your daughter Jane,
And adieu to you, my darlings.

My daughter Jane! – she is too young,
All in French garlands;
She cannot bide your flattering tongue,
And adieu to you, my darlings.

Be she young, or be she old,
   All in French garlands;
'Tis for a bride she must be sold,
   And adieu to you, my darlings.

A bride, a bride, she shall not be,
   All in French garlands;
Till she go through this world with me,
   And adieu to you, my darlings.

Then shall you keep your daughter Jane,
   All in French garlands;
Come once, we come not here again,
   And adieu to you, my darlings.

Turn back, turn back, you Spanish Knights,
   All in French garlands;
Scour, scour your spurs, till they be bright,
   And adieu to you, my darlings.

Sharp shine our spurs, all richly wrought,
   All in French garlands;
In towns afar our spurs were bought
   And adieu to you, my darlings.

Smell my lilies, smell my roses,
   All in French garlands;
Which of my maidens do you choose?
   And adieu to you, my darlings.

Not she. Not she. Thy youngest, Jane!
   All in French garlands;
We ride – and ride not back again,
   And adieu to you, my darlings.

In every pocket a thousand pound,
   All in French garlands;
On every finger a gay gold ring,
   And adieu to you, my darlings.
   And adieu to you, my darlings.

354. *The Whummil Bore*

Seven lang years I hae served the King,
    Fa fa fa fa lilly:
And I never got a sight of his daughter but ane:
    With my glimpy, glimpy, glimpy eedle,
    Lillum too tee a ta too a tee a ta a tally.

I saw her thro' a whummil bore,
    Fa fa fa fa lilly:
And I ne'er got a sight of her no more.
    With my glimpy, glimpy, glimpy eedle,
    Lillum too tee a ta too a tee a ta a tally.

Twa was putting on her gown,
    Fa fa fa fa lilly:
And ten was putting pins therein.
    With my glimpy, glimpy, glimpy eedle,
    Lillum too tee a ta too a tee a ta a tally.

Twa was putting on her shoon,
    Fa fa fa fa lilly:
And twa was buckling them again.
    With my glimpy, glimpy, glimpy eedle,
    Lillum too tee a ta too a tee a ta a tally.

Five was combing down her hair,
    Fa fa fa fa lilly:
And I ne'er got a sight of her nae mair.
    With my glimpy, glimpy, glimpy eedle,
    Lillum too tee a ta too a tee a ta a tally.

Her neck and breast was like the snow,
    Fa fa fa fa lilly:
Then from the bore I was forced to go.
    With my glimpy, glimpy, glimpy eedle,
    Lillum too tee a ta too a tee a ta a tally.

355. *Hey, Wully Wine*

Hey, Wully wine, and How, Wully wine,
I hope for hame ye'll no' incline;
Ye'll better light, and stay a' night,
And I'll gie thee a lady fine.

I maun ride hame, I maun ride hame,
    And bide nae langer here;
The road is lang, the mirk soon on,
    And howlets mak' me fear.

Light down, and bide wi' us a' night,
    We'll choose for ye a bonnie lass,
Ye'll get your wield and pick o' them a'
    And the time it soon awa' will pass.

Wha will ye gie, if I wi' ye bide,
To be my bonny bonny bride,
And lie down lovely by my side?

I'll gie thee Kate o' Dinglebell,
A bonny body like yersell.

I'll stick her high in yon pear-tree
Sweet and meek, and sae is she:
I lo'ed her ance, but she's no' for me,
Yet I thank ye for your courtesy.

I'll gie thee Rozie o' the Cleugh,
I'm sure she'll please thee weel eneugh.

Up wi' her on the bare bane dyke,
She'll be rotten or[1] I'll be ripe:
She's made for some ither, and no' me,
Yet I thank ye for your courtesy.

1. Ere

Then I'll gie ye Nell o' sweet Sprinkell,
Owre Galloway she bears the bell.

I'll set her up in my bed-head,
And feed her wi' new milk and bread;
She's for nae ither, but just for me,
Sae I thank ye for your courtesy.

356. *Down in Yonder Meadow*

Down in yonder meadow where the green grass grows,
Pretty Pollie Pillicote bleaches her clothes.
She sang, she sang, she sang, oh, so sweet,
She sang, *Oh, come over!* across the street.
He kissed her, he kissed her, he bought her a gown,
A gown of rich cramasie out of the town.
He bought her a gown and a guinea gold ring,
A guinea, a guinea, a guinea gold ring;
Up street, and down, shine the windows made of glass,
Oh, isn't Pollie Pillicote a braw young lass?
Cherries in her cheeks, and ringlets her hair,
Hear her singing *Handy*, *Dandy* up and down the stair.

357. *Quoth John to Joan*

Quoth John to Joan, Will thou have me:
I prithee now, wilt? and I'll marry thee,
My cow, my calf, my house, my rents,
And all my lands and tenements:
      Oh, say, my Joan, will not that do?
      I cannot come every day to woo.

I've corn and hay in the barn hard-by,
And three fat hogs pent up in the sty,
I have a mare and she is coal black,
I ride on her tail to save my back.
  Then, say, my Joan, will not that do?
  I cannot come every day to woo.

I have a cheese upon the shelf,
And I cannot eat it all myself;
I've three good marks that lie in a rag,
In a nook of the chimney, instead of a bag.
  Then, say, my Joan, will not that do?
  I cannot come every day to woo.

To marry I would have thy consent,
But faith I never could compliment;
I can say nought but 'Hoy, gee ho!'
Words that belong to the cart and the plough.
  Oh, say, my Joan, will not that do?
  I cannot come every day to woo.

358. *My Mistress Is as Fair as Fine*

My mistress is as fair as fine,
 Milk-white fingers, cherry nose.
Like twinkling day-stars look her eyne,
 Lightening all things where she goes.
Fair as Phoebe, though not so fickle,
Smooth as glass, though not so brickle.

My heart is like a ball of snow
 Melting at her lukewarm sight;
Her fiery lips like night-worms glow,
 Shining clear as candle-light.
Neat she is, no feather lighter;
Bright she is, no daisy whiter.

359. *Diaphenia*

Diaphenia, like the daffadowndilly,
White as the sun, fair as the lily,
      Heigh ho, how I do love thee!
I do love thee as my lambs
Are belovèd of their dams –
  How blest were I if thou wouldst prove me.

Diaphenia, like the spreading roses,
That in thy sweets all sweets encloses,
      Fair sweet, how I do love thee!
I do love thee as each flower
Loves the sun's life-giving power,
  For, dead, thy breath to life might move me.

Diaphenia, like to all things blessèd,
When all thy praises are expressèd,
      Dear joy, how I do love thee!
As the birds do love the Spring,
Or the bees their careful king.
  Then in requite, sweet virgin, love me!

HENRY CONSTABLE

360. *Aeglamour's Lament*

Here she was wont to go, and here, and here!
Just where those daisies, pinks, and violets grow:
The world may find the spring by following her;
For other print her airy steps ne'er left:
Her treading would not bend a blade of grass,
Or shake the downy blow-ball from his stalk;
But like the soft west-wind she shot along;
And where she went, the flowers took thickest root
As she had sowed them with her odourous foot.

BEN JONSON

361. *My True-Love Hath My Heart*

My true-love hath my heart, and I have his,
　　By just exchange one for the other given;
I hold his dear, and mine he cannot miss;
　　There never was a better bargain driven.

His heart in me keeps me and him in one,
　　My heart in him his thoughts and senses guides;
He loves my heart, for once it was his own;
　　I cherish his because in me it bides.

His heart his wound receivèd from my sight,
　　My heart was wounded with his wounded heart;
For as from me on him his heart did light,
　　So still methought in me his heart did smart.

Both equal hurt, in this change sought our bliss,
My true-love hath my heart, and I have his.

SIR PHILIP SIDNEY

362. *A Birthday*

My heart is like a singing bird
　　Whose nest is in a watered shoot;
My heart is like an apple-tree
　　Whose boughs are bent with thickest fruit.
My heart is like a rainbow shell
　　That paddles in a halcyon sea;
My heart is gladder than all these
　　Because my love is come to me.

597

Raise me a dais of silk and down;
　　Hang it with vair and purple dyes;
Carve it in doves and pomegranates,
　　And peacocks with a hundred eyes;
Work it in gold and silver grapes,
　　In leaves and silver fleurs-de-lys;
Because the birthday of my life
　　Is come, my love is come to me.

CHRISTINA ROSSETTI

363. *Life of Life*

'VOICE IN THE AIR, SINGING'

Life of Life! thy lips enkindle
　　With their love the breath between them
And thy smiles before they dwindle
　　Make the cold air flare; then screen them
In those looks, where whoso gazes
Faints, entangled in their mazes.

Child of Light! thy limbs are burning
　　Through the vest which seems to hide them;
As the radiant lines of morning
　　Through the clouds ere they divide them;
And this atmosphere divinest
Shrouds thee wheresoe'er thou shinest.

Fair are others; none beholds thee,
　　But thy voice sounds low and tender
Like the fairest, for it folds thee
　　From the sight, that liquid splendour,
And all feel, yet see thee never,
　　As I feel now, lost for ever!

Lamp of Earth! where'er thou movest
   Its dim shapes are clad with brightness,
And the souls of whom thou lovest
   Walk upon the winds with lightness,
Till they fail, as I am failing,
Dizzy, lost, yet unbewailing! . . .

PERCY BYSSHE SHELLEY

364. *A Sonnet of the Moon*

Look how the pale Queen of the silent night
Doth cause the Ocean to attend upon her,
And he, as long as she is in his sight,
With his full tide is ready her to honour:

But when the silver waggon of the Moon
Is mounted up so high he cannot follow,
The sea calls home his crystal waves to moan,
And with low ebb doth manifest his sorrow.

So you that are the sovereign of my heart,
Have all my joys attending on your will,
My joys low-ebbing when you do depart,
When you return, their tide my heart doth fill.

So as you come, and as you do depart,
Joys ebb and flow within my tender heart.

CHARLES BEST

365. *The Outlaw of Loch Lene*

O many a day have I made good ale in the glen,
That came not of stream or malt, like the brewing of men:
My bed was the ground; my roof, the green-wood above;
And the wealth that I sought, one far kind glance from my Love.

Alas, on that night when the horses I drove from the field
That I was not near from terror my angel to shield!
She stretched forth her arms; her mantel she flung to the wind,
And swam o'er Loch Lene, her outlawed lover to find.

O would that a freezing sleet-winged tempest did sweep,
And I and my love were alone, far off on the deep;
I'd ask not a ship, or a bark, or a pinnace, to save –
With her hand round my waist, I'd fear not the wind or the wave.

'Tis down by the lake where the wild tree fringes its sides,
The maid of my heart, my fair one of Heaven resides:
I think, as at eve she wanders its mazes among,
The birds go to sleep by the sweet wild twist of her song.

JEREMIAH JOHN CALLANAN

366. *O What If the Fowler*

O what if the fowler my blackbird has taken?
    The roses of dawn blossom over the sea;
Awaken, my blackbird, awaken, awaken,
    And sing to me out of my red fuchsia tree!

O what if the fowler my blackbird has taken?
    The sun lifts his head from the lip of the sea –
Awaken, my blackbird, awaken, awaken,
    And sing to me out of my red fuchsia tree!

O what if the fowler my blackbird has taken?
    The mountain grows white with the birds of the sea;
But down in my garden forsaken, forsaken,
    I'll weep all the day by my red fuchsia tree!

CHARLES DALMON

367. *Whither Away?*

'Where are you going, Master mine?'
  'Mistress of mine, farewell!
Pledge me a cup of golden wine!
Light shall be dark and darkness shine
    Before I tell!'

'O go you by the firwoods blue?
  And by the Fairies' Trysting Tree?'
'No, for the path is grown with rue
And nightshade's purple fruit, since you
    Walked there with me!'

'O go you by the pastures high –
  A grassy road and daisies fair?'
'No, for I saw them fade and die
On the bright evening, love, that I
    Sat with you there.'

MARY COLERIDGE

368. *Bonny Barbara Allan*

It was in and about the Martinmas time,
  When the green leaves were a falling,
That Sir John Graeme, in the West Country,
  Fell in love with Barbara Allan.

He sent his man down through the town,
  To the place where she was dwelling:
'O haste and come to my master dear,
  Gin ye be Barbara Allan.'

O hooly, hooly¹ rose she up,
　　To the place where he was lying,
And when she drew the curtain by; –
　　'Young man, I think, you're dying.'

'O it's I'm sick, and very, very sick,
　　And 'tis a' for Barbara Allan.' –
'O the better for me ye's never be,
　　Tho your heart's blood were a spilling.

'O dinna ye mind, young man,' said she,
　　'When ye was in the tavern a-drinking,
That ye eade the healths gae round and round,
　　And slighted Barbara Allan?'

He turned his face unto the wall,
　　And death was with him dealing:
'Adieu, adieu, my dear friends all,
　　And be kind to Barbara Allan.'

She had not gane a mile but twa,
　　When she heard the dead-bell ringing,
And every jow that the dead-bell gied,
　　It cryed, *Woe to Barbara Allan!*

'O mother, mother, make my bed!
　　O make it saft and narrow!
Since my love died for me to-day,
　　I'll die for him to-morrow.'

369. *Proud Maisie*

Proud Maisie is in the wood,
　　Walking so early;
Sweet Robin sits on the bush,
　　Singing so rarely.

1. Slowly, softly

'Tell me, thou bonny bird,
    When shall I marry me?'
'When six braw gentlemen
    Kirkward shall carry ye.'

'Who makes the bridal bed,
    Birdie, say truly?'
'The grey-headed sexton
    That delves the grave duly.'

'The glowworm o'er grave and stone
    Shall light thee steady;
The owl from the steeple sing
    Welcome, proud lady.'

SIR WALTER SCOTT

370. *A Leave Taking*

Let us go hence, my songs; she will not hear.
Let us go hence together without fear;
Keep silence now, for singing-time is over,
And over all old things and all things dear.
She loves not you nor me as all we love her.
Yea, though we sang as angels in her ear,
        She would not hear.

Let us rise up and part; she will not know.
Let us go seaward as the great winds go,
Full of blown sand and foam; what help is here?
There is no help, for all these things are so,
And all the world is bitter as a tear.
And how these things are, though ye strove to show,
        She would not know.

Let us go hence and rest; she will not love.
We gave love many dreams and days to keep,
Flowers without scent, and fruits that would not grow,
Saying, 'If thou wilt, thrust in thy sickle and reap.'
All is reaped now; no grass is left to mow;
And we that sowed, though all we feel on sleep,
        She would not weep.

Let us go hence and rest; she will not love.
She shall not hear us if we sing hereof,
Nor see love's ways, how sore they are and steep.
Come hence, let be, lie still; it is enough.
Love is a barren sea, bitter and deep;
And though she saw all heaven in flower above,
        She would not love.

Let us give up, go down; she will not care.
Though all the stars made gold of all the air,
And the sea moving saw before it move
One moon-flower making all the foam-flowers fair;
Though all those waves went over us, and drove
Deep down the stifling lips and drowning hair,
        She would not care.

Let us go hence, go hence; she will not see.
Sing all once more together; surely she,
She, too, remembering days and words that were,
Will turn a little toward us, sighing; but we,
We are hence, we are gone, as though we had not been there.
Nay, and though all men seeing had pity on me,
        She would not see.

       ALGERNON CHARLES SWINBURNE

371. *The Unquiet Grave*

'The wind doth blow to-day, my love,
   And a few small drops of rain;
I never had but one true love,
   In cold grave she was lain.

'I'll do as much for my true love
   As any young man may;
I'll sit and mourn all at her grave
   For a twelvemonth and a day.'

The twelvemonth and a day being up,
   The dead began to speak:
'Oh who sits weeping on my grave,
   And will not let me sleep?'

''Tis I, my love, sits on your grave,
   And will not let you sleep;
For I crave one kiss of your clay-cold lips,
   And that is all I seek.'

'You crave one kiss of my clay-cold lips;
   But my breath smells earthy strong;
If you have one kiss of my clay-cold lips,
   Your time will not be long.

''Tis down in yonder garden green,
   Love, where we used to walk,
The finest flower that ere was seen
   Is withered to a stalk.

'The stalk is withered dry, my love,
   So will our hearts decay;
So make yourself content, my love,
   Till God calls you away.'

372. *A Lament: 1547*

Departe, departe, departe –
Allace! I most departe
From hir that hes my hart,
    With hairt full soir;
Aganis my will in deid,
And can find no remeid:
I wait the pains of deid –
    Can do no moir . . .

Adew, my ain sueit thing,
My joy and comforting,
My mirth and sollesing
    Of erdly gloir:
Fair weill, my lady bricht,
And my remembrance rycht;
Fair weill and haif gud nycht:
    I say no moir.

ALEXANDER SCOTT

373. *I Died True*

Lay a garland on my hearse
    Of the dismal yew;
Maidens, willow branches bear;
    Say I died true.

My love was false, but I was firm
    From my hour of birth.
Upon my buried body lie
    Lightly, gentle earth!

JOHN FLETCHER

374. *Song*

How should I your true love know
  From another one?
By his Cockle hat and staffe,
  And his Sandal shoone.

He is dead and gone, Lady,
  He is dead and gone, –
At his head a grasse-greene Turfe,
  At his heeles a stone.

White his Shrowd as the Mountain Snow,
  Larded with sweet flowers:
Which bewept to the grave did not go,
  With true-love showres.

WILLIAM SHAKESPEARE

375. *It Was the Time of Roses*

It was not in the winter
Our loving lot was cast:
It was the time of roses –
We plucked them as we passed!

That churlish season never frowned
On early lovers yet!
O, no – the world was newly crowned
With flowers, when first we met.

'Twas twilight, and I bade you go,
But still you held me fast:
It was the time of roses –
We plucked them as we passed ...

THOMAS HOOD

376. *Auld Robin Gray*

When the sheep are in the fauld, and the kye¹ at hame,
And a' the warld to rest are gane,
The wares o' my heart fa' in showers frae my ee,
While my gudeman² lies sound by me.

Young Jamie lo'ed me weel, and sought for his bride,
But saving a croun he had naething else beside:
To make the croun a pund, young Jamie gaed to sea,
And the croun and the pund were baith for me.

He hadna been awa a week but only twa,
When my father brak his arm, and the cow was stown awa;
My mother she fell sick, and my Jamie at the sea –
And auld Robin Gray came a-courtin' me.

My father couldna work, and my mother couldna spin;
I toiled day and night, but their bread I couldna win;
Auld Rob maintained them baith, and wi' tears in his ee
Said, 'Jennie, for their sakes, O, marry me!'

My heart it said nay; I look'd for Jamie back;
But the wind it blew high, and the ship it was a wrack;
His ship it was a wrack ... Why didna Jamie dee?
Or why do I live to cry, Wae's me?

My father urgit sair: my mother didna speak,
But she looked in my face till my heart was like to break:
They gi'ed him my hand, but my heart was at the sea,
Sae auld Robin Gray he was gudeman to me.

I hadna been a wife a week but only four,
When mournfu' as I sat on the stane at the door,
I saw my Jamie's wraith, for I couldna think it he –
Till he said, 'I'm come home to marry thee.'

1. Cows   2. Husband

O, sair, sair did we greet,[3] and muckle[4] did we say;
We took but ae kiss, and I bad him gang away:
I wish that I were dead, but I'm no like to dee;
And why was I born to say, Wae's me!

I gang like a ghaist, and I carena to spin;
I daurna think on Jamie, for that wad be a sin;
But I'll do my best a gude wife aye to be,
For auld Robin Gray, he is kind unto me.

LADY ANNE LINDSAY

377. *The Lawlands o' Holland*

'The love that I hae chosen,
    I'll therewith be content;
The saut sea sall be frozen
    Before that I repent.
Repent it sall I never
    Until the day I dee;
But the Lawlands o' Holland
    Hae twinned my love and me.

'My love he built a bonny ship,
    And set her to the main,
Wi' twenty-four brave mariners
    To sail her out and hame.
But the weary wind began to rise,
    The sea began to rout,
And my love and his bonny ship
    Turned withershins about.

<hr>

3. Weep   4. Much

'There sall nae mantle cross my back,
    No kaim gae in my hair,
Neither sall coal nor candle-light
    Shine in my bower mair;
Nor sall I choose anither love,
    Until the day I dee,
Sin' the Lawlands o' Holland,
    Hae twinned my love and me.'

'Noo haud your tongue, my daughter dear,
    Be still, and bide content;
There's ither lads in Galloway;
    Ye needna sair lament.'
'O there is nane in Galloway,
    There's nane at a' for me.
I never lo'ed a lad but ane,
    And he's drowned in the sea.'

378. *The Churchyard on the Sands*

My love lies in the gates of foam,
    The last dear wreck of shore;
The naked sea-marsh binds her home,
    The sand her chamber door.

The gray gull flaps the written stones,
    The ox-birds chase the tide;
And near that narrow field of bones
    Great ships at anchor ride.

Black piers with crust of dripping green,
    One foreland, like a hand,
O'er intervals of grass between
    Dim lonely dunes of sand.

A church of silent weathered looks,
    A breezy reddish tower,
A yard whose wounded resting-nooks
    Are tinged with sorrel flower.

In peace the swallow's eggs are laid
    Along the belfry walls;
The tempest does not reach her shade,
    The rain her silent halls.

But sails are sweet in summer sky,
    The lark throws down a lay;
The long salt levels steam and dry,
    The cloud-heart melts away.

And patches of the sea-pink shine,
    The pied crows poise and come;
The mallow hangs, the bind-weeds twine,
    Where her sweet lips are dumb.

The passion of the wave is mute;
    No sound or ocean shock;
No music save the thrilling flute
    That marks the curlew flock . . .

                LORD DE TABLEY

379. *Rose Aylmer*

Ah, what avails the sceptred race,
    Ah, what the form divine!
What every virtue, every grace!
    Rose Aylmer, all were thine.

Rose Aylmer, whom these wakeful eyes
  May weep, but never see,
A night of memories and sighs
  I consecrate to thee.

WALTER SAVAGE LANDOR

380. *To Helen*

Helen, thy beauty is to me
  Like those Nicaean barks of yore,
That gently, o'er a perfumed sea,
    The weary, wayworn wanderer bore
    To his own native shore.

On desperate seas long wont to roam,
  The hyacinth hair, thy classic face,
Thy Naiad air, have brought me home
    To the glory that was Greece
    And the grandeur that was Rome.

Lo! in yon brilliant window-niche
  How statue-like I see thee stand,
The agate lamp within thy hand!
    Ah, Psyche, from the regions which
    Are Holy Land!

EDGAR ALLAN POE

381. *There Is a Lady Sweet and Kind*

There is a Lady sweet and kind,
Was never face so pleased my mind;
I did but see her passing by,
And yet I love her till I die.

Her gesture, motion, and her smiles,
Her wit, her voice, my heart beguiles,
Beguiles my heart, I know not why,
And yet I love her till I die . . .

Cupid is wingèd and doth range,
Her country so my love doth change:
But change she earth, or change she sky,
Yet will I love her till I die.

382. *Love Not Me for Comely Grace*

Love not me for comely grace,
For my pleasing eye or face,
Not for any outward part:
No, nor for my constant heart!
   For these may fail or turn to ill:
     So thou and I shall sever:
Keep therefore a true woman's eye,
And love me still, but know not why!
   So hast thou the same reason still
     To doat upon me ever.

383. *Now Wolde*

Now wolde I faine some merthes[1] make,
All only for my lady sake,
   When her I see;
But now I am so far fro her
   It will not be.

1. Praises

Though I be far out of her sight
I am her man both day and night
    And so will be.
Therefore wolde; as I love her,
    She lovèd me.

When she is mery, then I am glad;
When she is sory, then I am sad;
    And causè why,[2]
For he liveth not that loveth her
    As well as I.

She saith that she hath seen it written
That 'seldom seen is soon forgotten';
    It is not so.
For in good feith, save only her,
    I love no mo.[3]

384. *Egypt's Might Is Tumbled Down*

Egypt's might is tumbled down
    Down a-down the deeps of thought;
Greece is fallen and Troy town,
Glorious Rome hath lost her crown,
    Venice' pride is nought.

But the dreams their children dreamed
    Fleeting, unsubstantial, vain,
Shadowy as the shadows seemed,
Airy nothing, as they deemed,
    These remain.

MARY COLERIDGE

2. Good reason why   3. More

385. *Dream Love*

Young Love lies sleeping
  In May-time of the year.
Among the lilies,
  Lapped in the tender light:
White lambs come grazing,
  White doves come building there;
And round about him
  The May-bushes are white.

Soft moss the pillow
  For oh, a softer cheek;
Broad leaves cast shadow
  Upon the heavy eyes:
There winds and waters
  Grow lulled and scarcely speak;
There twilight lingers
  The longest in the skies.

Young Love lies dreaming;
  But who shall tell the dream?
A perfect sunlight
  On rustling forest tips;
Or perfect moonlight
  Upon a rippling stream;
Or perfect silence,
  Or song of cherished lips.

Burn odours round him
  To fill the drowsy air;
Weave silent dances
  Around him to and fro;
For oh, in waking
  The sights are not so fair,
And song and silence
  Are not like these below.

Young Love lies dreaming
  Till summer days are gone, –
Dreaming and drowsing
  Away to perfect sleep:
He sees the beauty
  Sun hath not looked upon,
And tastes the fountain
  Unutterably deep.

Him perfect music
  Doth hush unto his rest,
And through the pauses
  The perfect silence calms.
Oh, poor the voices
  Of earth from east to west,
And poor earth's stillness
  Between her stately palms.

Young Love lies drowsing
  Away to poppied death;
Cool shadows deepen
  Across the sleeping face:
So fails the summer
  With warm, delicious breath;
And what hath autumn
  To give us in its place?

Draw close the curtains
  Of branched evergreen;
Change cannot touch them
  With fading fingers sere:
Here the first violets
  Perhaps will bud unseen,
And a dove, may be,
  Return to nestle here.

CHRISTINA ROSSETTI

386. *At Common Dawn*

At common dawn there is a voice of bird
So sweet, 'tis kin to pain;
For love of earthly life it needs be heard,
And lets not sleep again.

This bird I did one time at midnight hear
In wet November wood
Say to himself his lyric faint and clear
As one at daybreak should.

He ceased; the covert breathed no other sound,
Nor moody answer made;
But all the world at beauty's worship found,
Was waking in the glade.

VIVIAN LOCKE ELLIS

'ECHO THEN SHALL AGAIN
TELL HER I FOLLOW'

387. Glycine's Song

A sunny shaft did I behold,
   From sky to earth it slanted:
And poised therein a bird so bold –
   Sweet bird, thou wert enchanted!

He sank, he rose, he twinkled, he trolled
   Within that shaft of sunny mist;
His eyes of fire, his beak of gold,
   All else of amethyst!

And thus he sang: 'Adieu! adieu!
Love's dreams prove seldom true.
The blossoms, they make no delay:
The sparkling dew-drops will not stay.
   Sweet month of May,
     We must away;
     Far, far away!
       To-day! to-day!'

SAMUEL TAYLOR COLERIDGE

388. The Crystal Cabinet

The Maiden caught me in the wild,
Where I was dancing merrily;
She put me into her Cabinet,
And locked me up with a golden key.

This Cabinet is formed of Gold
And Pearl and Crystal shining bright,
And within it opens into a World
And a little lovely Moony Night.

Another England there I saw
Another London with its Tower,
Another Thames and other Hills,
And another pleasant Surrey Bower.

Another Maiden like herself,
Translucent, lovely, shining clear,
Threefold each in the other closed –
O, what a pleasant trembling fear!

O, what a smile! a Threefold Smile
Filled me, that like a flame I burned;
I bent to kiss the lovely Maid,
And found a Threefold Kiss returned.

I strove to seize the inmost form
With ardour fierce and hands of flame,
But burst the Crystal Cabinet,
And like a Weeping Babe became –

A Weeping Babe upon the wild,
And Weeping Woman pale reclined,
And in the outward air again
I filled with woes the passing wind.

WILLIAM BLAKE

389. *The Chase*

Art thou gone in haste?
   I'll not forsake thee;
Runn'st thou ne'er so fast?
   I'll overtake thee:
O'er the dales, o'er the downs,
   Through the green meadows,
From the fields through the towns,
   To the dim shadows.

All along the plain,
    To the low fountains,
Up and down again
    From the high mountains;

Echo then shall again
    Tell her I follow,
And the floods to the woods
    Carry my holla!
        Holla!
    Ce! la! ho! ho! hu!

WILLIAM ROWLEY

390. *Tony O!*

Over the bleak and barren snow
A voice there came a-calling;
'Where are you going to, Tony O!
Where are you going this morning?'

'I am going where there are rivers of wine,
The mountains bread and honey;
There Kings and Queens do mind the swine,
And the poor have all the money.'

COLIN FRANCIS

391. *Romance*

When I was but thirteen or so
    I went into a golden land,
Chimborazo, Cotopaxi
    Took me by the hand.

623

My father died, my brother too,
  They passed like fleeting dreams.
I stood where Popocatapetl
  In the sunlight gleams.

I dimly heard the master's voice
  And boys far-off at play,
Chimborazo, Cotopaxi
  Had stolen me away.

I walked in a great golden dream
  To and fro from school –
Shining Popocatapetl
  The dusty streets did rule.

I walked home with a gold dark boy,
  And never a word I'd say,
Chimborazo, Cotopaxi
  Had taken my speech away:

I gazed entranced upon his face
  Fairer than any flower –
O shining Popocatapetl
  It was thy magic hour:

The houses, people, traffic seemed
  Thin fading dreams by day,
Chimborazo, Cotopaxi
  They had stolen my soul away!

WALTER J. TURNER

392. *Hallo My Fancy*

In melancholic fancy,
            Out of myself,
In the vulcan dancy,
            All the world surveying,
            Nowhere staying,
    Just like a fairy elf;
Out o'er the tops of highest mountains skipping,
Out o'er the hill, the trees and valleys tripping,
Out o'er the ocean seas, without an oar or shipping, –
    Hallo my fancy, whither wilt thou go?

            Amidst the misty vapours
            Fain would I know
            What doth cause the tapers;
            Why the clouds benight us
            And affright us.
    While we travel here below;
Fain would I know what makes the roaring thunder,
And what these lightnings be that rend the clouds asunder,
And what these comets are on which we gaze and wonder –
    Hallo my fancy, whither wilt thou go?

            Fain would I know the reason,
            Why the little ant,
            All the summer season,
            Layeth up provision
            On condition
    To know no winter's want.
And how housewives, that are so good and painful,
Do unto their husbands prove so good and gainful;
And why the lazy drones to them do prove disdainful –
    Hallo my fancy, whither wilt thou go? . . .

Amidst the foamy ocean,
Fain would I know
What doth cause the motion,
And returning
In its journeying,
And doth so seldom swerve?
And how the little fishes that swim beneath salt waters,
Do never blind their eye; methinks it is a matter
An inch above the reach of old Erra Pater! —
Hallo my fancy, whither wilt thou go?

Fain would I be resolvèd
How things are done;
And where the bull was calvèd
Of bloody Phalaris,
And where the tailor is
That works to the man i' the moon!
Fain would I know how Cupid aims so rightly;
And how the little fairies do dance and leap so lightly,
And where fair Cynthia makes her ambles nightly —
Hallo my fancy, whither wilt thou go?

In conceit like Phaeton
I'll mount Phoebus' chair
Having ne'er a hat on,
All my hair a-burning
In my journeying;
Hurrying through the air.
Fain would I hear his fiery horses neighing
And see how they on foamy bits are playing,
All the stars and planets I will be surveying! —
Hallo my fancy, whither wilt thou go?

O from what ground of nature
Doth the pelican,
That self devouring creature

        Prove so froward
        And untoward,
     Her vitals for to strain!
And why the subtle fox, while in death's wounds a-lying,
Do not lament his pangs by howling and by crying,
And why the milk-swan doth sing when she's a-dying –
   Hallo my fancy, whither wilt thou go?

        Fain would I conclude this,
        At least make essay;
        What similitude is:
        Why fowls of a feather
        Flock and fly together,
     And lambs know beasts of prey;
How Nature's alchemists, these small laborious creatures,
Acknowledge still a prince in ordering their matters,
And suffer none to live who slothing lose their features –
   Hallo my fancy, whither wilt thou go? . . .

        To know this world's centre
        Height, depth, breadth and length,
        Fain would I adventure
        To search the hid attractions
        Of magnetic actions
     And adamantine strength.
Fain would I know, if in some lofty mountain,
Where the moon sojourns, if there be tree or fountain;
If there be beasts of prey, or yet be fields to hunt in –
   Hallo my fancy, whither wilt thou go? . . .

        Hallo my fancy, hallo,
        Stay, stay at home with me,
        I can no longer follow,
        For thou hast betrayed me,
        And bewrayed me;
     It is too much for thee.

Stay, stay at home with me, leave off thy lofty soaring;
Stay then at home with me, and on thy books be poring;
For he that goes abroad, lays little up in storing –
Thou'rt welcome my fancy, welcome home to me.

WILLIAM CLELAND

393. *Sonnet*

There was an Indian, who had known no change,
   Who strayed content along a sunlit beach
Gathering shells. He heard a sudden strange
   Commingled noise: looked up; and gasped for speech.
For in the bay, where nothing was before,
   Moved on the sea, by magic, huge canoes,
With bellying clothes on poles, and not one oar,
   And fluttering coloured signs and clambering crews.

And he, in fear, this naked man alone,
   His fallen hands forgetting all their shells,
His lips gone pale, knelt low behind a stone,
   And stared, and saw, and did not understand,
   Columbus's doom-burdened caravels
   Slant to the shore, and all their seamen land.

J. C. SQUIRE

394. *On First Looking into Chapman's Homer*

Much have I travelled in the realms of gold,
   And many goodly states and kingdoms seen:
   Round many western islands have I been
Which bards in fealty to Apollo hold.

Oft of one wide expanse had I been told
    That deep-browed Homer ruled as his demesne;
    Yet did I never breathe its pure serene
Till I heard Chapman speak out loud and bold:

Then felt I like some watcher of the skies
    When a new planet swims into his ken;
Or like stout Cortez, when with eagle eyes

He stared at the Pacific – and all his men
    Looked at each other with a wild surmise –
Silent, upon a peak in Darien.

JOHN KEATS

395. *To Sea*

To sea, to sea! The calm is o'er;
The wanton water leaps in sport,
And rattles down the pebbly shore;
The dolphin wheels, the sea-cows snort,
And unseen Mermaids' pearly song
Comes bubbling up, the weeds among.
    Fling broad the sail, dip deep the oar:
To sea, to sea! the calm is o'er.

To sea, to sea! our wide-winged bark
Shall billowy cleave its sunny way,
And with its shadow, fleet and dark,
Break the caved Tritons' azure day,
Like mighty eagle soaring light
O'er antelopes on Alpine height.
    The anchor heaves, the ship swings free,
The sails swell full. To sea, to sea!

THOMAS LOVELL BEDDOES

396. *Bermudas*

Where the remote Bermudas ride,
In the Ocean's bosom unespied,
From a small boat, that rowed along,
The listening winds received this song:

    'What should we do but sing His praise,
That led us through the watery maze,
Unto an isle so long unknown,
And yet far kinder than our own?
Where He the huge sea-monsters wracks
That lift the deep upon their backs,
He lands us on a grassy stage,
Safe from the storms' and prelates' rage:
He gave us this eternal Spring
Which here enamels everything,
And sends the fowls to us in care
On daily visits through the air:
He hangs in shades the orange bright,
Like golden lamps in a green night,
And does in the pomegranates close
Jewels more rich than Ormus shows;
He makes the figs our mouths to meet,
And throws the melons at our feet;
But apples plants of such a price
No tree could ever bear them twice.
With cedars, chosen by His hand
From Lebanon, He stores the land,
And makes the hollow seas, that roar,
Proclaim the ambergris on shore.
He cast (of which we rather boast)
The Gospel's pearl upon our coast;
And in these rocks for us did frame
A temple where to sound His name.

Oh! let our voice His praise exalt,
Till it arrive at Heaven's vault,
Which, thence (perhaps) rebounding, may
Echo beyond the Mexique bay.'

Thus sung they, in the English boat,
A holy and a cheerful note;
And all the way, to guide their chime,
With falling oars they kept the time.

ANDREW MARVELL

397. *The Old Ships*

I have seen old ships sail like swans asleep
Beyond the village which men still call Tyre,
With leaden age o'ercargoed, dipping deep
For Famagusta and the hidden sun
That rings black Cyprus with a lake of fire;
And all those ships were certainly so old –
Who knows how oft with squat and noisy gun,
Questing brown slaves or Syrian oranges,
The pirate Genoese
Hell-raked them till they rolled
Blood, water, fruit and corpses up the hold.
But now through friendly seas they softly run,
Painted the mid-sea blue or shore-sea green,
Still patterned with the vine and grapes in gold.

But I have seen
Pointing her shapely shadows from the dawn
An image tumbled on a rose-swept bay
A drowsy ship of some yet older day;
And, wonder's breath indrawn,

Thought I – who knows – who knows – but in that same
(Fished up beyond Aeaea, patched up new
– Stern painted brighter blue —)
That talkative, bald-headed seaman came
(Twelve patient comrades sweating at the oar)
From Troy's doom-crimson shore,
And with great lies about his wooden horse
Set the crew laughing, and forgot his course.
It was so old a ship – who knows, who knows?
– And yet so beautiful, I watched in vain
To see the mast burst open with a rose,
And the whole deck put on its leaves again.

JAMES ELROY FLECKER

398. *The Rime of the Ancient Mariner*

IN SEVEN PARTS

ARGUMENT: *How a Ship having passed the Line is driven by storms to the cold Country towards the South Pole; and how from thence she made her course to the Tropical Latitude of the great Pacific Ocean; and of the strange things that befell; and in what manner the Ancient Mariner came back to his own Country.*

PART I

It is an ancient Mariner,
And he stoppeth one of three.
'By thy long grey beard and glittering eye,
Now wherefore stopp'st thou me?

The Bridegroom's doors are opened wide,
And I am next of kin;
The guests are met, the feast is set:
May'st hear the merry din.'

He holds him with his skinny hand,
'There was a ship,' quoth he.
'Hold off! unhand me, grey-beard loon!'
Eftsoons his hand dropt he.

He holds him with his glittering eye –
The Wedding-Guest stood still,
And listens like a three years' child:
The Mariner hath his will.

The Wedding-Guest sat on a stone:
He cannot choose but hear;
And thus spake on that ancient man,
The bright-eyed Mariner.

'The ship was cheered, the harbour cleared,
Merrily did we drop
Below the kirk, below the hill,
Below the lighthouse top.

The Sun came up upon the left,
Out of the sea came he!
And he shone bright, and on the right
Went down into the sea.

Higher and higher every day,
Till over the mast at noon –'
The Wedding-Guest here beat his breast,
For he heard the loud bassoon.

The bride hath paced into the hall,
Red as a rose is she;
Nodding their heads before her goes
The merry minstrelsy.

The Wedding-Guest he beat his breast,
Yet he cannot choose but hear;
And thus spake on that ancient man,
The bright-eyed Mariner.

'And now the STORM-BLAST came, and he
Was tyrannous and strong:
He struck with his o'ertaking wings,
And chased us south along.

With sloping masts and dipping prow,
As who pursued with yell and blow
Still treads the shadow of his foe,
And forward bends his head,
The ship drove fast, loud roared the blast,
And southward aye we fled.

And now there came both mist and snow,
And it grew wondrous cold:
And ice, mast-high, came floating by,
As green as emerald.

And through the drifts the snowy clifts
Did send a dismal sheen:
Nor shapes of men nor beasts we ken –
The ice was all between.

The ice was here, the ice was there,
The ice was all around:
It cracked and growled, and roared and howled,
Like noises in a swound!

At length did cross an Albatross,
Thorough the fog it came;
As if it had been a Christian soul,
We hailed it in God's name.

It ate the food it ne'er had eat,
And round and round it flew.
The ice did split with a thunder-fit;
The helmsman steered us through!

And a good south wind sprung up behind;
The Albatross did follow,
And every day, for food or play,
Came to the mariner's hollo!

In mist or cloud, on mast or shroud,
It perched for vespers nine;
Whiles all the night, through fog-smoke white,
Glimmered the white Moon-shine.'

'God save thee, ancient Mariner!
From the fiends, that plague thee thus! –
Why look'st thou so?'
                – 'With my cross-bow
I shot the ALBATROSS.'

PART II

The Sun now rose upon the right:
Out of the sea came he,
Still hid in mist, and on the left
Went down into the sea.

And the good south wind still blew behind,
But no sweet bird did follow,
Nor any day for food or play
Came to the mariner's hollo!

And I had done a hellish thing,
And it would work 'em woe:
For all averred, I had killed the bird
That made the breeze to blow.
Ah wretch! said they, the bird to slay,
That made the breeze to blow!

Nor dim nor red, like God's own head,
The glorious Sun uprist:
Then all averred, I had killed the bird
That brought the fog and mist.

'Twas right, said they, such birds to slay,
That bring the fog and mist.

The fair breeze blew, the white foam flew.
The furrow followed free;
We were the first that ever burst
Into that silent sea.

Down dropt the breeze, the sails dropt down,
'Twas sad as sad could be;
And we did speak only to break
The silence of the sea!

All in a hot and copper sky,
The bloody Sun, at noon,
Right up above the mast did stand,
No bigger than the Moon.

Day after day, day after day,
We stuck, nor breath nor motion;
As idle as a painted ship
Upon a painted ocean.

Water, water, every where,
And all the boards did shrink;
Water, water, every where,
Nor any drop to drink.

The very deep did rot: O Christ!
That ever this should be!
Yea, slimy things did crawl with legs
Upon the slimy sea.

About, about, in reel and rout
The death-fires danced at night;
The water, like a witch's oils,
Burnt green, and blue, and white.

And some in dreams assurèd were
Of the Spirit that plagued us so;
Nine fathom deep he had followed us
From the land of mist and snow.

And every tongue, through utter drought,
Was withered at the root;
We could not speak, no more than if
We had been choked with soot.

Ah! well a-day! what evil looks
Had I from old and young!
Instead of the cross, the Albatross
About my neck was hung.

PART III

'There passed a weary time. Each throat
Was parched, and glazed each eye.
A weary time! a weary time!
How glazed each weary eye,
When looking westward, I beheld
A something in the sky.

At first it seemed a little speck,
And then it seemed a mist;
It moved and moved, and took at last
A certain shape, I wist.

A speck, a mist, a shape, I wist!
And still it neared and neared:
As if it dodged a water-sprite,
It plunged and tacked and veered.

With throats unslaked, with black lips baked,
We could nor laugh nor wail;
Through utter drought all dumb we stood!
I bit my arm, I sucked the blood,
And cried, A sail! a sail!

With throats unslaked, with black lips baked,
Agape they heard me call:
Gramercy! they for joy did grin,
And all at once their breath drew in,
As they were drinking all.

See! see! (I cried) she tacks no more!
Hither to work us weal;
Without a breeze, without a tide,
She steadies with upright keel!

The western wave was all a-flame,
The day was well nigh done!
Almost upon the western wave
Rested the broad bright Sun;
When that strange shape drove suddenly
Betwixt us and the Sun.

And straight the Sun was flecked with bars,
(Heaven's Mother send us grace!)
As if through a dungeon-grate he peered
With broad and burning face.

Alas! (thought I, and my heart beat loud)
How fast she nears and nears!
Are those *her* sails that glance in the Sun,
Like restless gossameres?

Are those *her* ribs through which the Sun
Did peer, as through a grate?
And is that Woman all her crew?
Is that a DEATH? and are there two?
Is DEATH that woman's mate?

Her lips were red, *her* looks were free,
Her locks were yellow as the gold:
Her skin was as white as leprosy,
The Night-mare LIFE-IN-DEATH was she,
Who thicks man's blood with cold.

The naked hulk alongside came,
And the twain were casting dice;
'The game is done! I've won! I've won!'
Quoth she, and whistles thrice.

The Sun's rim dips: the stars rush out:
At one stride comes the dark;
With far-heard whisper, o'er the sea,
Off shot the spectre-bark.

We listened and looked sideways up!
Fear at my heart, as at a cup,
My life-blood seemed to sip!
The stars were dim, and thick the night,
The steersman's face by his lamp gleamed white:

From the sails the dew did drip –
Till clomb above the eastern bar
The hornèd Moon, with one bright star
Within the nether tip.

One after one, by the star-dogged Moon,
Too quick for groan or sigh,
Each turned his face with a ghastly pang,
And cursed me with his eye.

Four times fifty living men,
(And I heard nor sigh nor groan)
With heavy thump, a lifeless lump,
They dropped down one by one.

The souls did from their bodies fly, –
They fled to bliss or woe!
And every soul, it passed me by,
Like the whizz of my cross-bow!'

PART IV

'I fear thee, ancient Mariner!
I fear thy skinny hand!
And thou art long, and lank, and brown,
As is the ribbed sea-sand.

I fear thee and thy glittering eye,
And thy skinny hand, so brown.' –
'Fear not, fear not, thou Wedding-Guest!
This body dropt not down.

Alone, alone, all, all alone,
Alone on a wide wide sea!
And never a saint took pity on
My soul in agony.

The many men, so beautiful!
And they all dead did lie:
And a thousand thousand slimy things
Lived on; and so did I.

I looked upon the rotting sea,
And drew my eyes away;
I looked upon the rotting deck,
And there the dead men lay.

I looked to heaven, and tried to pray;
But or ever a prayer had gusht,
A wicked whisper came, and made
My heart as dry as dust.

I closed my lids, and kept them close,
And the balls like pulses beat;
For the sky and the sea, and the sea and the sky
Lay like a load on my weary eye,
And the dead were at my feet.

The cold sweat melted from their limbs,
Nor rot nor reek did they:
The look with which they looked on me
Had never passed away.

An orphan's curse would drag to hell
A spirit from on high;
But oh! more horrible than that
Is the curse in a dead man's eye!
Seven days, seven nights, I saw that curse,
And yet I could not die.

The moving Moon went up the sky,
And no where did abide:
Softly she was going up,
And a star or two beside —

Her beams bemocked the sultry main,
Like April hoar-frost spread;
But where the ship's huge shadow lay,
The charmèd water burnt alway
A still and awful red.

Beyond the shadow of the ship,
I watched the water-snakes:
They moved in tracks of shining white,
And when they reared, the elfish light
Fell off in hoary flakes.

Within the shadow of the ship
I watched their rich attire:
Blue, glossy green, and velvet black,
They coiled and swam; and every track
Was a flash of golden fire.

O happy living things! no tongue
Their beauty might declare:
A spring of love gushed from my heart,
And I blessed them unaware:
Sure my kind saint took pity on me,
And I blessed them unaware.

The self-same moment I could pray;
And from my neck so free
The Albatross fell off, and sank
Like lead into the sea.

PART V

Oh sleep! it is a gentle thing,
Beloved from pole to pole!
To Mary Queen the praise be given!
She sent the gentle sleep from Heaven,
That slid into my soul.

The silly buckets on the deck,
That had so long remained,
I dreamt that they were filled with dew;
And when I awoke, it rained.

My lips were wet, my throat was cold,
My garments all were dank;
Sure I had drunken in my dreams,
And still my body drank.

I moved, and could not feel my limbs:
I was so light – almost
I thought that I had died in sleep,
And was a blessèd ghost.

And soon I heard a roaring wind:
It did not come anear;
But with its sound it shook the sails,
That were so thin and sere.

The upper air burst into life!
And a hundred fire-flags sheen,
To and fro they were hurried about!
And to and fro, and in and out,
The wan stars danced between.

And the coming wind did roar more loud,
And the sails did sigh like sedge;
And the rain poured down from one black cloud;
The Moon was at its edge.

The thick black cloud was cleft, and still
The Moon was at its side:
Like waters shot from some high crag,
The lightning fell with never a jag,
A river steep and wide.

The loud wind never reached the ship,
Yet now the ship moved on!
Beneath the lightning and the Moon
The dead men gave a groan.

They groaned, they stirred, they all uprose,
Nor spake, nor moved their eyes;
It had been strange, even in a dream,
To have seen those dead men rise.

The helmsman steered, the ship moved on;
Yet never a breeze up-blew;
The mariners all 'gan work the ropes,
Where they were wont to do;
They raised their limbs like lifeless tools —
We were a ghastly crew.

The body of my brother's son
Stood by me, knee to knee:
The body and I pulled at one rope,
But he said nought to me.' —

'I fear thee, ancient Mariner!' –
'Be calm, thou Wedding-Guest!
'Twas not those souls that fled in pain,
Which to their corses came again,
But a troop of spirits blest:

For when it dawned – they dropped their arms,
And clustered round the mast;
Sweet sounds rose slowly through their mouths,
And from their bodies passed.

Around, around, flew each sweet sound,
Then darted to the Sun;
Slowly the sounds came back again,
Now mixed, now one by one.

Sometimes a-dropping from the sky
I heard the sky-lark sing;
Sometimes all little birds that are,
How they seemed to fill the sea and air
With their sweet jargoning!

And now 'twas like all instruments,
Now like a lonely flute;
And now it is an angel's song,
That makes the heavens be mute.

It ceased; yet still the sails made on
A pleasant noise till noon,
A noise like of a hidden brook
In the leafy month of June,
That to the sleeping woods all night
Singeth a quiet tune.

Till noon we silently sailed on,
Yet never a breeze did breathe:
Slowly and smoothly went the ship,
Moved onward from beneath.

Under the keel nine fathom deep,
From the land of mist and snow,
The spirit slid: and it was he
That made the ship to go.
The sails at noon left off their tune,
And the ship stood still also.

The Sun, right up above the mast,
Had fixed her to the ocean;
But in a minute she 'gan stir,
With a short uneasy motion –
Backwards and forwards half her length
With a short uneasy motion.

Then like a pawing horse let go,
She made a sudden bound:
It flung the blood into my head,
And I fell down in a swound.

How long in that same fit I lay,
I have not to declare;
But ere my living life returned,
I heard and in my soul discerned
Two voices in the air.

'Is it he?' quoth one, 'Is this the man?
By him who died on cross,
With his cruel bow he laid full low
The harmless Albatross.

The spirit who bideth by himself
In the land of mist and snow,
He loved the bird that loved the man
Who shot him with his bow.'

The other was a softer voice,
As soft as honey-dew:
Quoth he, 'The man hath penance done,
And penance more will do.'

PART VI

First Voice. 'But tell me, tell me! speak again,
    Thy soft response renewing –
    What makes that ship drive on so fast?
    What is the ocean doing?'

Second Voice. 'Still as a slave before his lord,
    The ocean hath no blast;
    His great bright eye most silently
    Up to the Moon is cast –

    If he may know which way to go;
    For she guides him smooth or grim.
    See, brother, see! how graciously
    She looketh down on him.'

First Voice. 'But why drives on that ship so fast,
    Without or wave or wind?'

Second Voice. 'The air is cut away before,
    And closes from behind.

    Fly, brother, fly! more high, more high!
    Or we shall be belated:
    For slow and slow that ship will go,
    When the Mariner's trance is abated.' –

    I woke and we were sailing on
    As in a gentle weather:
    'Twas night, calm night, the moon was high;
    The dead men stood together.

    All stood together on the deck,
    For a charnel-dungeon fitter:
    All fixed on me their stony eyes,
    That in the Moon did glitter.

The pang, the curse, with which they died,
Had never passed away:
I could not draw my eyes from theirs,
Nor turn them up to pray.

And now this spell was snapt: once more
I viewed the ocean green,
And looked far forth, yet little saw
Of what had else been seen –

Like one, that on a lonesome road
Doth walk in fear and dread,
And having once turned round walks on,
And turns no more his head;
Because he knows, a frightful fiend
Doth close behind him tread.

But soon there breathed a wind on me,
Nor sound nor motion made:
Its path was not upon the sea,
In ripple or in shade.

It raised my hair, it fanned my cheek
Like a meadow-gale of spring –
It mingled strangely with my fears,
Yet it felt like a welcoming.

Swiftly, swiftly flew the ship,
Yet she sailed softly too:
Sweetly, sweetly blew the breeze –
On me alone it blew.

Oh! dream of joy! is this indeed
The light-house top I see?
Is this the hill? is this the kirk?
Is this mine own countree?

We drifted o'er the harbour-bar,
And I with sobs did pray –
O let me be awake, my God!
Or let me sleep alway.

The harbour-bay was clear as glass,
So smoothly it was strewn!
And on the bay the moonlight lay,
And the shadow of the Moon.

The rock shone bright, the kirk no less,
That stands above the rock:
The moonlight steeped in silentness
The steady weathercock.

And the bay was white with silent light,
Till rising from the same,
Full many shapes, that shadows were,
In crimson colours came.

A little distance from the prow
Those crimson shadows were:
I turned my eyes upon the deck –
Oh, Christ! what saw I there!

Each corse lay flat, lifeless, and flat,
And, by the holy rood!
A man all light, a seraph-man,
On every corse there stood.

This seraph-band, each waved his hand:
It was a heavenly sight!
They stood as signals to the land,
Each one a lovely light;

This seraph-band, each waved his hand,
No voice did they impart –
No voice; but oh! the silence sank
Like music on my heart.

But soon I heard the dash of oars,
I heard the Pilot's cheer;
My head was turned perforce away,
And I saw a boat appear.

The Pilot and the Pilot's boy,
I heard them coming fast:
Dear Lord in Heaven! it was a joy
The dead men could not blast.

I saw a third – I heard his voice:
It is the Hermit good!
He singeth loud his godly hymns
That he makes in the wood.
He'll shrieve my soul, he'll wash away
The Albatross's blood.

PART VII

This Hermit good lives in that wood
Which slopes down to the sea.
How loudly his sweet voice he rears!
He loves to talk with marineres
That come from a far countree.

He kneels at morn, and noon, and eve –
He hath a cushion plump:
It is the moss that wholly hides
The rotted old oak-stump.

The skiff-boat neared: I heard them talk,
'Why, this is strange, I trow!
Where are those lights so many and fair,
That signal made but now?'

'Strange, by my faith!' the Hermit said –
'And they answered not our cheer!
The planks looked warped! and see those sails,
How thin they are and sere!
I never saw aught like to them,
Unless perchance it were

Brown skeletons of leaves that lag
My forest-brook along;
When the ivy-tod is heavy with snow,
And the owlet whoops to the wolf below,
That eats the she-wolf's young.'

'Dear Lord! it hath a fiendish look –
(The Pilot made reply)
I am a-feared' – 'Push on, push on!'
Said the Hermit cheerily.

The boat came closer to the ship,
But I nor spake nor stirred;
The boat came close beneath the ship,
And straight a sound was heard.

Under the water it rumbled on,
Still louder and more dread:
It reached the ship, it split the bay;
The ship went down like lead.

Stunned by that loud and dreadful sound,
Which sky and ocean smote,
Like one that hath been seven days drowned
My body lay afloat;
But swift as dreams, myself I found
Within the Pilot's boat.

Upon the whirl, where sank the ship,
The boat spun round and round;
And all was still, save that the hill
Was telling of the sound.

I moved my lips – the Pilot shrieked
And fell down in a fit;
The holy Hermit raised his eyes,
And prayed where he did sit.

I took the oars: the Pilot's boy,
Who now doth crazy go,
Laughed loud and long, and all the while
His eyes went to and fro.
'Ha! ha!' quoth he, 'full plain I see,
The Devil knows how to row.'

And now, all in my own countree,
I stood on the firm land!
The Hermit stepped forth from the boat,
And scarcely he could stand.

'O shrieve me, shrieve me, holy man!'
The Hermit crossed his brow.
'Say quick,' quoth he, 'I bid thee say –
What manner of man art thou?'

Forthwith this frame of mine was wrenched
With a woful agony,
Which forced me to begin my tale;
And then it left me free.

Since then, at an uncertain hour,
That agony returns:
And till my ghastly tale is told,
This heart within me burns.

I pass, like night, from land to land;
I have strange power of speech;
That moment that his face I see,
I know the man that must hear me:
To him my tale I teach.

What loud uproar bursts from that door!
The wedding-guests are there:
But in the garden-bower the bride
And bride-maids singing are:
And hark the little vesper bell,
Which biddeth me to prayer!

O Wedding-Guest! this soul hath been
Alone on a wide wide sea:
So lonely 'twas, that God himself
Scarced seemèd there to be.

O sweeter than the marriage-feast,
'Tis sweeter far to me,
To walk together to the kirk
With a goodly company! –

To walk together to the kirk,
And all together pray,
While each to his great Father bends,
Old men, and babes, and loving friends
And youths and maidens gay!

Farewell, farewell! but this I tell
To thee, thou Wedding-Guest!
He prayeth well, who loveth well
Both man and bird and beast.

He prayeth best, who loveth best
All things both great and small;
For the dear God who loveth us,
He made and loveth all.' –

The Mariner, whose eye is bright,
Whose beard with age is hoar,
Is gone: and now the Wedding-Guest
Turned from the bridegroom's door.

He went like one that hath been stunned,
And is of sense forlorn:
A sadder and a wiser man,
He rose the morrow morn.

SAMUEL TAYLOR COLERIDGE

399. *The Child and the Mariner*

This sailor knows of wondrous lands afar,
More rich than Spain, when the Phoenicians shipped
Silver for common ballast, and they saw
Horses at silver mangers eating grain;
This man has seen the wind blow up a mermaid's hair
Which, like a golden serpent, reared and stretched
To feel the air away beyond her head . . .
He many a tale of wonder told: of where,
At Argostoli, Cephalonia's sea
Ran over the earth's lip in heavy floods;
And then again of how the strange Chinese
Conversed much as our homely Blackbirds sing.
He told us how he sailed in one old ship
Near that volcano Martinique, whose power
Shook like dry leaves the whole Caribbean seas;
And made the sun set in a sea of fire
Which only half was his; and dust was thick
On deck, and stones were pelted at the mast . . .
He told how isles sprang up and sank again,
Between short voyages, to his amaze;
How they did come and go, and cheated charts;
Told how a crew was cursed when one man killed
A bird that perched upon a moving barque;
And how the sea's sharp needles, firm and strong,
Ripped open the bellies of big, iron ships;
Of mighty icebergs in the Northern seas,
That haunt the far horizon like white ghosts.

He told of waves that lift a ship so high.
That birds could pass from starboard unto port
Under her dripping keel.
                                Oh, it was sweet
To hear that seaman tell such wondrous tales . . .

WILLIAM H. DAVIES

400. *The Parrots*

Somewhere, somewhen I've seen,
But where or when I'll never know,
Parrots of shrilly green
With crests of shriller scarlet flying
Out of black cedars as the sun was dying
Against cold peaks of snow.

From what forgotten life
Of other worlds I cannot tell
Flashes that screeching strife:
Yet the shrill colour and shrill crying
Sing through my blood and set my heart replying
And jangling like a bell.

WILFRID GIBSON

401. *Ozymandias of Egypt*

I met a traveller from an antique land
Who said: Two vast and trunkless legs of stone
Stand in the desert . . . Near them, on the sand,
Half sunk, a shattered visage lies, whose frown
And wrinkled lip, and sneer of cold command
Tell that its sculptor well those passions read
Which yet survive, stamped on these lifeless things,
The hand that mocked them, and the heart that fed:

And on the pedestal these words appear:
'My name is Ozymandias, king of kings:
Look on my works, ye Mighty, and despair!'
Nothing beside remains. Round the decay
Of that colossal wreck, boundless and bare
The lone and level sands stretch far away.

                    PERCY BYSSHE SHELLEY

402. St Anthony's Township

The trees of the elder lands,
Give ear to the march of Time,
To his steps that are heavy and slow
In the streets of ruined cities
That were great awhile ago –
Skeletons bare to the skies
Or mummies hid in the sands,
Wasting to rubble and lime.
Ancient are they and wise;

But the gum-trees down by the creek,
Gnarled, archaic and grey,
Are even as wise as they.
They have learned in a score of years
The lore that their brethren know;
For they saw a town arise,
Arise and pass.

There are pits by the dry, dead river,
Whence the diggers won their gold,
A circle traced in the grass,
A hearthstone long a-cold,
A path none come to seek –
The trail of the pioneers –

Where the sheep wind to and fro;
And the rest is a tale that is told
By voices quavering and weak
Of men grown old.

GILBERT SHELDON

403. *Silence*

There is a silence where hath been no sound,
   There is a silence where no sound may be,
    In the cold grave – under the deep – deep sea,
Or in wide desert where no life is found,
Which hath been mute, and still must sleep profound;
   No voice is hushed – no life treads silently,
    But clouds and cloudy shadows wander free,
That never spoke, over the idle ground:
But in green ruins, in the desolate walls
   Of antique palaces, where Man hath been,
Though the dun fox, or wild hyaena, calls,
   And owls, that flit continually between,
Shriek to the echo, and the low winds moan,
There the true Silence is, self-conscious and alone.

THOMAS HOOD

404. *Kubla Khan*

In Xanadu did Kubla Khan
A stately pleasure-dome decree:
Where Alph, the sacred river, ran
Through caverns measureless to man
   Down to a sunless sea.
So twice five miles of fertile ground
With walls and towers were girdled round:

And here were gardens bright with sinuous rills
Where blossomed many an incense-bearing tree;
And here were forests ancient as the hills,
Enfolding sunny spots of greenery.

But oh! that deep romantic chasm which slanted
Down the green hill athwart a cedarn cover!
A savage place! as holy and enchanted
As e'er beneath a waning moon was haunted
By woman wailing for her demon-lover!
And from this chasm, with ceaseless turmoil seething,
As if this earth in fast thick pants were breathing,
A mighty fountain momently was forced:
Amid whose swift half-intermitted burst
Huge fragments vaulted like rebounding hail,
Or chaffy grain beneath the thresher's flail:

And 'mid these dancing rocks at once and ever
It flung up momently the sacred river.
Five miles meandering with a mazy motion
Through wood and dale the sacred river ran,
Then reached the caverns measureless to man,
And sank in tumult to a lifeless ocean:
And 'mid this tumult Kubla heard from far
Ancestral voices prophesying war!
        The shadow of the dome of pleasure
        Floated midway on the waves;
        Where was heard the mingled measure
        From the fountain and the caves.
It was a miracle of rare device,
A sunny pleasure-dome with caves of ice!

        A damsel with a dulcimer
        In a vision once I saw:
        It was an Abyssinian maid,
        And on her dulcimer she played,
        Singing of Mount Abora.

Could I revive within me
　　Her symphony and song,
To such a deep delight 'twould win me,
That with music loud and long
I would build that dome in air,
That sunny dome! those caves of ice!
And all who heard should see them there,
And all should cry, Beware! Beware!
His flashing eyes, his floating hair!
Weave a circle round him thrice,
And close your eyes with holy dread,
For he on honey-dew hath fed,
And drunk the milk of Paradise . . .

SAMUEL TAYLOR COLERIDGE

405. *Lost Love*

His eyes are quickened so with grief,
He can watch a grass or leaf
Every instant grow; he can
Clearly through a flint wall see,
Or watch the startled spirit flee
From the throat of a dead man.
　　Across two countries he can hear,
And catch your words before you speak.
The woodlouse, or the maggot's weak
Clamour rings in his sad ear;
And noise so slight it would surpass
Credence: – drinking sound of grass,
Worm talk, clashing jaws of moth
Chumbling holes in cloth:
The groan of ants who undertake
Gigantic loads for honour's sake,
Their sinews creak, their breath comes thin:
Whir of spiders when they spin,

And minute whispering, mumbling, sighs
Of idle grubs and flies.
    This man is quickened so with grief,
He wanders god-like or like thief
Inside and out, below, above,
Without relief seeking lost love.

ROBERT GRAVES

406. *Ecstasy*

I saw a frieze on whitest marble drawn
Of boys who sought for shells along the shore,
Their white feet shedding pallor in the sea,
The shallow sea, the spring-time sea of green
That faintly creamed against the cold, smooth pebbles . . .

One held a shell unto his shell-like ear
And there was music carven in his face,
His eyes half-closed, his lips just breaking open
To catch the lulling, mazy, coralline roar
Of numberless caverns filled with singing seas.

And all of them were hearkening as to singing
Of far-off voices thin and delicate,
Voices too fine for any mortal wind
To blow into the whorls of mortal ears –
And yet those sounds flowed from their grave, sweet faces.

And as I looked I heard that delicate music,
And I became as grave, as calm, as still
As those carved boys. I stood upon that shore,
I felt the cool sea dream around my feet,
My eyes were staring at the far horizon . . .

WALTER J. TURNER

407. *The Sea of Death*

... And there were spring-faced cherubs that did sleep
Like water-lilies on that motionless deep,
How beautiful! with bright unruffled hair
On sleek unfretted brows, and eyes that were
Buried in marble tombs, a pale eclipse!
And smile-bedimpled cheeks, and pleasant lips,
Meekly apart, as if the soul intense
Spake out in dreams of its own innocence ...
So lay they garmented in torpid light,
Under the pall of a transparent night,
Like solemn apparitions lulled sublime
To everlasting rest, – and with them Time
Slept, as he sleeps upon the silent face
Of a dark dial in a sunless place.

408. *The Frozen Ocean*

The sea would flow no longer,
    It wearied after change,
It called its tide and breakers in,
    From where they might range.

It sent an icy message
    To every wave and rill;
They lagged, they paused, they stiffened,
    They froze; and were still.

It summoned in its currents,
    They reached not where they led;
It bound its foaming whirlpools.
    'Not the old life,' it said,

'Not fishes for the fisherman,
    Not bold ships as before,
Not beating loud for ever
    Upon the seashore,

'But cold white foxes stepping
    On to my hard proud breast,
And a bird coming sweetly
    And building a nest.

'My icebergs shall be mountains,
    My silent fields of snow
Unmarked shall join the land's snowfields –
    Where, no man shall know.'

VIOLA MEYNELL

409. *The End of the World*

The snow had fallen many nights and days;
The sky was come upon the earth at last,
Sifting thinly down as endlessly
As though within the system of blind planets
Something had been forgot or overdriven.
The dawn now seemed neglected in the grey
Where mountains were unbuilt and shadowless trees
Rootlessly paused or hung upon the air.
There was no wind, but now and then a sigh
Crossed that dry falling dust and rifted it
Through crevices of slate and door and casement.
Perhaps the new moon's time was even past.
Outside, the first white twilights were too void
Until a sheep called once, as to a lamb,
And tenderness crept everywhere from it;
But now the flock must have strayed far away.
The lights across the valley must be veiled,

The smoke lost in the greyness or the dusk.
For more than three days now the snow had thatched
That cow-house roof where it had ever melted
With yellow stains from the beasts' breath inside;
But yet a dog howled there, though not quite lately.
Someone passed down the valley swift and singing,
Yes, with locks spreaded like a son of morning;
But if he seemed too tall to be a man
It was that men had been so long unseen,
Or shapes loom larger through a moving snow.
And he was gone and food had not been given him.
When snow slid from an overweighted leaf,
Shaking the tree, it might have been a bird
Slipping in sleep or shelter, whirring wings;
Yet never bird fell out, save once a dead one –
And in two days the snow had covered it.
The dog had howled again – or thus it seemed
Until a lean fox passed and cried no more.
All was so safe indoors where life went on
Glad of the close enfolding snow – O glad
To be so safe and secret at its heart,
Watching the strangeness of familiar things.
They knew not what dim hours went on, went by,
For while they slept the clock stopt newly wound
As the cold hardened. Once they watched the road,
Thinking to be remembered. Once they doubted
If they had kept the sequence of the days,
Because they heard not any sound of bells.
A butterfly, that hid until the Spring
Under a ceiling's shadow, dropt, was dead.
The coldness seemed more nigh, the coldness deepened
As a sound deepens into silences;
It was of earth and came not by the air;
The earth was cooling and drew down the sky.
The air was crumbling. There was no more sky.
Rails of a broken bed charred in the grate,
And when he touched the bars he thought the sting

Came from their heat – he could not feel such cold . . .
She said, 'O do not sleep,
Heart, heart of mine, keep near me. No, no; sleep.
I will not lift his fallen, quiet eyelids,
Although I know he would awaken then –
He closed them thus but now of his own will.
He can stay with me while I do not lift them.'

GORDON BOTTOMLEY

OLD TALES AND BALLADRY

410. *Flannan Isle*

'Though three men dwell on Flannan Isle
To keep the lamp alight,
As we steered under the lee, we caught
No glimmer through the night.' –

A passing ship at dawn had brought
The news; and quickly we set sail,
To find out what strange thing might ail
The keepers of the deep-sea light.

The Winter day broke blue and bright,
With glancing sun and glancing spray,
While o'er the swell our boat made way,
As gallant as a gull in flight.

But as we neared the lonely Isle,
And looked up at the naked height,
And saw the lighthouse towering white,
With blinded lantern, that all night
Had never shot a spark
Of comfort through the dark,
So ghostly in the cold sunlight
It seemed, that we were struck the while
With wonder all too dread for words.

And as into the tiny creek
We stole beneath the hanging crag,
We saw three queer, black, ugly birds –
Too big, by far, in my belief,
For cormorant or shag –
Like seamen sitting bolt-upright
Upon a half-tide reef:
But, as we neared, they plunged from sight,
Without a sound, or spurt of white.

And still too mazed to speak,
We landed; and made fast the boat;
And climbed the track in single file,
Each wishing he were safe afloat,
On any sea, however far,
So it be far from Flannan Isle:
And still we seemed to climb, and climb,
As though we'd lost all count of time,
And so must climb for evermore.
Yet, all too soon, we reached the door
The black, sun-blistered lighthouse-door
That gaped for us ajar.

As, on the threshold, for a spell,
We paused, we seemed to breathe the smell
Of limewash and of tar,
Familiar as our daily breath,
As though 'twere some strange scent of death:
And so, yet wondering, side by side,
We stood a moment, still tongue-tide:
And each with black foreboding eyed
The door, ere we should fling it wide,
To leave the sunlight for the gloom:
Till, plucking courage up, at last,
Hard on each other's heels we passed,
Into the living-room.

Yet, as we crowded through the door,
We only saw a table, spread
For dinner, meat and cheese and bread;
But, all untouched; and no one there:
As though, when they sat down to eat,
Ere they could even taste,
Alarm had come; and they in haste
Had risen and left the bread and meat:
For at the table-head a chair
Lay tumbled on the floor.
We listened; but we only heard

The feeble cheeping of a bird
That starved upon its perch:
And, listening still, without a word,
We set about our hopeless search.
We hunted high, we hunted low;
And soon ransacked the empty house;
Then o'er the Island, to and fro,
We ranged, to listen and to look
In every cranny, cleft or nook
That might have hid a bird or mouse;
But, though we searched from shore to shore,
We found no sign in any place:
And soon again stood face to face
Before the gaping door:
And stole into the room once more
As frightened children steal.
Ay: though we hunted high and low,
And hunted everywhere,
Of the three men's fate we found no trace
Of any kind in any place,
But a door ajar, and an untouched meal,
And an overtoppled chair.
And as we listened in the gloom
Of that forsaken living-room –
A chill clutch on our breath –
We thought how ill-chance came to all
Who kept the Flannan Light:
And how the rock had been the death
Of many a likely lad:
How six had come to a sudden end,
And three had gone stark mad:
And one whom we'd all known as friend
Had leapt from the lantern one still night,
And fallen dead by the lighthouse wall:
And long we thought
On the three we sought,
And of what might yet befall.

Like curs a glance has brought to heel,
We listened, flinching there:
And looked, and looked, on the untouched meal,
And the overtoppled chair.

We seemed to stand for an endless while,
Though still no word was said,
Three men alive on Flannan Isle,
Who thought on three men dead.

WILFRID GIBSON

411. *The Golden Vanity*

There was a gallant ship, and a gallant ship was she,
    Eck iddle du, and the Lowlands low;
And she was called The Goulden Vanitie.
    As she sailed to the Lowlands low.

She had not sailed a league, a league but only three,
When she came up with a French gallee.
    As she sailed to the Lowlands low.

Out spoke the little cabin-boy, out spoke he;
'What will you give me if I sink that French gallee?
    As ye sail to the Lowlands low.'

'I'll give thee gold, and I'll give thee fee,
And my eldest daughter thy wife shall be
    If you sink her off the Lowlands low.'

'Then row me up ticht in a black bull's skin,
And throw me oer deck-buird, sink I or swim.
    As ye sail to the Lowlands low.'

So they've rowed him up ticht in a black bull's skin,
And have thrown him oer deck-buird, sink he or swim.
    As they sail to the Lowlands low.

About, and about, and about went he,
Until he cam up with the French gallee.
As they sailed to the Lowlands low.

O some were playing cards, and some were playing dice,
The boy he had an auger bored holes two at twice;
He let the water in, and it dazzled in their eyes,
As they sailed to the Lowlands low.

Then some they ran with cloaks, and some they ran with caps,
To try if they could stap the saut-water draps.
As they sailed to the Lowlands low.

About, and about, and about when he,
Until he cam back to The Goulden Vanitie.
As they sailed to the Lowlands low.

'Now throw me oer a rope and pu me up on buird,
And prove unto me as guid as your word.
As we sail to the Lowlands low.'

'We'll no throw ye oer a rope, nor pu you up on buird,
Nor prove unto you as guid as our word.
As we sail to the Lowlands low.'

'You promised me gold, and you promised me fee,
Your eldest daughter my wife she should be.
As we sail to the Lowlands low.'

'You shall have gold, and you shall have fee,
But my eldest daughter your wife shall never be.
As we sail to the Lowlands low.'

Out spoke the little cabin-boy, out spoke he;
'Then hang me, I'll sink ye as I sunk the French gallee.
As ye sail to the Lowlands low.'

The boy he swam round all by the starboard side,
When they pu'd him up on buird it's there he soon died;
They threw him o'er deck-buird to go down with the tide,
And sink off the Lowlands low.

412. *Brown Robyn*

It fell upon a Wednesday
Brown Robyn's men went to sea,
But they saw neither moon nor sun,
    Nor starlight with their ee.

'We'll cast kevels us amang,
    See what the unhappy man may be':
The kevel fell on Brown Robyn,
    The master-man was hee.

'It is nae wonder,' said Brown Robyn,
    'Altho I dinna thrive;
(For if the deidly sins be seven,
    Befallen me hae five.)

'But tie me to a plank o wude,
    And throw me in the sea;
And if I sink, ye may bid me sink,
    But if I swim, lat me bee.'

They've tyed him to a plank o wude,
    And thrown him in the sea;
He didna sink, tho they bade him sink;
    He swimd, and they lat him be –

He hadna been into the sea
    An hour but barely three,
Till by and came Our Blessed Lady,
    Her dear young son her wi.

'Will ye gang to your men again?
    Or will ye gang wi me?
Will ye gang to the high heavens,
    Wi my dear son and me?'

'I winna gang to my men again,
    For they would be feared at mee;
But I would gang to the high heavens,
    Wi thy dear son and thee.'

'It's for nae honour ye did to me, Brown Robyn,
    It's for nae guid ye did to mee;
But a' is for your fair confession
    You've made upon the sea.'

413. *One Friday Morn*

One Friday morn when we set sail,
    Not very far from land,
We there did espy a fair pretty maid
    With a comb and a glass in her hand, her hand, her hand,
    With a comb and a glass in her hand.

While the raging seas did roar,
    And the stormy winds did blow,
While we jolly sailor-boys were up into the top,
And the land-lubbers lying down below, below, below,
And the land-lubbers lying down below.

Then up starts the captain of our gallant ship,
    And a brave young man was he:

'I've a wife and a child in fair Bristol town,
　　But a widow I fear she will be.'
　　　　And the raging seas did roar,
　　　　　　And the stormy winds did blow.

Then up starts the mate of our gallant ship,
　　And a bold young man was he:
'Oh! I have a wife in fair Portsmouth town,
　　But a widow I fear she will be.'
　　　　And the raging seas did roar,
　　　　　　And the stormy winds did blow.

Then up starts the cook of our gallant ship,
　　And a gruff old soul was he:
'Oh! I have a wife in fair Plymouth town,
　　But a widow I fear she will be.'
　　　　And the raging seas did roar,
　　　　　　And the stormy winds did blow.

And then up spoke the little cabin-boy,
　　And a pretty little boy was he;
'Oh! I am more grieved for my daddy and my mammy
　　Than you for your wives all three.'
　　　　And the raging seas did roar,
　　　　　　And the stormy winds did blow.

Then three times round went our gallant ship,
　　And three times round went she;
And three times round went our gallant ship,
　　And she sank to the bottom of the sea . . .

　　　And the raging seas did roar,
　　　　And the stormy winds did blow.
　　While we jolly sailor-boys were up into the top,
　　　And the land-lubbers lying down below, below, below,
　　　And the land-lubbers lying down below.

414. *The Ship*

There was no song nor shout of joy
　　Nor beam of moon or sun,
When she came back from the voyage
　　Long ago begun;
But twilight on the waters
　　Was quiet and grey,
And she glided steady, steady and pensive,
　　Over the open bay.

Her sails were brown and ragged,
　　And her crew hollow-eyed,
But their silent lips spoke content
　　And their shoulders pride;
Though she had no captives on her deck,
　　And in her hold
There were no heaps of corn or timber
　　Or silks or gold.

J. C. SQUIRE

415. *The Moon-Child*

A little lonely child am I
　　That have not any soul:
God made me as the homeless wave,
　　That has no goal.

A seal my father was, a seal
　　That once was man;
My mother loved him tho' he was
　　'Neath mortal ban.

He took a wave and drownèd her,
   She took a wave and lifted him:
And I was born where shadows are
   In sea-depths dim.

All through the sunny blue-sweet hours
   I swim and glide in waters green:
Never by day the mournful shores
   By me are seen.

But when the gloom is on the wave
   A shell unto the shore I bring:
And then upon the rocks I sit
   And plaintive sing.

I have no playmate but the tide
   The seaweed loves with dark brown eyes:
The night-waves have the stars for play,
   For me but sighs.

FIONA MACLEOD

416. *The Mermaid*

To yon fause stream that, by the sea,
   Hides mony an elf and plum,[1]
And rives wi' fearful din the stanes,
   A witless knicht did come.

The day shines clear. Far in he's gane,
   Whar shells are silver bright;
Fishes war loupin'[2] a' aroun'
   An' sparklin' to the light.

1. Pool   2. Leaping

When, as he laved, sounds came sae sweet
    Frae ilka rock ajee;[3]
The brief[4] was out; 'twas him it doomed
    The mermaid's face to see.

Frae 'neath a rock sune, sune she rose,
    An' stately on she swam,
Stopped i' the midst, and becked and sang
    For him to stretch his han';

Gowden glist the yellow links
    That roun' her neck she'd twine;
Her een war o' the skyie blue,
    Her lips did mock the wine.

The smile upon her bonnie cheek
    Was sweeter than the bee;
Her voice excelled the birdie's sang
    Upon the birchen tree.

Sae couthie, couthie did she look,
    And meikle had she fleeched;[5]
Out shot his hand – alas! alas!
    Fast in the swirl he screeched.

The mermaid leuched;[6] her brief was dane;
    The kelpie's blast was blawin':
Fu' low she dived, ne'er cam' again;
    For deep, deep was the fawin'.

Aboon the stream his wraith was seen:
    Warlocks tirled lang at gloamin':
That e'en was coarse;[7] the blast blew hoarse
    Ere lang the waves war foamin'.

3. Crooked, awry   6. Laughed
4. Spell   7. Foul
5. Charmed and cozened

417. *Quo' the Tweed*

Quo' the Tweed to the Till,
  'What gars ye gang sae still?'
Quo' the Till to the Tweed,
  'Though ye rin wi' speed,
And I rin slaw,
For ilka ane that ye droon,
  I droon twa.'

418. *Sir Patrick Spence*

The king sits in Dumferling toune,
  Drinking the blude-reid wine:
'O whar will I get a guid sailor,
  To sail this schip of mine?'

Up and spak an eldlern knicht,
  Sat at the king's richt kne;
'Sir Patrick Spence is the best sailor
  That sails upon the se.'

The king has written a braid letter,
  And signed it wi his hand,
And sent it to Sir Patrick Spence,
  Was walking on the sand.

The first line that Sir Patrick red,
  A loud lauch lauched he;
The next line that Sir Patrick red,
  The teir blinded his ee.

'O wha is this has done this deid,
  This ill deid don to me,
To send me out this time o' the yeir,
  To sail upon the se!

'Mak haste, mak haste, my mirry men all,
    Our guid schip sails the morne:'
'O say na sae, my master deir,
    Fir I feir a deadlie storme.

'Late, late yestreen I saw the new moone,
    Wi' the auld moone in his arme,
And I feir, I feir, my deir master,
    That we will cum to harme.'

O our Scots nobles wer richt laith[1]
    To weet[2] their cork-heil'd schoone;
Bot lang owre[3] a' play wer playd,
    Thair hats they swam aboone.

O lang, lang may their ladies sit
    Wi' thair fans into their hand,
Or eir they se Sir Patrick Spence
    Cum sailing to the land.

O lang, lang may the ladies stand,
    Wi' thair gold kems in their hair,
Waiting for thair ain deir lords,
    For they'll se thame na mair.

Haf owre, haf owre to Aberdour,
    Its fiftie fadom deip,
And thair lies guid Sir Patrick Spence,
    Wi' the Scots lords at his feit.

419. *Allison Gross*

O Allison Gross, that lives in yon towr,
    The ugliest witch i the north country,
Has trysted me ae day up till her bowr,
    An monny fair speech she made to me.

1. Right   3. But long ere
2. Wet

She stroaked my head, an she kembed my hair,
 An she set me down saftly on her knee;
Says, Gin¹ ye will be my luver so true,
 Sae monny braw things as I would you gi'e.

She showed me a mantle o red scarlet,
 Wi gouden flowrs an fringes fine;
Says, Gin ye will be my luver so true,
 This goodly gift it sal be thine.

'Awa, awa, ye ugly witch,
 Haud far awa, an lat me be;
I never will be your luver sae true,
 An I wish I were out o your company.'

She neist brought a sark o the saftest silk,
 Well wrought wi pearles about the ban;
Says, Gin you will be my ain true love,
 This goodly gift you sal comman.

She showd me a cup of the good red gold,
 Well set wi jewls sae fair to see;
Says, Gin you will be my luver sae true,
 This goodly gift I will you gi'e.

'Awa, awa, ye ugly witch,
 Haud far awa, and lat me be;
For I woudna ance kiss your ugly mouth
 For a' the gifts that ye could gi'e.'

She's turnd her right and roun about,
 And thrice she blaw on a grass-green horn,
An she sware by the moon and the stars aboon,
 That she'd gar me rue the day I was born.

1. If

Then out has she taen a silver wand,
    An she's turned her three times roun an roun;
She's muttered sich words till my strength it faild,
    An I fell down senceless upon the groun.

She's turnd me into an ugly worm,
    And gard me writhle about the tree;
An ay, on ilka Saturdays night,
    My sister Maisry came to me,

Wi silver bason an silver kemb,
    To kemb my heady upon her knees;
But or I had kissd her ugly mouth,
    I'd rather a writhled about the tree.

But as it fell out on last Hallow-even,
    When the seely court was ridin by,
The queen lighted down on a gowany bank,
    Nae far frae the tree where I wont to lye.

She took me up in her milk-white han,
    An she's strokd me three times oer her knee;
She chang'd me again to my ain proper shape,
    An I nae mair maun writhle about the tree.

420. *Sir Hugh, or The Jew's Daughter*

Four and twenty bonny boys
    Were playing at the ba',
And by it came him sweet Sir Hugh,
    And he playd o'er them a'.

He kicked the ba' with his right foot,
    And catchd it wi' his knee,
And throuch-and-thro the Jew's window
    He gard the bonny ba' flee.

He's doen him to the Jew's castell,
   And walkd it round about;
And there he saw the Jew's daughter,
   At the window looking out.

'Throw down the ba', ye Jew's daughter,
   Throw down the ba' to me!'
'Never a bit,' says the Jew's daughter,
   'Till up to me come ye.'

'How will I come up? How can I come up?
   How can I come to thee?
For as ye did to my auld father
   The same ye'll do to me.'

She's gane till her father's garden,
   And pu'd an apple red and green;
'T was a' to wyle him – sweet Sir Hugh,
   And to entice him in.

She's led him in through ae dark door,
   And sae has she thro nine;
She's laid him on a dressing-table,
   And stickit him like a swine.

And first came out the thick, thick blood,
   And syne came out the thin,
And syne came out the bonny heart's blood;
   There was nae mair within.

She's rowd him in a cake o' lead,
   Bade him lie still and sleep;
She's thrown him in Our Lady's draw-well,
   Was fifty fathom deep.

When bells were rung, and mass was sung,
   And a' the bairns came hame,
When every lady gata hame her son,
   The Lady Maisry gat nane.

She's ta'en her mantle her about,
  Her coffer[1] by the hand,
And she's gane out to seek her son,
  And wanderd o'er the land.

She's doen her to the Jew's castell,
  Where a' were fast asleep:
'Gin ye be there, my sweet Sir Hugh,
  I pray you to me speak.'

She's doen her to the Jew's garden,
  Thought he had been gathering fruit:
'Gin ye be there, my sweet Sir Hugh,
  I pray you to me speak!'

She heard Our Lady's deep draw-well,
  Was fifty fathom deep:
'Whareer ye be, my sweet Sir Hugh,
  I pray you to me speak.'

'Gae hame, gae hame, my mither dear,
  Prepare my winding sheet,
And at the birks[2] o' merry Lincoln
  The morn I will you meet.'

Now Lady Maisry is gane hame,
  Made him a winding sheet,
And at the birks o' merry Lincoln
  The dead corpse did her meet.

And a' the bells o' merry Lincoln
  Without men's hands were rung,
And a' the books o' merry Lincoln
  Were read without man's tongue,

1. Hand-bag 2. Birch-wood

When bells war rung, and mass was sung
    And a' man bound for bed,
Every mither had her son,
    But sweet Sir Hugh was dead.

421. *Edward*

'Why does your brand so drop wi' blood,
                        Edward, Edward,
Why does your brand so drop wi' blood,
    And why so sad go ye O?'
'O I have killed my hawk so good,
                        Mother, mother,
O I have killed my hawk so good,
    And I had no more but he O.'

'Your hawk's blood was never so red,
                        Edward, Edward,
Your hawk's blood was never so red,
    My dear son I tell thee O.'
'O I have killed my red-roan steed,
                        Mother, mother,
O I have killed my red-roan steed,
    That erst was so fair and free O.'

'Your steed was old, and ye have got more,
                        Edward, Edward,
Your steed was old, and ye have got more,
    Some other grief you bear O.'

'O I have killed my father dear,
                        Mother, mother,
O I have killed my father dear,
    Alas, and woe is me O!'

'And what penance will ye do for that,
                    Edward, Edward?
And what penance will ye do for that?
   My dear son, now tell me O.'
'I'll set my foot in yonder boat,
                    Mother, mother,
I'll set my foot in yonder boat,
   And I'll fare over the sea O.'

'And what will ye do wi' your towers and your hall,
                    Edward, Edward?
And what will ye do wi' your towers and your hall,
   That were so fair to see O?'
'I'll let them stand till they down fall,
                    Mother, mother,
I'll let them stand till they down fall.
   For here never more may I be O.'

'And what will ye leave to your bairns and your wife,
                    Edward, Edward?
And what will ye leave to your bairns and your wife,
   When ye go over the sea O?'
'The world's wide, let them beg their life,
                    Mother, mother,
The world's wide, let them beg their life,
   For them never more will I see O.'

'And what will ye leave to your own mother dear,
                    Edward, Edward?
And what will ye leave to your own mother dear?
   My dear son, now tell me O.'
'The curse of hell from me shall ye bear,
                    Mother, mother,
The curse of hell from me shall ye bear,
   Such counsels ye gave to me O.'

422. *The Laird o' Logie*

I will sing, if ye will hearken,
    If ye will hearken unto me;
The King has ta'en a poor prisoner,
    The wanton laird of Young Logie.

Young Logie's laid in Edinburgh chapel,
    Carmichael's the keeper o' the key;
I heard a May[1] lamenting sair
    A' for the laird of Young Logie.

'Lament, lament, na, May Margaret,
    And o' your weeping let me be;
For ye maun to the king yoursell,
    And ask the life of Young Logie.'

May Margaret has kilted her green cleiding,[2]
    And she's currlld back her yellow hair;
'If I canna get young Logie's life,
    Farewell to Scotland for ever mair!'

When she came before the king,
    She knelit low doon on her knee:
'It's what's your will wi' me, May Margaret,
    And what needs a' this courtesie?'

'A boon, a boon, my noble leige,
    A boon, a boon, I beg o' thee!
And the first boon that I come to crave,
    It's to grant me the life o' Young Logie.'

'O na, O na, May Margaret,
    Na, in sooth it mauna[3] be;
For the[4] morn, ere I taste meat or drink,
    Hee[5] hangèd shall Young Logie be.'

1. The young wife   4. This
2. Skirts of bright green   5. High
3. Must not

She has stolen the king's redding-kaim,[6]
    Likewise the queen her wedding-knife;
And sent the tokens to Carmichael,
    To cause Young Logie get[7] his life.

She sent him a purse o' the red gowd,
    Another o' the white monie;
And sent him a pistol for each hand,
    And bade him shoot when he gat free.

When he came to the Tolbooth stair,
    There he let his volley flee,
It made the king in his chamber start,
    E'en in the bed where he might be.

'Gae out, gae out, my merrie men a',
    And gar Carmichael come speak wi' me,
For I'll lay my life the pledge o' that,
    That yon's the volley of Young Logie.'

When Carmichael came before the king,
    He fell low down upon his knee;
The very first word that the king spake,
    Was, 'Where's the laird o' Young Logie?'

Carmichael turn'd him round about,
    I wat the salt tear blinded his ee,
'There came a token frae your grace,
    Has ta'en the laird awa frae me.'

'Hast thou played me that Carmichael? –
    Hast thou played me that?' quoth he;
'The morn the Justice Court's to stand,
    And Logie's place ye maun supplie.'

6. Hair-comb   7. Save

Carmichael's awa to May Margaret's bower,
   Even as fast as he may dree;
'O if Young Logie be within,
   Tell him to come and speak with me.'

May Margaret's turn'd her round about,
   I wat a loud laughter gae she:
'The egg is chipp'd, the bird is flown,
   Ye'll see nae mair o' Young Logie.'

Tane[8] is shipped at the pier o' Leith,
   T'other at the Queen's Ferrie,
And she's gotten a father to her bairn,
   The wanton laird of Young Logie.

423. *Fair Annie*

The reivers[1] they stole Fair Annie,
   As she walked by the sea;
But a noble knight was her ransom soon,
   Wi' gowd and white monie.[2]

She bided in strangers' land wi' him,
   And none knew whence she cam;
She lived in the castle wi' her love,
   But never told her name. –

'It's narrow, narrow, mak your bed,
   And learn to lie your lane;[3]
For I'm gaun owre the sea, Fair Annie,
   A braw Bride to bring hame.
Wi' her I will get gowd and gear,
   Wi' you I ne'er gat nane.

8. The one   2. Gold and silver
1. Raiders   3. Alone

'But wha will bake my bridal bread,
    Or brew my bridal ale?
And what will welcome my bright Bride,
    That I bring owre the dale?'

'It's I will bake your bridal bread,
    And brew your bridal ale;
And I will welcome your bright Bride,
    That you bring owre the dale.'

'But she that welcomes my bright Bride
    Maun gang like maiden fair;
She maun lace on her robe sae jimp,
    And comely braid her hair.

'Bind up, bind up your yellow hair,
    And tie it on your neck;
And see you look as maiden-like
    As the day that first we met.'

'O how can I gang maiden-like,
    When maiden I am nane?
Have I not borne six sons to thee,
    And am wi' child again?'

'I'll put cooks into my kitchen,
    And stewards in my hall,
And I'll have bakers for my bread,
    And brewers for my ale;
But you're to welcome my bright Bride,
    That I bring owre the dale.'

Three months and a day were gane and past,
    Fair Annie she gat word
That her love's ship was come at last,
    Wi' his bright young Bride aboard.

She's ta'en her young son in her arms,
    Anither in her hand;
And she's gane up to the highest tower.
    Looks over sea and land.

'Come doun, come doun, my mother dear,
    Come aff the castle wa'!
I fear if langer ye stand there,
    Ye'll let yourself doun fa'.'

She's ta'en a cake o' the best bread,
    A stoup o' the best wine,
And a' the keys upon her arm,
    And to the yett is gane.[4]

'O ye're welcome hame, my ain gude lord,
    To your castles and your towers;
Ye're welcome hame, my ain gude lord,
    To your ha's,[5] but and your bowers.
And welcome to your hame, fair lady!
    For a' that's here is yours.'

'O whatna lady's that, my lord,
    That welcomes you and me?
Gin[6] I be lang about this place,
    Her friend I mean to be.' —

Fair Annie served the lang tables
    Wi' the white bread and the wine;
But ay she drank the wan water
    To keep her colour fine.

And she gaed by the first table,
    And smiled upon them a';
But ere she reached the second table,
    The tears began to fa'.

4. To the gate is gone   6. If
5. Halls

She took a napkin lang and white,
    And hung it on a pin;
It was to wipe away the tears,
    As she gaed out and in.

When bells were rung and mass was sung,
    And a' men bound for bed,
The bridegroom and the bonny Bride
    In ae[7] chamber were laid. –

Fair Annie's ta'en a harp in her hand,
    To harp thir twa[8] asleep;
But ay, as she harpit and she sang,
    Fu' sairly did she weep.

'O gin my sons were seven rats,
    Rinnin' on the castle wa',
And I myself a grey grey cat,
    I soon wad worry them a'!

'O gin my sons were seven hares,
    Rinnin' owre yon lily lea,
And I mysell a good greyhound,
    Soon worried they a' should be!' –

Then out and spak the bonny young Bride,
    In bride-bed where she lay:
'That's like my sister Annie,' she says;
    'Wha is it doth sing and play?'

'I'll put on my gown,' said the new-come Bride
    'And my shoes upon my feet;
I will see wha doth sae sadly sing.
    And what is it gars her greet.[9]

7. One   9. Make her weep
8. The twain

'What ails you, what ails you, my housekeeper,
    Tha ye mak sic a mane?[10]
Has ony wine-barrell cast its girds,
    Or is a' your white bread gane?'

'It isna because my wine is spilt,
    Or that my white bread's gane;
But because I've lost my true love's love,
    And he's wed to anither ane.'

'Noo tell me wha was your father?' she says,
    'Noo tell me wha was your mother?
And had ye ony sister?' she says,
    'And had ye ever a brother?'

'The Earl of Wemyss was my father,
    The Countess of Wemyss my mother,
Young Elinor she was my sister dear,
    And Lord John he was my brother.'

'If the Earl of Wemyss was your father,
    I wot sae was he mine;
And it's O my sister Annie!
    Your love ye sallna tyne.[11]

'Tak your husband, my sister dear;
    You ne'er were wrangd for me,
Beyond a kiss o' his merry mouth
    As we came owre the sea.

'Seven ships, loaded weel,
    Cam owre the sea wi' me;
Ane o' them will tak me hame,
    And six I'll gie to thee.'

10. Such lament   11. Shall not lose

424. *Helen of Kirconnell*

. . . I wish I were where Helen lies,
Night and day on me she cries;
O that I were where Helen lies,
    On fair Kirconnell lea!

Curst be the heart that thought the thought,
And curst the hand that fired the shot,
When in my arms burd Helen dropt,
    And died to succour me!

O think na ye my heart was sair
When my love dropt down and spak nae mair;
There did she swoon, wi' meickle care,
    On fair Kirconnell lea.

As I went down the water side,
None but my foe to be my guide,
None but my foe to be my guide,
    On fair Kirconnell lea;

I lighted down, my sword to draw,
I hackèd him in pieces sma',
I hackèd him in pieces sma',
    For her that died for me.

O Helen fair, beyond compare,
I'll make a garland of thy hair
Shall bind my heart for evermair,
    Until the day I die.

O that I were where Helen lies,
Night and day on me she cries;
Out of my bed she bids me rise,
    Says, 'Haste and come to me!'

O Helen fair! O Helen chaste!
If I were with thee I were blest,
Where thou lies low, and takes thy rest
      On fair Kirconnell lea.

I wish my grave were growing green,
A winding-sheet drawn ower my e'en,
And I in Helen's arms lying
      On fair Kirconnell lea.

I wish I were where Helen lies,
Night and day on me she cries;
And I am weary of the skies,
      For her sake that died for me.

425. *The Bonnie Bower*

THE LAMENT OF THE BORDER WIDOW

My love he built me a bonnie bower,
And clad it a' wi' lily flower;
A brawer bower ye ne'er did see,
Than my true-love he built for me.

There came a man, by middle day,
He spied his sport, and went away;
And brought the king that very night,
Who brake my bower, and slew my knight.

He slew my knight, to me sae dear;
He slew my knight, and poin'd his gear:[1]
My servants all for life did flee,
And left me in extremitie.

1. Seized his all

694

I sewed his sheet, making my mane;
I watched the corpse, mysel alane;
I watched his body night and day;
No living creature came that way.

I took his body on my back,
And whiles I gaed, and whiles I sat;
I digged a grave, and laid him in,
And happed him with the sod sae green.

But think na' ye my heart was sair,
When I laid the moul' on his yellow hair?
O, think na' ye my heart was wae,
When I turned about, away to gae?

Nae living man I'll love again,
Since that my lovely knight is slain;
Wi' ae lock o' his yellow hair
I'll chain my heart for evermair.

426. *Weep No More*

Weep no more, nor sigh nor groan,
Sorrow calls no time that's gone:
Violets plucked, the sweetest rain
Makes not fresh nor grow again;
Trim thy locks, look cheerfully,
Fate's hidden ends eyes cannot see.
Joys as wingèd dreams fly fast,
Why should sadness longer last?
Grief is but a wound to woe;
   Gentlest fair, mourn, mourn no moe.[1]

JOHN FLETCHER

1. More

427. *The Twa Sisters*

There were twa sisters sat in a bowr;
   Binnorie, O Binnorie:
There came a knight to be their wooer
   By the bonny mill-dams of Binnorie.

He courted the eldest wi' glove an ring,
But he lovd the youngest above a' thing.[1]

He courted the eldest wi' brotch an knife,
But lovd the youngest as his life.

The eldest she was vexèd sair,
An' much envi'd her sister fair.

Into[2] her bowr she could not rest,
Wi' grief an spite she almos brast.

Upon a morning fair an' clear,
She cried upon her sister dear: –

'O sister, come to yon sea stran,
An see our father's ships come to lan.'

She's ta'en her by the milk-white han,
An led her down to yon sea stran.

The youngest stood upon a stane,
The eldest came an threw her in.

She tooke her by the middle sma',
An dashed her bonny back to the jaw.[3]

1. Everything   3. And dashed her backwards into the waves
2. Within

'O sister, sister, tak my han,
And Ise mack[4] you heir to a' my lan.

'O sister, sister, tak my middle,
An yes get[5] my goud and my gouden girdle.

'O sister, sister, save my life,
An I swear Ise never be nae man's wife.'

'Foul fa' the han that I should tacke,
It twin'd me an my wardles make.[6]

'Your cherry cheeks an yellow hair
Gars me gae maiden for evermair.'

Sometimes she sank, and sometimes she swam,
Till she came down yon bonny mill-dam.

O out it came the miller's son.
An' saw the fair maid swimmin in.

'O father, father, draw your dam,
Here's either a mermaid or a swan.'

The miller quickly drew the dam,
An there he found a drown'd woman.

You couldna see her yellow hair
For gold and pearle that were so rare.

You couldna see her middle sma'
For gouden girdle that was sae braw.

You couldna see her fingers white,
For gouden rings that was sae gryte.[7]

---

4. And I'll make   6. It parted me and my world's mate
5. You shall have   7. Great

An by there came a harper fine,
That harpèd to the king at dine.

When he did look that lady upon,
He sigh'd and made a heavy moan.

He's taen three locks o' her yellow hair,
An wi' them strung his harp sae fair.

The first tune he did play and sing,
Was, 'Farewell to my father the king.'

The nextin tune that he play'd syne,
Was, 'Farewell to my mother the queen.'

The lastin tune that he play'd then,
Was, 'Wae to my sister, fair Ellen.'

428. *Sweet William and May Margaret*

There came a ghost to Margret's door,
    With many a grievous groan;
And aye he tirlèd at the pin,
    But answer made she none . . .

'Is that my father Philip?
    Or is't my brother John?
Or is't my true-love Willie,
    From Scotland new come home?'

' 'Tis not thy father Philip,
    Nor yet thy brother John,
But 'tis thy true-love Willie,
    From Scotland new come home.

'O sweet Margret, O dear Margret,
   I pray thee speak to me;
Give me my faith and troth, Margret,
   As I gave it to thee.'

'Thy faith and troth thou's never get,
   Nor yet will I thee lend,
Till that thou come within my bower
   And kiss me cheek and chin.'

'If I shou'd come within thy bower,
   I am no earthly man;
And shou'd I kiss thy ruby lips,
   Thy days would not be lang.

'O sweet Margret, O dear Margret,
   I pray thee speak to me;
Give me my faith and troth, Margret,
   As I give it to thee.'

'Thy faith and troth thou's never get,
   Nor yet will I thee lend,
Till thou take me to yon kirk-yard,
   And wed me with a ring.'

'My bones are buried in yon kirk-yard
   Afar beyond the sea;
And it is but my spirit, Margret,
   That's now speaking to thee.'

She stretched out her lily-white hand,
   And, for to do her best:
'Hae, there's your faith and troth, Willie;
   God send your soul good rest.' . . .

Now she has kilted her robes o' green
   A piece below her knee,
And a' the live-lang winter night
   The dead corp followed she.

'Is there any room at your head, Willie,
   Or any room at your feet?
Or any room at your side, Willie,
   Wherein that I may creep?'

'There's nae room at my head, Margret,
   There's nae room at my feet;
There's nae room at my side, Margret,
   My coffin's made so meet.'

Then up and crew the red, red cock,
   And up and crew the grey;
' 'Tis time, 'tis time, my dear Margret,
   That you were gane awa'.'

429. *The Wife of Usher's Well*

There lived a wife at Usher's Well
   And a wealthy wife was she;
She had three stout and stalwart sons,
   And sent them o'er the sea.

They hadna been a week from her,
   A week but barely ane,
Whan word came to the carline wife
   That her three sons were gane.

They hadna been a week from her,
   A week but barely three,
Whan word came to the carline wife
   That her sons she'd never see.

'I wish the wind may never cease,
  Nor fashes in the flood,[1]
Till my three sons come hame to me,
  In earthly flesh and blood.' –

It fell about the Martinmass,
  When nights are lang and mirk,
The carline wife's three sons came hame,
  And their hats were o the birk.

It neither grew in syke[2] nor ditch,
  Nor yet in ony sheugh;
But at the gates o' Paradise
  That birk grew fair enough . . .

'Blow up the fire, my maidens,
  Bring water from the well;
For a' my house shall feast this night.
  Since my three sons are well.'

And she has made to them a bed,
  She's made it large and wide;
And she's ta'en her mantle her about,
  Sat down at the bedside.

Up then crew the red, red cock,
  And up and crew the grey;
The eldest to the youngest said,
  ' 'Tis time we were away!'

The cock he hadna crawed but once,
  And clapped his wings at a',
When the youngest to the eldest said,
  'Brother, we must awa'.

1. Travail on the deep   2. Marsh

'The cock doth craw, the day doth daw,
    The channerin worm doth chice;
Gin we be mist out o' our place,
    A sair pain we maun bide.

'Lie still, lie still but a little wee while,
    Lie still but if we may;
Gin my mother should miss us when she wakes
    She'll go mad ere it be day.

'Fare ye weel, my mother dear!
    Fareweel to barn and byre!
And fare ye well, the bonny lass
    That kindles my mother's fire!'

EVENING AND DREAM

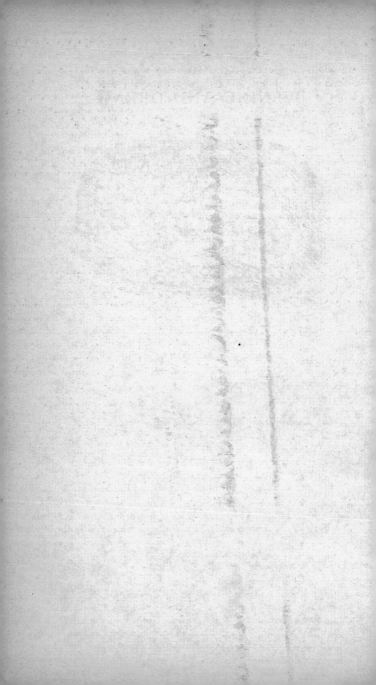

430. *Dream-Pedlary*

If there were dreams to sell,
  What would you buy?
Some cost a passing bell;
  Some a light sigh,
That shakes from Life's fresh crown
Only a rose-leaf down.
If there were dreams to sell,
Merry and sad to tell,
And the crier rang the bell,
  What would you buy?

A cottage lone and still,
  With bowers nigh,
Shadowy, my woes to still,
  Until I die.
Such peace from Life's fresh crown
Fain would I shake me down.
Were dreams to have at will,
This would best heal my ill,
  This would I buy.

    THOMAS LOVELL BEDDOES

431. *The Evening Sun*

The evening sun was sinking down
 On low green hills and clustered trees;
It was a scene as fair and lone
 As ever felt the soothing breeze

That cools the grass when day is gone,
 And gives the waves a brighter blue,
And makes the soft white clouds sail on –
 Like spirits of ethereal dew

Which all the morn had hovered o'er
  The azure flowers, where they were nursed,
And now return to Heaven once more,
  Where their bright glories shone at first.

EMILY BRONTË

432. *To the Evening Star*

Thou fair-haired angel of the evening,
Now, whilst the sun rests on the mountains, light
Thy bright torch of love; thy radiant crown
Put on, and smile upon our evening bed!
Smile on our loves, and, while thou drawest the
Blue curtains of the sky, scatter thy silver dew
On every flower that shuts its sweet eyes
In timely sleep. Let thy west wind sleep on
The lake; speak silence with thy glimmering eyes,
And wash the dusk with silver. Soon, full soon,
Dost thou withdraw; then the wolf rages wide,
And the lion glares thro' the dun forest:
The fleeces of the flocks are covered with
Thy sacred dew: protect them with thine influence.

WILLIAM BLAKE

433. *To Daisies, Not to Shut So Soon*

Shut not so soon; the dull-eyed night
  Hath not as yet begun
To make a seisure on the light,
  Or to seale up the Sun.

No Marigolds yet closèd are;
  No shadowes great appeare:
Nor doth the early Shepheard's Starre
  Shine like a spangle here.

Stay but till my *Julia* close
  Her life-begetting eye;
And let the whole world then dispose
  It selfe to live or dye.

ROBERT HERRICK

434. *Of the Going Down of the Sun*

What, hast thou run thy Race? Art going down?
Thou seemest angry, why dost on us frown?
Yea wrap thy heads with Clouds, and hide thy face,
As threatning to withdraw from us thy Grace?
Oh leave us not! When once thou hid'st thy head,
Our Hórizon with darkness will be spread.
Tell's, who hath thee offended? Turn again:
Alas! too late – Entreaties are in vain! . . .

JOHN BUNYAN

435. *Virtue*

Sweet day, so cool, so calm, so bright
  The bridal of the earth and skie:
The dew shall weep thy fall to-night,
          For thou must die.

Sweet rose, whose hue angry and brave
  Bids the rash gazer wipe his eye,
Thy root is ever in its grave,
          And thou must die.

Sweet spring, full of sweet days and roses,
  A box where sweets compacted lie,
My music shows ye have your closes,
          And all must die.

Only a sweet and vertuous soul,
  Like seasond timber, never gives;
But though the whole world turn to coal,
          Then chiefly lives.

GEORGE HERBERT

436. *Night*

The sun descending in the west,
The evening star does shine;
The birds are silent in their nest,
And I must seek for mine.
  The moon, like a flower,
  In heaven's high bower,
  With silent delight
  Sits and smiles on the night.

Farewell green fields and happy groves,
Where flocks have took delight.
Where lambs have nibbled, silent moves
The feet of angels bright;
  Unseen they pour blessing,
  And joy without ceasing,
  On each bud and blossom,
  And each sleeping bosom.

They look in every thoughtless nest,
Where birds are covered warm;
They visit caves of every beast,
To keep them all from harm.
  If they see any weeping,
  That should have been sleeping,
  They pour sleep on their head,
  And sit down by their bed.

When wolves and tygers howl for prey,
They pitying stand and weep;
Seeking to drive their thirst away,
And keep them from the sheep.
 But if they rush dreadful,
 The angels, most heedful,
 Receive each mild spirit,
 New worlds to inherit.

And there the lion's ruddy eyes
Shall flow with tears of gold,
And pitying the tender cries,
And walking round the fold,
 Saying, 'Wrath, by his meekness,
 And by his health, sickness
 Is driven away
 From our immortal day.

'And now beside thee, bleating lamb
I can lie down and sleep;
Or think on him who bore thy name,
Graze after thee and weep.
 For, washed in life's river,
 My bright mane for ever
 Shall shine like the gold,
 As I guard o'er the fold.'

WILLIAM BLAKE

437. Nurse's Song

When the voices of children are heard on the green
And laughing is heard on the hill,
My heart is at rest within my breast
And everything else is still.

'Then come home, my children, the sun is gone down,
And the dews of night arise;
Come, come, leave off play, and let us away
Till the morning appears in the skies.'

'No, no, let us play, for it is yet day
And we cannot go to sleep;
Besides, in the sky the little birds fly,
And the hills are all covered with sheep.'

'Well, well, go and play till the light fades away,
And then go home to bed.'
The little ones leaped and shouted and laughed.
And all the hills ecchoèd.

WILLIAM BLAKE

438. *The Evening Primrose*

When once the sun sinks in the west,
And dew-drops pearl the evening's breast;
Almost as pale as moonbeams are,
Or its companionable star,
The evening primrose opes anew
Its delicate blossoms to the dew;
And, shunning hermit of the light,
Wastes its fair bloom upon the night;
Who, blindfold to its fond caresses,
Knows not the beauty he possesses.
Thus it blooms on till night is bye
And day looks out with open eye,
Abashed at the gaze it cannot shun,
It faints and withers, and is done.

JOHN CLARE

439. *Time, You Old Gipsy Man*

Time, you old gipsy man,
Will you not stay,
Put up your caravan
Just for one day?

All things I'll give you
Will you be my guest.
Bells for your jennet
Of silver the best,
Goldsmiths shall beat you
A great golden ring
Peacocks shall bow to you,
Little boys sing,
Oh, and sweet girls will
Festoon you with may.
Time, you old gipsy,
Why hasten away?

Last week in Babylon,
Last night in Rome,
Morning, and in the crush
Under Paul's dome;
Under Paul's dial
You tighten your rein –
Only a moment,
And off once again;
Off to some city
Now blind in the womb,
Off to another
Ere that's in the tomb.

Time, you old gipsy man,
Will you not stay,
Put up your caravan
Just for one day?

RALPH HODGSON

440. *Afterwards*

When the Present has latched its postern behind my tremulous
    stay,
  And the May month flaps its glad green leaves like wings,
Delicate-filmed as new-spun silk, will the neighbours say,
  'He was a man who used to notice such things'?

If it be in the dusk when, like an eyelid's soundless blink,
  The dewfall-hawk comes crossing the shades to alight
Upon the wind-warped upland thorn, a gazer may think,
  'To him this must have been a familiar sight.'

If I pass during some nocturnal blackness, mothy and warm,
  When the hedgehog travels furtively over the lawn,
One may say, 'He strove that such innocent creatures should come
    to no harm,
  But he could do little for them; and now he is gone.'

If, when hearing that I have been stilled at last, they stand at the
    door,
  Watching the full-starred heavens that winter sees,
Will this thought rise on those who will meet my face no more,
  'He was one who had an eye for such mysteries'?

And will any say when my bell of quittance is heard in the gloom,
  And a crossing breeze cuts a pause in its outrollings,
Till they rise again, as they were a new bell's boom,
  'He hears it not now, but used to notice such things'?

THOMAS HARDY

441. *Stepping Westward*

'What, you are stepping westward?' – 'Yea.'
  – 'Twould be a wildish destiny,

If we, who thus together roam
In a strange land, and far from home,
Were in this place the guests of chance;
Yet who would stop, or fear to advance,
Though home or shelter he had none,
With such a sky to lead him on?

The dewy ground was dark and cold;
Behind, all gloomy to behold;
And stepping westward seemed to be
A kind of heavenly destiny;
I liked the greeting; 'twas a sound
Of something without place or bound;
And seemed to give me spiritual right
To travel through that region bright.

The voice was soft, and she who spake
Was walking by her native lake;
The salutation had to me
The very sound of courtesy;
Its power was felt; and while my eye
Was fixed upon the glowing sky,
The echo of the voice enwrought
A human sweetness with the thought
Of travelling through the world that lay
Before me in my endless way.

WILLIAM WORDSWORTH

442. *Folding the Flocks*

Shepherds all, and Maidens fair,
Fold your Flocks up; for the Air
'Gins to thicken, and the Sun
Already his great course hath run.

See the Dew-drops how they kiss
Every little Flower that is:
Hanging on their Velvet Heads,
Like a Rope of Cristal Beads.
See the heavy Clouds low falling,
And bright *Hesperus* down calling
The dead Night from under Ground,
At whose rising, Mists unsound,
Damps and Vapours fly apace,
Hov'ring o'er the smiling Face
Of these Pastures, where they come,
Striking dead both Bud and Bloom;
Therefore, from such Danger, lock
Ev'ry one his lovèd Flock;
And let your Dogs lie loose without,
Lest the Wolf come as a scout
From the Mountain, and, ere day,
Bear a Lamb or Kid away;
Or the crafty, thievish Fox
Break upon your simple Flocks:
To secure yourself from these
Be not too secure in ease;
Let one Eye his watches keep,
While the other Eye doth sleep;
So shall you good Shepherds prove,
And deserve your Master's love.
Now, good night! may Sweetest Slumbers
And soft Silence fall in numbers
On your Eye-lids: So, farewell;
Thus I end my Evening knell.

JOHN FLETCHER

443. *To the Night*

Swiftly walk over the western wave,
      Spirit of Night!
Out of the misty eastern cave,
Where, all the long and lone daylight,
Thou wovest dreams of joy and fear,
Which make thee terrible and dear, –
      Swift be thy flight!

Wrap thy form in a mantle gray,
      Star-inwrought;
Blind with thine hair the eyes of Day;
Kiss her until she be wearied out,
Then wander o'er city, and sea, and land,
Touching all with thine opiate wand –
      Come, long-sought!

When I arose and saw the dawn,
      I sighed for thee;
When light rode high, and the dew was gone,
And noon lay heavy on flower and tree,
And the weary Day turned to his rest,
Lingering like an unloved guest,
      I sighed for thee.

Thy brother Death came, and cried,
      Wouldst thou me?
Thy sweet child Sleep, the filmy-eyed,
Murmured like a noon-tide bee,
Shall I nestle near thy side?
Wouldst thou me? – And I replied
      No, not thee!

Death will come when thou art dead,
      Soon, too soon –
Sleep will come when thou art fled;

Of neither would I ask the boon
I ask of thee, belovèd Night –
Swift be thine approaching flight,
          Come soon, soon!

PERCY BYSSHE SHELLEY

444. *Light the Lamps Up, Lamplighter!*

(FOR A LAMPLIGHTER, A GRANDMOTHER, THE ANGEL
GABRIEL, AND ANY NUMBER OF OTHERS)

Light the lamps up, Lamplighter,
The people are in the street –
          Without a light
          They have no sight,
And where will they plant their feet?
Some will tread in the gutter,
And some in the mud – oh dear!
Light the lamps up, Lamplighter,
Because the night is here.

Light the candles, Grandmother,
The children are going to bed –
          Without a wick
          They'll stumble and stick,
And where will they lay their head?
Some will lie on the staircase,
And some in the hearth – oh dear!
Light the candles, Grandmother,
Because the night is here.

Light the stars up, Gabriel,
The cherubs are out to fly –
          If heaven is blind
          How will they find
Their way across the sky?

Some will splash in the Milky Way,
Or bump on the moon – oh dear!
Light the stars up, Gabriel,
Because the night is here.

ELEANOR FARJEON

445. *Will You Come?*

Will you come?
Will you come?
Will you ride
So late
At my side?
O, will you come?

Will you come?
Will you come
If the night
Has a moon,
Full and bright?
O, will you come?

Would you come?
Would you come
If the noon
Gave light,
Not the moon?
Beautiful, would you come?

Would you have come?
Would you have come
Without scorning,
Had it been
Still morning?
Beloved, would you have come?

If you come
Haste and come.
Owls have cried;
It grows dark
To ride.
Beloved, beautiful, come!

EDWARD THOMAS

446. *Come!*

Wull ye come in eärly Spring,
Come at Easter, or in Mäy?
Or when Whitsuntide mid bring
Longer light to show your wäy?
Wull ye come, if you be true,
Vor to quicken love anew?
Wull ye call in Spring or Fall?
Come now soon by zun or moon?
Wull ye come?

Come wi' väice to väice the while
All their words be sweet to hear;
Come that feäce to feäce mid smile,
While their smiles do seem so dear;
Come within the year to seek
Woone you have sought woonce a week?
Come while flow'rs be on the bow'rs.
And the bird o' songs a-heärd.
Wull ye come?
Ess come *to* ye, an' come *vor* ye, is my word,
I wull come.

WILLIAM BARNES

447. *Hymn to Diana*

Queen and huntress, chaste and fair,
  Now the sun is laid to sleep,
Seated in thy silver chair,
    State in wonted manner keep;
      Hesperus entreats thy light,
      Goddess excellency bright.

Earth, let not thy envious shade
  Dare itself to interpose;
Cynthia's shining orb was made
    Heaven to clear when day did close:
      Bless us then with wishèd sight,
      Goddess excellently bright.

Lay the bow of pearl apart,
  And thy crystal shining quiver;
Give unto the flying hart
    Space to breathe, how short soever:
      Thou that mak'st a day of night,
      Goddess excellently bright.

BEN JONSON

448. *The Clouds Have Left the Sky*

The clouds have left the sky,
The wind hath left the sea,
The half-moon up on high
Shrinketh her face of dree.

She lightens on the comb
Of leaden waves, that roar
And thrust their hurried foam
Up on the dusky shore.

Behind the western bars
The shrouded day retreats,
And unperceived the stars
Steal to their sovran seats.

And whiter grows the foam,
The small moon lightens more;
And as I turn me home,
My shadow walks before.

ROBERT BRIDGES

449. *With How Sad Steps*

With how sad steps, O Moon, thou climb'st the skies!
How silently, and with how wan a face!
What! may it be that even in heavenly place
That busy archer his sharp arrows tries?
Sure, if that long-with-love-acquainted eyes
Can judge of love, thou feel'st a lover's case:
I read it in thy looks; thy languished grace
To me, that feel the like, thy state descries.

Then, even of fellowship, O Moon, tell me,
Is constant love deemed there but want of wit?
Are beauties there as proud as here they be?
Do they above love to be loved, and yet
Those lovers scorn whom that love doth possess?
Do they call virtue there ungratefulness?

SIR PHILIP SIDNEY

450. *In Dispraise of the Moon*

I would not be the Moon, the sickly thing,
To summon owls and bats upon the wing;

For when the noble Sun is gone away,
She turns his night into a pallid day.

She hath no air, no radiance of her own,
That world unmusical of earth and stone.
She wakes her dim, uncoloured, voiceless hosts,
Ghost of the Sun, herself the sun of ghosts.

The mortal eyes that gaze too long on her
Of Reason's piercing ray defrauded are.
Light in itself doth feed the living brain;
That light, reflected, but makes darkness plain.

MARY COLERIDGE

451. *The Waning Moon*

And like a dying lady, lean and pale,
Who totters forth, wrapt in a gauzy veil
Out of her chamber, led by the insane
And feeble wanderings of her fading brain,
The moon arose up in the murky East, -
A white and shapeless mass. –

PERCY BYSSHE SHELLEY

452. *We'll Go No More A-roving*

So, we'll go no more a-roving
    So late into the night,
Though the heart be still as loving,
    And the moon be still as bright.

For the sword outwears its sheath,
    And the soul wears out the breast,
And the heart must pause to breathe,
    And love itself have rest.

Though the night was made for loving,
  And the day returns too soon,
Yet we'll go no more a-roving
  By the light of the moon.

GEORGE GORDON, LORD BYRON

453. *Song of the Night at Daybreak*

All my stars forsake me,
And the dawn-winds shake me.
Where shall I betake me?

Whither shall I run
Till the set of sun,
Till the day be done?

To the mountain-mine,
To the boughs o' the pine,
To the blind man's eyne,

To a brow that is
Bowed upon the knees,
Sick with memories.

ALICE MEYNELL

454. *The Night Will Never Stay*

The night will never stay,
The night will still go by,
Though with a million stars
You pin it to the sky;
Though you bind it with the blowing wind
And buckle it with the moon,
The night will slip away
Like sorrow or a tune.

ELEANOR FARJEON

455. *Lines for a Bed at Kelmscott Manor*

The wind's on the wold
And the night is a-cold,
And Thames runs chill
'Twixt mead and hill,
But kind and dear
Is the old house here,
And my heart is warm
Midst winter's harm.
Rest then and rest,
And think of the best
'Twixt summer and spring
When all birds sing
In the town of the tree,
And ye lie in me
And scarce dare move
Lest earth and its love
Should fade away
Ere the full of the day.

I am old and have seen
Many things that have been,
Both grief and peace,
And wane and increase.
No tale I tell
Of ill or well,
But this I say,
Night treadeth on day,
And for worst and best
Right good is rest.

WILLIAM MORRIS

456. *Rock, Ball, Fiddle*

He that lies at the stock,
Shall have the gold rock;
He that lies at the wall,
Shall have the gold ball;
He that lies in the middle,
Shall have the gold fiddle.

457. *Before Sleeping*

Matthew, Mark, Luke, and John,
Bless the bed that I lie on.
Before I lay me down to sleep
I give my soul to Christ to keep.
Four corners to my bed,
Four angels there aspread,
Two to foot, and two to head,
And four to carry me when I'm dead.
I go by sea, I go by land,
The Lord made me with His right hand.
If any danger come to me,
Sweet Jesus Christ deliver me.
He's the branch and I'm the flower,
Pray God send me a happy hour,
And if I die before I wake,
I pray that Christ my soul will take.

458. *On a Quiet Conscience*

Close thine eyes, and sleep secure;
Thy soul is safe, thy body sure.

He that guards thee, he that keeps,
Never slumbers, never sleeps.
A quiet conscience in the breast
Has only peace, has only rest.
The wisest and the mirth of kings
Are out of tune unless she sings:
Then close thine eyes in peace and sleep secure,
No sleep so sweet as thine, no rest so sure.

CHARLES I

459. *Song*

While Morpheus thus does gently lay
   His powerful charge upon each part
Making thy spirits even obey
   The silver charms of his dull art;

I, thy Good Angel, from thy side, –
   As smoke doth from the altar rise,
Making no noise as it doth glide, –
   Will leave thee in this soft surprise;

And from the clouds will fetch thee down
   A holy vision, to express
Thy right unto an earthly crown;
   No power can make this kingdom less.

But gently, gently, lest I bring
   A start in sleep by sudden flight,
Playing aloof, and hovering,
   Till I am lost unto the sight.

This is a motion still and soft;
   So free from noise and cry,
That Jove himself, who hears a thought,
   Knows not when we pass by.

HENRY KILLIGREW

460. *The Eve of Saint Mark*

Upon a Sabbath-day, it fell;
Twice holy was the Sabbath-bell,
That called the folk to evening prayer;
The city streets were clean and fair
From wholesome drench of April rains;
And, on the western window panes,
The chilly sunset faintly told
Of unmatured green vallies cold,
Of the green thorny bloomless hedge,
Of rivers new with spring-tide sedge,
Of primroses by sheltered rills,
And daisies on the aguish hills.
Twice holy was the Sabbath-bell:
The silent streets were crowded well
With staid and pious companies,
Warm from their fire-side oratories;
And moving, with demurest air,
To even-song, and vesper-prayer.
Each archèd porch, and entry low,
Was filled with patient folk and slow,
With whispers hush, and shuffling feet,
While played the organ loud and sweet.
The bells had ceased, the prayers begun,
And Bertha had not yet half done
A curious volume, patched and torn,
That all day long, from earliest morn,
Had taken captive her two eyes,
Among its golden broideries;
Perplexed her with a thousand things,—
The stars of Heaven, and angels' wings,
Martyrs in a fiery blaze,
Azure saints in silver rays,
Moses' breastplate, and the seven
Candlesticks John saw in Heaven,

The winged Lion of Saint Mark,
And the Covenantal Ark,
With its many mysteries,
Cherubim and golden mice.

Bertha was a maiden fair,
Dwelling in the old Minster-square;
From her fire-side she could see,
Sidelong, its rich antiquity,
Far as the Bishop's garden-wall;
Where sycamores and elm-trees tall,
Full-leaved the forest had outstript,
By no sharp north-wind ever nipt,
So sheltered by the mighty pile,
Bertha arose, and read awhile,
With forehead 'gainst the window-pane.
Again she tryed, and then again,
Until the dusk eve left her dark
Upon the legend of St. Mark.
From plaited lawn-frill, fine and thin,
She lifted up her soft warm chin,
With aching neck and swimming eyes,
And dazed with saintly imageries.

All was gloom, and silent all,
Save now and then the still foot-fall
Of one returning homewards late,
Past the echoing minster-gate.
The clamorous daws, that all the day
Above tree-tops and towers play,
Pair by pair had gone to rest,
Each in its ancient belfry-nest,
Where asleep they fall be times,
To music of the drowsy chimes.

All was silent, all was gloom,
Abroad and in the homely room:

Down she sat, poor cheated soul!
And struck a lamp from the dismal coal;
Leaned forward, with bright drooping hair
And slant book, full against the glare.
Her shadow, in uneasy guise,
Hovered about, a giant size,
On ceiling-beam and old oak chair
The parrot's cage, and panel square;
And the warm angled winter screen,
On which were many monsters seen,
Called doves of Siam, Lima mice,
And legless birds of Paradise,
Macaw, and tender Avadavat,
And silken-furred Angora cat.
Untired she read, her shadow still
Glowered about, as it would fill
The room with wildest forms and shades,
As though some ghostly queen of spades
Had come to mock behind her back,
And dance, and ruffle her garments black.
Untired she read the legend page,
Of holy Mark, from youth to age,
On land, on sea, in pagan chains,
Rejoicing for his many pains.
Sometimes the learned eremite,
With golden star, or dagger bright,
Referred to pious poesies
Written in smallest crow-quill size
Beneath the text; and thus the rhyme
Was parcelled out from time to time: –

‘ "Gif ye wol stonden[1] hardie wight –
Amiddès of the blackè night –
Righte in the churchè porch, pardie
Ye wol behold a companie
Approchen thee full dolourouse:

1. If you will stand

For soothe to sain from everich house
Be it in city or villàge
Wol come the Phantom and imàge
Of ilka² gent and ilka carle
Whom coldè Deathè hath in parle
And wol some day that very year
Touchen with foulè venime spear
And sadly do them all to die. –
Hem all shalt thou see verilie –
And everichon shall be thee pass
All who must die that year, Alas."

'Als³ writith he of swevenis,⁴
Men han beforne they wake in bliss,
Whanne that hir friendès thinke hem bound
In crimpèd shroude farre under grounde;
And how a litling child mote be
A saint er its nativitie,
Gif that the modre – God her blesse! –
Kepen in solitarinesse,
And kissen devoute the holy croce –
Of Goddès love, and Sathan's force, –
He writith; and thinges many mo,
Of swichè things I may not show.
Bot I must tellen verilie
Somdel of Saintè Cicilie,
And chieflie what he auctoriethe
Of Saintè Markis life and dethe:'

At length her constant eyelids come
Upon the fervent martyrdom;
Then lastly to his holy shrine.
Exalt amid the tapers' shine
At Venice . . .

JOHN KEATS

2. Every 4. Visions
3. Likewise

461. *Laid in My Quiet Bed*

Laid in my quiet bed, in study as I were,
I saw within my troubled head a heap of thoughts appear;
And every thought did shew so lively in mine eyes,
That now I sighed, and then I smiled, as cause of thought did rise.
I saw the little boy in thought how oft that he
Did wish of God, to scape the rod, a tall young man to be.
The young man eke that feels his bones with pains opprest,
How he would be a rich old man, to live and lie at rest.
The rich old man that sees his end draw on so sore,
How he would be a boy again, to live so much the more.
Whereat full oft I smiled, to see how all these three,
From boy to man, from man to boy, would chop and change
    degree . . .

HENRY HOWARD, EARL OF SURREY

462. *At Night*

Home, home from the horizon far and clear,
    Hither the soft wings sweep;
Flocks of the memories of the day draw near
    The dovecote doors of sleep.

Oh, which are they that come through sweetest light
    Of all these homing birds?
Which with the straightest and the swiftest flight?
    Your words to me, your words!

ALICE MEYNELL

463. *Echo*

Come to me in the silence of the night;
   Come in the speaking silence of a dream;
Come with soft rounded cheeks and eyes as bright
    As sunlight on a stream;
      Come back in tears,
O memory, hope, love of finished years.

O dream how sweet, too sweet, too bitter sweet,
   Whose wakening should have been in Paradise,
Where souls brimfull of love abide and meet;
    Where thirsting longing eyes
      Watch the slow door
That opening, letting in, lets out no more.

Yet come to me in dreams, that I may live
   My very life again though cold in death:
Come back to me in dreams, that I may give
    Pulse for pulse, breath for breath:
      Speak low, lean low,
As long ago, my love, how long ago.

CHRISTINA ROSSETTI

464. *The Shadow of Night*

How strange it is to wake
   And watch while others sleep,
Till sight and hearing ache
   For objects that may keep
The awful inner sense
   Unroused, lest it should mark
The life that haunts the emptiness
   And horror of the dark.

How strange the distant bay
    Of gods; how wild the note
Of cocks that scream for day,
    In homesteads far remote;
How strange and wild to hear
    The old and crumbling tower,
Amidst the darkness, suddenly
    Take life and speak the hour . . .

The nightingale is gay,
    For she can vanquish night;
Dreaming, she sings of day,
    Notes that make darkness bright:
But when the refluent gloom
    Suddens the gaps of song,
We charge on her the dolefulness,
    And call her crazed with wrong.

COVENTRY PATMORE

465. *Out in the Dark*

Out in the dark over the snow
The fallow fawns invisible go
With the fallow doe;
And the winds blow
Fast as the stars are slow.

Stealthily the dark haunts round
And, when the lamp goes, without sound
At a swifter bound
Then the swiftest hound,
Arrives, and all else is drowned;

And I and star and wind and deer,
Are in the dark together, – near,
Yet far, – and fear

Drums on my ear
In that sage company drear.

How weak and little is the light,
All the universe of sight,
Love and delight,
Before the might,
If you love it not, of night.

EDWARD THOMAS

466. *Nocturne*

The red flame flowers bloom and die,
    The embers puff a golden spark.
Now and again a horse's eye
    Shines like a topaz in the dark.

A prowling jackal jars the hush,
    The drowsy oxen chump and sigh –
The ghost moon lifts above the bush
    And creeps across the starry sky.

Low in the south the 'Cross' is bright,
    And sleep comes dreamless, undefiled,
Here in the blue and silver night,
    In the star-chamber of the Wild.

CROSBIE GARSTIN

467. *The Angel*

I dreamt a Dream! what can it mean?
And that I was a maiden Queen
Guarded by an Angel mild:
Witless woe was ne'er beguiled!

And I wept both night and day,
And he wiped my tears away;
And I wept both day and night,
And hid from him my heart's delight.

So he took his wings and fled;
Then the morn blushed rosy red;
I dried my tears, and armed my fears
With ten thousand shields and spears.

Soon my Angel came again;
I was armed, he came in vain;
For the time of youth was fled,
And grey hairs were on my head.

WILLIAM BLAKE

468. *Angel Spirits of Sleep*

Angel spirits of sleep,
White-robed, with silver hair,
In your meadows fair,
Where the willows weep,
And the sad moonbeam
On the gliding stream
Writes her scattered dream:

Angel spirits of sleep,
Dancing to the weir
In the hollow roar
Of its waters deep;
Know ye how men say
That ye haunt no more
Isle and grassy shore
With your moonlit play;
That ye dance not here,

White-robed spirits of sleep,
All the summer night
Threading dances light?

ROBERT BRIDGES

469. *A Dream*

Once a dream did weave a shade
O'er my Angel-guarded bed,
That an Emmet lost its way
Where on grass methought I lay.

Troubled, 'wildered, and forlorn,
Dark, benighted, travel-worn,
Over many a tangled spray,
All heart-broke I heard her say:

'O my children! do they cry?
Do they hear their father sigh?
Now they look abroad to see:
Now return and weep for me.'

Pitying, I dropped a tear;
But I saw a glow-worm near,
Who replied: 'What wailing wight
Calls the watchman of the night?

'I am set to light the ground,
While the beetle goes his round:
Follow now the beetle's hum;
Little wanderer, hie thee home.'

WILLIAM BLAKE

470. *The Land of Dreams*

Awake, awake, my little Boy!
Thou wast thy Mother's only joy:
Why dost thou weep in thy gentle sleep?
Awake! thy Father does thee keep.

'O, what land is the Land of Dreams,
What are its mountains, and what are its streams?
O Father! I saw my Mother there,
Among the Lillies by waters fair.

'Among the lambs clothèd in white,
She walked with her Thomas in sweet delight.
I wept for joy, like a dove I mourn;
O! when shall I again return?'

Dear Child, I also by pleasant streams
Have wandered all night in the Land of Dreams,
But tho' calm and warm the waters wide,
I could not get to the other side.

'Father, O Father! what do we here,
In this Land of unbelief and fear?
The Land of Dreams is better far
Above the light of the Morning Star.'

WILLIAM BLAKE

THE GARDEN

471. *I Know a Little Garden-Close*

I know a little garden-close
Set thick with lily and red rose,
Where I would wander if I might
From dewy dawn to dewy night,
And have one with me wandering.

And though within it no birds sing,
And though no pillared house is there,
And though the apple boughs are bare
Of fruit and blossom, would to God,
Her feet upon the green grass trod,
And I beheld them as before.

There comes a murmur from the shore,
And in the close two fair streams are,
Drawn from the purple hills afar,
Drawn down unto the restless sea;
Dark hills whose heath-bloom feeds no bee,
Dark shores no ship has ever seen,
Tormented by the billows green
Whose murmur comes unceasingly
Unto the place for which I cry.

For which I cry both day and night,
For which I let slip all delight,
Whereby I grow both deaf and blind,
Careless to win, unskilled to find,
And quick to lose what all men seek.

Yet tottering as I am, and weak,
Still have I left a little breath
To seek within the jaws of death
An entrance to that happy place,

To seek the unforgotten face,
Once seen, once kissed, once reft from me
Anight the murmuring of the sea.

WILLIAM MORRIS

472. *Follow*

Follow thy fair sun, unhappy shadow,
Though thou be black as night,
And she made all of light,
Yet follow thy fair sun, unhappy shadow.

Follow her whose light thy light depriveth,
Though here thou liv'st disgraced,
And she in heaven is placed,
Yet follow her whose light the world reviveth.

Follow those pure beams whose beauty burneth,
That so have scorchèd thee,
As thou still black must be,
Till her kind beams thy black to brightness turneth.

Follow her while yet her glory shineth:
There comes a luckless night,
That will dim all her light;
And this the black unhappy shade divineth.

Follow still since so thy fates ordainèd;
The Sun must have his shade,
Till both at once do fade –
The Sun still proud, the shadow still disdainèd.

THOMAS CAMPION

473. *Up-hill*

Does the road wind up-hill all the way?
   Yes, to the very end.
Will the day's journey take the whole long day?
   From morn to night, my friend.

But is there for the night a resting-place?
   A roof for when the slow dark hours begin.
May not the darkness hide it from my face?
   You cannot miss that inn.

Shall I meet other wayfarers at night?
   Those who have gone before.
Then must I knock or call when just in sight?
   They will not keep you standing at the door.

Shall I find comfort, travel-sore and weak?
   Of labour you shall find the sum.
Will there be beds for me and all who seek?
   Yea, beds for all who come.

CHRISTINA ROSSETTI

474. *Love*

Love bade me welcome; yet my soul drew back,
    Guilty of dust and sin.
But quick-eyed Love, observing me grow slack
    From my first entrance in,
Drew nearer to me, sweetly questioning
    If I lacked anything.

'A guest,' I answered, 'worthy to be here':
      Love said, 'You shall be he.'
'I, the unkind, ungrateful? Ah, my dear!
      I cannot look on Thee.'
Love took my hand, and smiling did reply,
      'Who made the eyes but I?'

'Truth, Lord; but I have marred them; let my shame
      Go where it doth deserve.'
'And know you not,' says Love, 'who bore the blame?'
      'My dear, then I will serve.'
'You must sit down,' says Love, 'and taste my meat.'
      So I did sit and eat.

GEORGE HERBERT

475. *A Royal Guest*

. . . Yet if His Majesty our sovereign lord
      Should of his own accord
    Friendly himself invite,
And say, 'I'll be your guest to-morrow night.'
How should we stir ourselves, call and command
All hands to work! 'Let no man idle stand!

'Set me fine Spanish tables in the hall,
      See they be fitted all;
    Let there be room to eat,
And order taken that there want no meat.
See every sconce and candlestick made bright,
That without tapers they may give a light.

'Look to the presence: are the carpets spread,
      The dazie[1] o'er the head,
    The cushions in the chairs,

1. Canopy over dais

And all the candles lighted on the stairs?
Perfume the chambers, and in any case
Let each man give attendance in his place!'

Thus, if the king were coming, would we do,
  And 'twere good reason too;
   For 'tis a duteous thing
To show all honour to an earthly king,
And after all our travail and our cost.
So he be pleased, to think no labour lost.

But at the coming of the King of Heaven
  All's set at six and seven:
   We wallow in our sin,
Christ cannot find a chamber in the inn.
We entertain Him always like a stranger,
And, as at first, still lodge Him in a manger.

476. *Eve*

Eve, with her basket, was
Deep in the bells and grass,
Wading in bells and grass
Up to her knees,
Picking a dish of sweet
Berries and plums to eat,
Down in the bells and grass
Under the trees.

Mute as a mouse in a
Corner the cobra lay,
Curled round a bough of the
Cinnamon tall . . .
Now to get even and
Humble proud heaven and –
Now was the moment or
Never at all.

'Eva!' Each syllable
Light as a flower fell,
'Eva!' he whispered the
Wondering maid,
Soft as a bubble sung
Out of a linnet's lung,
Soft and most silverly
'Eva!' he said.

Picture that orchard sprite,
Eve, with her body white,
Supple and smooth to her
Slim finger tips,
Wondering, listening,
Listening, wondering,
Eve with a berry
Half-way to her lips.

Oh, had our simple Eve
Seen through the make-believe!
Had she but known the
Pretender he was!
Out of the boughs he came,
Whispering still her name,
Tumbling in twenty rings
Into the grass.

Here was the strangest pair
In the world anywhere,
Eve in the bells and grass
Kneeling, and he
Telling his story low . . .
Singing birds saw them go
Down the dark path to
The Blasphemous Tree.

Oh, what a clatter when
Titmouse and Jenny Wren
Saw him successful and
Taking his leave!
How the birds rated him,
How they all hated him!
How they all pitied
Poor motherless Eve!

Picture her crying,
Outside in the lane,
Eve, with no dish of sweet
Berries and plums to eat,
Haunting the gate of the
Orchard in vain . . .
Picture the lewd delight
Under the hill to-night –
'Eva!' the toast goes round,
'Eva!' again.

                              RALPH HODGSON

477. *Eve*

'While I sit at the door,
Sick to gaze within,
Mine eye weepeth sore
For sorrow and sin:
As a tree my sin stands
To darken all lands;
Death is the fruit it bore.

'How have Eden bowers grown
Without Adam to bend them!
How have Eden flowers blown,
Squandering their sweet breath,
Without me to tend them!

The Tree of Life was ours,
Tree twelvefold-fruited,
Most lofty tree that flowers,
Most deeply rooted:
I chose the Tree of Death.

'Hadst thou but said me nay,
Adam, my brother,
I might have pined away;
I, but none other:
God might have let thee stay
Safe in our garden
By putting me away
Beyond all pardon.

'I, Eve, sad mother
Of all who must live,
I, not another,
Plucked bitterest fruit to give
My friend, husband, lover.
O wanton eyes run over;
Who but I should grieve? –
Cain hath slain his brother:
Of all who must die mother,
Miserable Eve!'
Thus she sat weeping,
Thus Eve our mother,
Where one lay sleeping
Slain by his brother.
Greatest and least
Each piteous beast
To hear her voice
Forgot his joys
And set aside his feast.

The mouse paused in his walk
And dropped his wheaten stalk;
Grave cattle wagged their heads

In rumination;
The eagle gave a cry
From his cloud station:
Larks on thyme beds
Forbore to mount or sing;
Bees drooped upon the wing;
The raven perched on high
Forgot his ration;
The conies in their rock,
A feeble nation,
Quaked sympathetical;
The mocking-bird left off to mock;
Huge camels knelt as if
In deprecation;
The kind hart's tears were falling;
Chattered the wistful stork;
Dove-voices with a dying fall
Cooed desolation
Answering grief by grief.
Only the serpent in the dust,
Wriggling and crawling,
Grinned an evil grin and thrust
His tongue out with its fork.

CHRISTINA ROSSETTI

478. *Adam*

Adam lay i'bowndyn,
  bowndyn in a bond.
Fowre thowsand wynter
  thowt he not to long;

And al was for an appil,
  an appil that he tok,
As clerkes fyndyn wretyn
  in here Book.

Ne hadde the appil takė ben,
    the appil taken ben,
Ne hadde never our lady
    a ben hevene qwen.

Blyssid be the tyme
    that appil take was!
Therefore we mown syngyn
    Deo gracias.

479. *The Seven Virgins*

All under the leaves and the leaves of life
    I met with virgins seven,
And one of them was Mary mild,
    Our Lord's mother of Heaven.

'Oh, what are you seeking, you seven fair maids
    All under the leaves of life?
Come tell, come tell, what seek you
    All under the leaves of life?'

'We're seeking for no leaves, Thomas,
    But for a friend of thine;
We're seeking for sweet Jesus Christ,
    To be our guide and thine.'

'Go down, go down, to yonder town,
    And sit in the gallery,
And there you'll see sweet Jesus Christ
    Nailed to a big yew-tree.'

So down they went to yonder town
    As fast as foot could fall,
And many a grievous bitter tear
    From the virgins' eyes did fall.

'O peace, Mother, O peace, Mother,
　　Your weeping doth me grieve:
I must suffer this,' He said,
　　'For Adam and for Eve.

'O Mother, take you John Evangelist
　　All for to be your son,
And he will comfort you sometimes,
　　Mother, as I have done.'

'O come, thou John Evangelist,
　　Thou'rt welcome unto me;
But more welcome my own dear Son,
　　Whom I nursèd on my knee.'

Then he laid his head on His right shoulder,
　　Seeing death it struck Him nigh –
'The Holy Ghost be with your soul,
　　I die, Mother dear, I die.' . . .

480. *Lully, Lulley*

Lully, lalley, lully, lulley;
The faucon hath borne my make[1] away.

He bare him up, he bare him down,
He bare him in to an orchard browne.

In that orchard there was an halle
That was hanged with purpill and pall.

An in that hall there was a bede,[2]
Hit was hanged with gold so rede.

1. Mate　　2. Bed

And in that bede there lithe a knyght,
His woundes bleding day and night.

By that bede side kneleth a may,
And she wepeth both night and day.

And by that bede side there stondeth a stone,
Corpus Christi wretyen there on.

481. *Balme*

... There grew a goodly tree him faire beside,
   Loaden with fruit and apples rosie red,
   As they in pure vermilion had beene dide,
   Whereof great vertues over all were red:[1]
   For happie life to all, which thereon fed,
   And life eke everlasting did befall:
   Great God it planted in that blessed sted
   With his almightie hand, and did it call
The tree of life, the crime of our first father's fall.

In all the world like was not to be found,
   Save in that soile, where all good things did grow,
   And freely sprong out of the fruitfull ground,
   As incorrupted Nature did them sow,
   Till that dread Dragon all did overthrow.
   Another like faire tree eke grew thereby,
   Whereof who so did eat, eftsoones did know
   Both good and ill: O mornefull memory:
That tree through one man's fault hath doen us all to dy.

From that first tree forth flowd, as from a well,
   A trickling streame of Balme, most soveraine
   And daintie deare, which on the ground still fell,
   And overflowèd all the fertill plaine,

1. Told

And it had deawèd bene with timely raine:
Life and long health that gratious ointment gave,
And deadly woundes could heale, and reare againe
The senselesse corse appointed for the grave.
Into that same he fell: which did from death him save . . .

EDMUND SPENSER

482. *My Master Hath a Garden*

My master hath a garden, full-filled with divers flowers,
Where thou mayst gather posies gay, all times and hours,
    Here nought is heard
    But paradise-bird,
    Harp, dulcimer, and lute,
      With cymbal,
      And timbrel,
    And the gentle sounding flute.

Oh! Jesus, Lord, my heal and weal, my bliss complete,
Make thou my heart thy garden-plot, true, fair and neat
    That I may hear
    This music clear,
    Harp, dulcimer, and lute,
      With cymbal,
      And timbrel,
    And the gentle sounding flute.

483. *This Is the Key*

This is the Key of the Kingdom:
In that Kingdom is a city;
In that city is a town;
In that town there is a street;

751

In that street there winds a lane;
In that lane there is a yard;
In that yard there is a house;
In that house there waits a room;
In that room an empty bed;
And on that bed a basket –
A Basket of Sweet Flowers:
  Of Flowers, of Flowers;
  A Basket of Sweet Flowers.

Flowers in a Basket;
Basket on the bed;
Bed in the chamber;
Chamber in the house;
House in the weedy yard;
Yard in the winding lane;
Lane in the broad street;
Street in the high town;
Town in the city;
City in the Kingdom –
This is the Key of the Kingdom;
  Of the Kingdom this is the Key.

ABOUT AND ROUNDABOUT

(continued from volume 1)

264. 'Woe weeps out her division when she sings'

This means, I think, that she adds her own grieved cadences to the melody, as may one, among many voices, singing in harmony.

265. 'Is like a bubble'

This rainbow 'bubble' – like Shelley's dome of 'many-coloured glass' in his *Adonais* – seems, before our very eyes, to be hovering in the empty blue heavens, until it smalls into a bead of gold, and vanishes. It brings to memory – though I am uncertain of the first line – an epitaph in the church at Zennor, a village clustered above the Atlantic on the dreamlike coast of Cornwall. The epitaph has been cut in fine lettering into its slate slab, and at each corner of the slab Cherubs' heads representing the winds of the world puff out their round and solemn cheeks:

> Sorrow, and sin, false hope, and trouble –
> These the Four Winds that hourly vex this Bubble:
> His breath a Vapour, and his life a Span;
> 'Tis Glorious Misery to be born a Man.

266. 'O, sweet content!'

> There is a jewel which no Indian mines
> Can buy, no chymic art can counterfeit;
> It makes men rich in greatest poverty;
> Makes water wine, turns wooden cups to gold,
> The homely whistle to sweet music's strain:
>   Seldom it comes, to few from heaven sent,
>   That much in little, all in naught – Content.

'*Art thou poor, . . .*
Art thou rich . . . ?'

He that spendeth much;
   And getteth nought;
He that oweth much,
   And hath nought;
He that looketh in his purse
   And findeth nought, –
He may be sorry,
   And say nought.
He that may and will not,
He then that would shall not.
He that would not and cannot
May repent and sigh not.

He that sweareth
   Till no man trust him;
He that lieth
   Till no man believe him;
He that borroweth
   Till no man will lend him;
Let him go where
   No man knoweth him.

He that hath a good master,
   And cannot keep him;
He that hath a good servant,
   And is not content with him;
He that hath such conditions,
   That no man loveth him;
May well know other,
   But few men will know him.

HUGH RHODES (1550)

And, to make trebly sure:
Three false sisters: 'Perhaps,' 'May be,' 'I dare say.'
Three timid brothers: 'Hush!' 'Stop!' 'Listen!'
Three deeps: Well! *well!* WELL!
A useful pair: *Almost* and *Very nigh*
                    Saved many a lie.

Also and finally: 'Be aisy, and if you can't be aisy, be as aisy as you can.'

269. '*Lord Rameses of Egypt sighed*'

The most ancient poem I know of consists of such a sigh. It comes from an Egyptian tomb, was composed about 5000 years ago, and might have been written by some serene and melancholy soul at his sick-room window yesterday afternoon. For, after all, these men whose mummies are now a mere wonder to the curious, once lived, as Raleigh says, 'in the same newness of time which we call "old time".'

Death is before me to-day
Like the recovery of a sick man,
Like going forth into a garden after sickness.

Death is before me to-day
Like the odour of myrrh,
Like sitting under the sail on a windy day . . .

Death is before me to-day
Like the course of the freshet,
Like the return of a man from the war-galley to his house . . .

Death is before me to-day
As a man longs to see his house
When he had spent years in captivity.

He is so keenly (if not contentedly) aware and alive that every simile of tribute to death that he uses refers to some intensely happy experience in his own remembrance.

272. 'These Strong and Fair'

And here is another poem by William Barnes which I have ventured to spell not as it appears in its original dialect, but in the usual way:

> If souls should only shine as bright
> In heaven as in earthly light,
> And nothing better were the case,
> How comely still, in shape and face,
> Would many reach that happy place, –
> The hopeful souls that in their prime,
> Have seemed a-taken before their time –
>   The young that died in beauty.
>
> But when one's limbs have lost their strength
> A-toiling through a lifetime's length,
> And over cheeks a-growing old
> The slowly-wasting years have rolled
> The deepening wrinkles' hollow fold;
> When life is ripe, then death do call
> For less of thought, than when it fall
>   On young folks in their beauty . . .
>
> But still the dead shall more than keep
> The beauty of their early sleep;
> Where comely looks shall never wear
> Uncomely, under toil and care,
> The fair, at death be always fair,
> Still fair to living, thought and love,
> And fairer still to God above,
>   Then when they died in beauty.

273

I remember actually coming upon this poem (in Mr Nahum's second book), and how I suddenly turned my head and looked up at the dark-socketed skull in its alcove in the turret room; it had no alarm for me then, though I can recall cold moments of dread or confusion, when I was a boy, at the thought of death. Then – or was it some time after? – I turned the page, and found the following poem by Thomas Campion, and, in Mr Nahum's writing, this scrawl at the foot of it: 'Yes, but the vision first.'

> The man of life upright,
>   Whose guiltless heart is free
> From all dishonest deeds,
>   Or thought of vanity;
>
> The man whose silent days
>   In harmless joys are spent,
> Whom hopes cannot delude
>   Nor sorrow discontent:
>
> That man needs neither towers
>   Nor armour for defence,
> Nor secret vaults to fly
>   From thunder's violence:
>
> He only can behold
>   With unaffrighted eyes
> The horrors of the deep
>   And terrors of the skies.
>
> Thus scorning all the cares
>   That fate or fortune brings,
> He makes the heaven his book,
>   His wisdom heavenly things;

Good thoughts his only friends,
His wealth a well-spent age,
The earth his sober inn
And quiet pilgrimage.

'. . . Yet suffer us, O Lord, not to repine, whether in the morning, at noon, or at midnight, that is to say, in our cradle, in our youth, or old age, we go to take our long sleep; but let us make this reckoning of our years, that if we can live no longer, *that* is unto us our old age; for he that liveth so long as thou appointest him (though he die in the pride of his beauty) dieth an old man . . .'

274

This solemn dirge was written in 'time of pestilence', – such a visitation as Daniel Defoe tells of in his 'Journal of the Plague Year'. So too this nameless writer (of 1625) – in a fragment of verse that is scarcely better than doggerel, though 'Who yesterday sate singing' and 'morning Mattens' and line 7 touch it with a *poetic* actuality Defoe seldom achieved:

This was that yeere of wonder, when this Land,
Was Ploughed up into Graves, and graves did stand
From morne, till next morne, gaping still for more.
The Bells (like our lowde sinnes) ne'er giving ore.
Then, life look't pale, and sicklier then the Moone,
Whole Households, well i'th morne, lying dead at Noone.
Then sicknesse was of her owne face affrayde,
And frighting all, yet was her self dismayde . . .
Paules Organs (then) were passing-bells, to call
This day a Quirist to his Funerall
Who yesterday sate singing; Men did come
To morning Mattens, yet ere they got home,
Had Tokens sent them that they should no more
Hear Anthems there; They were to goe before
Him, to whose name, those Anthems were all sung,
To instruments, which were by Angels strung.

The Elizabethan poets brooded endlessly on the mystery of death. A music haunts their words like that of muffled bells, as in John Fletcher's poem:

> . . . Come hither, you that hope, and you that cry,
> Leave off complaining!
> Youth, strength, and beauty, that shall never die,
> Are here remaining.
> Come hither, fools, and blush you stay so long
> From being blessed,
> And mad men, worse than you, that suffer wrong,
> Yet seek no rest! . . .

And in William Davenant's:

> Wake, all the dead! What ho! what ho!
> How soundly they sleep whose pillows lie low!
> They mind not poor lovers, who walk above
> On the decks of the world in storms of love.
> No whisper now nor glance shall pass
> Through wickets or through panes of glass,
> For our windows and doors are shut and barred.
> Lie close in the church, and in the churchyard!
> In every grave make room, make room!
> The world's at an end, and we come, we come! . . .

275. '*I, who loved with all my life, Love with all my death*'

> Not full twelve years twice-told, a weary breath
> I have exchangèd for a wishèd death.
> My course was short, the longer is my rest,
> God takes them soonest whom he loveth best;
> For he that's born to-day dies to-morrow,
> Loseth some days of mirth, but months of sorrow.

There is an epitaph that instantly calls these words to mind in the steep-sloping graveyard at Manorbier whose ruinous castle towers above the turf of its narrow ocean inlet, as if it were keeping a long tryst with the church tower on the neighbouring height:

> Weep not for her ye friends that's dear,
> Weep for your sins, for death is near –
> You see by her, she [was] cut down soon:
> Her morning Sun went down at noon.

Not much better than doggerel; and yet it is not easy to forget such things – chancing on the weathered stone in the long grasses in the summer sunshine – birds, bees, and butterflies one's only company and the distant lully of the sea.

And then there are these two unforgettable fragments, the one from the Scots of John Wedderburn (1542), and the other of a century before, its authorship unknown:

Who's at My Window?

> Who's at my window, who, who?
> Go from my window, go, go!
> Who calleth there so like a stranger?
>   Go from my window – go!
> Lord, I am here, a wretched mortal
> That for Thy mercy does cry and call –
>   Unto Thee, my Lord Celestial,
>   See who is at my window, who.

The Call

> . . . Come home again, come home again;
> Mine own sweet heart, come home again!
>   You are gone astray
>   Out of your way,
> Therefore, sweet heart, come home again!

277. '*Hark! now everything is still*'

Death stands above me, whispering low
    I know not what into my ear;
Of his strange language all I know
    Is, there is not a word of fear.

            WALTER SAVAGE LANDOR

'*'Tis now full tide 'tween night and day*'

Leave me, O Love, which reachest but to dust;
And thou, my mind, aspire to higher things;
Grow rich in that which never taketh rust;
Whatever fades, but fading pleasure brings.

Draw in thy beams, and humble all thy might
To that sweet yoke where lasting freedoms be;
Which breaks the clouds, and opens forth the light,
That doth both shine and give us sight to see.

O, take fast hold! let that light be thy guide
In this small course which birth draws out to death –
And think how evil becometh him to slide,
Who seeketh heaven, and comes of heavenly breath.

    Then farewell, world; thy uttermost I see:
    Eternal Love, maintain thy life in me.

            SIR PHILIP SIDNEY

278

Of the *Lyke-Wake Dirge* is known neither the age nor the author. The body from which the 'saule' or spirit within fled away lies in its shroud, and the dirge tells of that spirit's journey. Its word 'sleet', says Mr Sidgwick, means either salt, for it was the custom to place in a wooden platter beside the dead, earth and salt for emblems, the one of corruption, the other of the immortal; or, as some suppose, 'sleet' should be *fleet*, meaning embers or water or houseroom. 'Whinnies' means gorse. To explain the full meaning of Bridge of Dread would need many pages.

279

Next this poem in Mr Nahum's book was 'Lead, Kindly Light', and there was a strange picture for it hanging in the round tower – the picture of a becalmed ship, clumsy of rig and low in the water which was smooth and green as glass. In the midst of the ship there was piled high what might be taken for a vast heap of oranges, their fair reddish colour blazing in the rays of the sun that was about to plunge out of the greenish sky below the line of the west. But what even more particularly attracted my eye at the time was that ship's figurehead – a curious head and shoulders, as if with wings, and of a kind of far beauty or wonder beyond me to describe.

281

Philaster.   Fie, fie,
So young and so dissembling! fear'st thou not death?
Can boys contemn that?

Bellario.   O, what boy is he
Can be content to live to be a man,
That sees the best of men thus passionate,
Thus without reason?

Philaster.   O, but thou dost not know what 'tis to die.

Bellario.   Yes, I do know, my Lord!
'Tis less than to be born; a lasting sleep,
A quiet resting from all jealousy;
A thing we all pursue; I know besides
It is but giving over of a game
That must be lost.

From *Philaster*, FRANCIS BEAUMONT and JOHN FLETCHER

284. '*All the flowers*'

'. . . But those which perfume the air most delightfully, not passed by as the rest, but being trodden upon and crushed, are three – that is, burnet, wild thyme, and watermints. Therefore you are to set whole alleys of them, to have the pleasure when you walk or tread.'

An Essay on Gardens, FRANCIS BACON

> Bring, too, some branches forth of Daphne's hair,
> And gladdest myrtle for the posts to wear,
> With spikenard weaved and marjorams between
> And starred with yellow-golds and meadows-queen.

The very names indeed of the aromatic herbs seem to 'perfume the air' – bergamot, lavender, meadowsweet, costmary, southern-wood, woodruff, balm, germander. And flowers even though dead remain sweet in their dust, as every bowl of pot-pourri will tell. To have 'a repository of odours' always with them, when streets were foul and pestilence was a peril, gentle-people would in old times carry fresh nosegays or pomanders. The pomanders were of many kinds; an orange stuffed with cloves, etc., for the hand; or – for pocket or chatelaine – some little curiously-devised receptacle of silver containing tiny phials of precious essences – possibly no bigger than a plum. Or they might be compounded of rare ingredients: 'Your only way to make a good pomander is this. Take an ounce of the purest garden mould, cleansed and steeped seven days in change of motherless rose water. Then take the best labdanum, benjoin, both storaxes, ambergris, civet, and musk. Incorporate them together, and work them into what form you please. This, if your breath be not too valiant, will make you smell as sweet as any lady's dog.'

285

Francis Beaumont, who wrote this memorable 'Meditation', was himself to lie in Westminster Abbey not many years afterwards. The 'once' in the eighteenth line means *once for all;* but I am a little uncertain of the meaning of 'bones of birth' in the thirteenth.

Nearly a hundred years before him, Stephen Hawes had shared his thought:

> O Mortal folk, you may behold and see
> How I lie here, sometime a mighty knight.
> The end of joy and all prosperity
> Is death at last, thorough his course and might:
> For though the day be never so long,
> At last the bell ringeth to evensong.

And this is an epitaph of the second century:

'Fair indeed is the secret from the Blessed Ones – that for mortals Death is not alone no evil, but a good.'

And this of the sixteenth:

> IGO: TO SLE   AND WEE
> EPE: BEFO   SHAL WAKE
> RE: YOU   TOGEATHER

The following lines, too, are said to have been found between the pages of Sir Walter Raleigh's Bible in the Gate House at Westminster, having been written by him, it is surmised, during the night of 28 October, 1618, and a few hours before he was beheaded:

> Even such is Time, that takes in trust
> Our youth, our joys, our all we have,
> And pays us but with earth and dust;
> Who, in the dark and silent grave,
> When we have wandered all our ways,
> Shuts up the story of our days.

But from this earth, this grave, this dust,
My God shall raise me up, I trust.

Having put off his gown and doublet he turned his eyes to the headsman with his axe. 'I pr'ythee let me see it,' he said, 'lest thou sayest that I am afraid of it. It is sharp medicine, but it is a sound cure for all diseases'; and when he was instructed how he should kneel, he added, 'If the heart be right it is no matter which way the head lies.'

Sir Thomas More had taken the same journey as Raleigh, but eighty-three years before him. On Monday, 5 July, 1535, the night before he was beheaded, he wrote ('with a cole') this letter of farewell to his daughter Margaret Roper. He had seen her for the last time when she openly met and kissed him in the midst of his enemies and of the throngs on Tower Wharf, as he came from Judgment:

'Oure Lorde Blesse you, good daughter, & youre good husbande, & youre lyttle boye, & all yours, & all my children, & all my Godde chyldren and all oure frendes . . . I comber you good *Margaret* much, but I would be sory, if it should be any lenger than tomorrow. For it is saint *Thomas* even, & the utas of saint *Peter :* & therefore tomorrow long I to go to God: it were a day verye mete & convenient for me. I never liked your maner toward me better, than whan you kissed me laste: for I love when doughterly love, and deere charitye, hath no laysure to loke to worldlye courtesy. Farewell my dere chylde, & praye for me, & I shall for you & all youre frendes, that we maye merilye mete in heaven . . .'

286. '*Sidney, O Sidney is dead*'

'Sir Philip Sydney, Knight,' says John Aubrey, 'was the most accomplished courtier of his time. He was not only of an excellent witt, but extremely beautiful; he much resembled his sister. He was a person of great courage. Among others Mr Edmund Spenser made his addresse to him, and brought his *Faery Queen*. Sir Philip was busy at his study, and his servant delivered Mr Spenser's booke to his master, who layd it by, thinking it might be such kind of stuffe as he was frequently troubled with. When Sir Philip persued it, he was so exceedingly delighted with it, that he was extremely sorry he was gonne, and where to send for him he knew not. After much enquiry he learned his lodgeing, and sent for him, and mightily caressed him . . . From this time there was a great friend-ship between them, to his dying day . . . His body was putt in a leaden coffin (which after the firing of Paule's, I myself sawe), and with wonderful great state was carried to St Paule's church, when he was buried in our Ladie's Chapell. There solempnized this funerall all the nobility and great officers of Court.'

Here is part of a letter written to him, by his father, Sir Henry Sidney, in 1566, when Philip was a boy at Shrewsbury School:

Son Philip . . . Above all things, tell no untruth. No, not in trifles. The custom of it is nought: and let it not satisfy you that, for a time, the hearers take it for a truth; yet after it will be known as it is, to your shame. For there cannot be a greater reproach to a gentleman, than to be accounted a liar . . . Remember, my son! the noble blood you are descended of by your mother's side: and think that only by virtuous life and good action you may be an ornament to that illustrious family; otherwise, through vice and sloth, you may be counted *labes generis*, 'a spot of your kin,' one of the greatest curses that can happen to man.

This next fragment is from a letter written on October 18, 1580, by Sir Philip Sidney himself to his younger brother Robert (then seventeen). This Robert six years afterwards fought with him at Zutphen. He grew up a gallant gentleman, was created Earl of Leicester, and in his leisure wrote words to fit the music of John Dowland – afterwards lutenist to Charles I.

My Dear Brother,
   For the money you have received, assure yourself (for it is true), there is nothing I spend so pleaseth me; as that which is for you. If ever I have ability, you shall find it so: if not, yet shall not any brother living be better beloved than you, of me . . . Look to your diet, sweet Robin!

and hold your heart in courage and virtue. Truly, great part of my comfort is in you! ... Be careful of yourself, and I shall never have cares ... I write this to you as one, that for myself have given over the delight in the world; but wish to you as much, if not more, than to myself ... God bless you, sweet Boy! and accomplish the joyful hope I conceive of you ... Lord how I have babbled! Once again, farewell, dearest Brother!

> Your most loving and careful brother,
> *Philip Sidney*

And here in a few words is a fleeting glimpse of this renowned man as he appeared amidst the splendour and magnificence of the Tournament during the Anjou Fêtes in London, in 1581, five years before his death:

'Then proceeded Master Philip Sidney, in very sumptuous manner with armour part blue and the rest gilt and engraven ... He had four pages that rode on his four spare horses [richly caparisoned in gold and pearls and feathers of silver] who had cassock hats and Venetian hose all of cloth of silver laid with gold lace and hats of the same with gold bands and white feathers: and each one a pair of white buskins.' ... There followed him in as rich and splendid array his gentlemen, yeomen, and trumpeters.

> Was never eie, did see that face,
> Was never eare, did heare that tong.
> Was never minde, did minde his grace,
> That ever thought the travell long;
> But eies, and eares, and ev'ry thought,
> Were with his sweete perfections caught.

> EDMUND SPENSER

287. '*His Picture in a sheet*'

Of John Donne's Book of Poems there was nothing in Mr Nahum's first volume, much in the others. But what I then read of them I little understood. It is a poetry that awaits the mind as the body grows older, and when we have ourselves learned the experience of life with which it is concerned. Not that the simplest poetry will then lose anything of its grace and truth and beauty – far rather it shines the more clearly, since age needs it the more.

'His Picture in a sheet' refers to a drawing (prefixed to Donne's *Poems*) of his stone effigy in St Paul's Cathedral, where a few days before his death he preached his last valedictory, or farewell, sermon.

288. '*Do thou the same!*'

So too Walter Savage Landor:

> . . . Quieter is his breath, his breast more cold
>   Than daisies in the mould,
> Where children spell, athwart the churchyard gate,
>   His name, and life's brief date.
> Pray for him, gentle souls, whoe'er you be,
>   And, O, pray too for me!

289. '*Lamps in sepulchres*'

'One morning, as I was sitting by the fire, a great cloud came over me, and a temptation beset me, and I sate still. And it was said [in me], All things come by nature; and the Elements and Stars came over me, so that I was in a moment quite clouded with it; but, inasmuch as I sate still and said nothing, the people of the house perceived nothing.

'And as I sate still under it and let it alone, a living hope rose in me, and a true voice arose in me which cried: There is a living God who made all things. And immediately the cloud and temptation vanished away, and the life rose over it all, and my heart was glad, and I praised the living God.'

From GEORGE FOX'S *Journal*

290. 'A pretty bud'

'To die young,' in William Drummond's words, 'is to do that soon, and in some fewer Days, which once thou must do; it is but the giving over of a Game, that after never so many Hazards must be lost.'

Here is the last stanza of an epitaph written by Edmund Waller in memory of the 'only son of the Lord Andover,' who also died young. He lies in the chancel of the serene and ancient parish Church of Ewelme, and near by, lovely and undefaced, are the tombs of Geoffrey Chaucer's son and daughter.

> . . . Like Buds appearing ere the Frosts are past,
> To become Man he made such fatal hast,
> And to Perfection labour'd so to climb,
> Preventing[1] slow Experience and Time,
> That 'tis no wonder Death our Hopes beguil'd;
> He's seldom Old, that will not be a Child.

Nor can he ever be said to be 'old' who remains in some degree childlike in mind and nature. Even in the depths of winter there are well-springs that never cease to flow. And so it was with Waller himself. Like Herrick he lived to be over eighty, and during the last years of his life wrote one – and that perhaps the best – of the few poems by which he is remembered. This is its last stanza:

> . . . The soul's dark cottage, battered and decayed,
> Lets in new light through chinks that Time has made
> Stronger, by weakness, wiser men become
> As they draw near to their eternal home.
> Leaving the old, both worlds at once they view
> That stand upon the threshold of the new.

1. Hastening on before

771

And in those who have not become old but who are soon to die the radiance of this new light is sometimes seen to shine. As if by a secret forewarning they have made haste to live in mind and spirit far beyond their years – Keats, Emily Brontë, Katherine Mansfield.

291. 'A-left asleep'

May! Be thou never graced with birds that sing,
    Nor Flora's pride!
In thee all flowers and roses spring –
    Mine, only died.
In obitum MS. X⁰ Maij. 1614, WILLIAM BROWNE

293. 'Sunk Lyonnesse'

There is a legend – recorded in an ancient monastic chronicle – that in the days of Arthur there stretched between Land's End and the Scillies a country of castles, of fair towns, and landscapes, named Lyonnesse. When the tumult of the last great Arthurian battle was over, there befell a cataclysm of nature, and in a night of tempest this whole region was engulfed beneath the seas.

What truth is in this legend no certain history relates. But when the vast Atlantic breakers begin to lull after storm, to lie listening in the watches of the night is to hear, it would seem, deep-sunken belfries of bells sounding in the waters, and siren-like lamentations. I have myself heard this, and fancy though it may be, if the ear is once beguiled into its deceit, the bells clash and chime on and on in the imagination, mingled with the enormous lully of the surges, until at last, one falls asleep.

296

The 'basin of boxwood' refers to a custom in the North of England of preparing sprays of box before a funeral. The mourners carried these little emblems to the graveside, and at the last dropped them down upon the coffin for a remembrance to the one who was gone.

299. 'Sings no sad songs for me'

– and here is another such happy and tender word of farewell – but from one unknown:

> When from the world I should be ta'en,
> And from earth's necessary pain,
> Then let no blacks be worn for me,
> Not in a ring, my dear, by thee.
> But this bright diamond, let it be
> Worn in remembrance of me.
> And when it sparkles in your eye,
> Think 'tis my shadow passeth by.

302

This poem, again, is spelt as the words would be pronounced by the people of Dorsetshire, the county in which William Barnes was born and lived nearly all his long life. This way of speech is slower than in common English, and the words, especially those with the two dots, or diæresis, over them, should be lingered over a little in pronouncing them.

Londoners are apt to be scornfully amused at country speech – in their ignorance that much of it is older and most of it far more beautiful than their own clipped and nasal manner of pronouncing their words. There are two extremes of this Cockney talk – though even that is constantly changing, and Sam Weller might be taken for a foreigner if he returned to his old haunts today. The downright, full-throated coster-monger in the abundance of his heart opens his mouth as wide as possible, and so broadens his vowels, converting 'tape' into *taip*, 'type' into *toip*, 'go on' into *gurn*, and 'out' into *aht*; while the too, too genteel, practised in 'prunes and prisms', narrow theirs, and for 'coin' say *co-in*, for 'type' say *tape,* and for 'tape' say *tepe.* They may, on occasion, say 'Listen to darlingest little Carlo; he is *snawing* in his sleep,' having been warned against saying 'Meh! the snow is thoring!'

For contrast (and for its own sake), I am adding (from Halliwell's *Dictionary*) a scrap of Derbyshire dialect in which a farmhand, Thomas Lide, tells his master that he could *do* if only it were waiting to be done.

'Tummus,' says the Farmer, 'why dunner yo mend meh shoom?'

'Becoz, mester,' replies Tummas, ''tis zo cood, I conner work the tachin [waxed thread] at aw. I've brockn it ten times I'm shur to de [day] – it freezes so hard. Why, Hester hung out a smockdrock to dry, and in three minits it wor frozzen as stiff as a proker, an I conner afford to keep a good fire; I wish I cud. I'd soon mend yore shoon, and uthers tow. I'd soon yarn [earn] sum munney, I warrant ye. Conner [cannot] yo find sum work for m', mester, these hard times? I'll doo onnythink to addle [make] a penny. I con thresh – I con split wood – I con make spars – I con thack [thatch] – I con skower a dike, and I can trench tow [too], bit it freezes so hard. I con winner [winnow] – I con fother [litter] or milk, if there be need on't. I wondner mind drivin plow or onnythink.'

But half an hour with the great *Dialect Dictionary* will prove how inexhaustibly rich the English language once was and still is in words made, used, and loved by those who were unlearned in books, but had keen and lively eyes in their heads, quick to see the delight and livingness of a thing, and the wits to give it a name fitting it as close as a skin.

'*The verse wer short, but very good*'

This is not true of most inscriptions upon tombstones. Like poetry itself they are a test of the age in which they were written. The quiet and noble words on Spenser's tomb in Westminster Abbey are of 1598:

Here lyes (expecting the Second Comminge of our Saviour *Christ Jesus*) the body of Edmond Spencer the Prince of

Poets in his tyme whose divine Spirrit needs noe other wit-
nesse than the works which he left behind him.

He was born in London in the

Yeare 1553 and Died

In the yeare

1598.

'Michaell Draiton' is near by – 'his bust in alablaster' above his
tomb. 'A memorable Poet of this age who Exchanged his Lawrell
for a Crowne of Glorye A.D. 1631.' And this his epitaph 'made by
Mr Francis Quarles, who was a great friend . . . and a very good
man':

Doe pious marble let thy Readers knowe
What they and what their children owe
To DRAITON'S Name whose sacred dust
Hee recommend unto thy TRUST.
Protect his Mem'ry and Preserve his Storye,
Remaine a lasting Monument of his Glorye,
And when thy Ruines shall disclame
To be the Treas'rer of his NAME,
His Name, that canot fade, shall be
An everlasting MONUMENT to thee.

Not far distant lies Margaret Cavendish, Duchess of Newcastle.
She was, we read, 'the youngest sister to the Lord Lucas of Col-
chester, a noble familie, for all the Brothers were valiant and all the
Sisters virtuous. This Dutches was a wise wittie and learned Lady,
which her many books do well testify, she was a most virtuous
and a Loving and careful wife, and was with her Lord all the time
of his banishment and miseries, and when he came home never
parted with him in his solitary confinement.'

This inscription is of 1674.

In 1740, a belated and 'preposterous' monument was erected to
Shakespeare, in whose inscription an attempt to amend the lines
taken from *The Tempest* ruined their poetry and their sense!

Later still (1771) – in a windy effort to hit off two poets on one slab – we have:

> No more the *Graecian* Muse unrival'd reagns
> To *Britain* let the Nations homage pay:
> She felt a Homer's fire in Milton's strains,
> A Pindar's rapture in the lyre of Gray.

If, then, even epitaphs in clear and simple prose are rare, how much rarer must be epitaphs with poetry in them. It is, therefore, an unusual and haunting experience to chance on an epitaph in church aisle or yard that calls as if with a human voice out of the silent past. The three that follow I owe to the kindness of a friend, Mrs Graham Wallis:

The first is from the Galilee Chapel, Durham, where in the sixteenth century John Brinley was organist. It is dated October 13, A.D. 1576:

> Jno Brinlyes body here doth ly
> Who praysèd GOD with hand and voice:
> By musickes Heavenlie harmonie
> Dull myndes he made in God rejoice:
> His soul into heavens is lyft
> To prayse him still that gave the gyft.

The next is from Chaldon Church, Surrey:

> GOOD REDAR, WARNE ALL MEN AND WOMEN WHIL THEY
> BE HERE TO BE EVER GOOD TO THE POORE AND NEDY!
> THE POORE EVER IN THIS WORLD SHALL YE HAVE:
> GOD GRAUNTE US SUMWAT IN STORE FOR TO SAVE.
> THE CRY OF THE POORE IS EXTREME AND VERY SORE:
> GOD GRAUNTE US TO BE GOOD EVER MORE.
> IN THIS WORLDE WE RUN OUR RASE:
> GOD GRAUNTE US TO BE WITH CHRIST IN TYME AND SPACE

This – of June 1668 in Burford – is a memorial of three generations of one family named Bartholomew – mercers:

Lo, Huddled up together lye
Gray age, greene youth, white Infantcy;
If death doth Natures laws dispence
And Reconciles all difference
Tis fit one Flesh, one House, should have
One Tombe, one Epitaph, one Grave;
And they that lived and loved either
Should dye and Lye and sleep together.

Go reader – whether go or stay –
Thou canst not hence be long away.

And this, of 2 April, 1777, is from the Churchyard of Strath-fieldsaye:

Asleep beneath this humble Stone
Lies honest, harmless, simple John;
Who free from Guilt & Care & Strife,
Here closed his inoffensive Life;
He practised all the good he knew,
And did no harm. His only Sin
Was that he loved a drop of Gin;
And when his favourites was not near
Contented took his horn of Beer,
Tho' weak his head, to make amendes
Heav'n gave him Health, Content & Friends;
This little Village Nursed and Bred him
And Good Lord Rivers cloathed and fed him,
T'was there he Lived, Caressed by all,
The favourite of the Servant's Hall;
With them he eat his daily Bread;
They loved him Living, mourn him Dead,
And now have kindly Joined to Raise
This little Tombstone to his praise.
Nor should the learned and the wise
Such humble merit e'en despise;

Who knows but John may find a place
Where wit must never show its face?
Farewell John: [and] Grant Heaven that we
Harmless may live, and die, like thee.

It seemed no offence in earlier days than our own to refer to 'a
drop of Gin' on a tomb-stone, or, like the grave-diggers in *Hamlet*,
to keep up one's spirits with a jest or two on a dismal occasion. I
came, for example, quite by accident, on John Archer's epitaph in
Selby Abbey:

Near to this Stone lies Archer (John)
  Late Saxon (I aver)
Who, without tears, thirty-four years,
  Did carcases inter.

But, Death at last, for his work's past,
  Unto him thus did say:
'Leave off thy trade, be not afraid,
  But forthwith come away.'

Without reply or asking why,
  The summons he obey'd,
In Seventeen hundred and sixty-eight
  Resigned his life and spade.

And (owing to the good fellowship of the man who cut his stone)
every stranger who reads his epitaph bids him a warm farewell and
carries off a pinch of courage in his poke.

In the Church at Iver, Buckinghamshire, I found:

Beneath this place lies interned the body of Venturus Mandey,
Bricklayer, son of Michael Mandey, Bricklayer, and grandson
to Venturus Mandey, of this parish, Bricklayer, who had the
honour of being Bricklayer to the Honble. Society of Lincolns
Inn from the year of Our Lord 1667 to the day of his death.
... He also translated into English DIRECTORIUM

GENERALE URANOMETRICUM and TRIGONOMETRICA
PLANA ET SPHERICA, LINEARIS ET LOGARITHMICA...

There proper pride in an ancient Craft rings out like a cockcrow, dull though the words may be. Nor was Venturus Mandey the only Bricklayer connected with Lincoln's Inn who turned to letters, for 'when a little child', rare Ben Jonson 'lived in Hartshorn-lane near Charing Cross where his Mother married a Bricklayer for her second Husband.' On leaving Westminster School he was admitted into St John's College, Cambridge, but was there only a few weeks owing to lack of money, and was 'fain to return to the trade of his father-in-law. And let not them blush that have, but those that have not, a lawful calling. He help'd in the building of the new structure of Lincolns-Inn, when having a Trowell in his hand, he had a book in his pocket.'

Just as Charlotte Brontë remembered seeing her sister Emily standing at the table in the tiny kitchen of the parsonage at Haworth, kneading dough, and with a copy of Plato propped up against a pudding-basin.

303. 'Care is heavy'

Dear God, though Thy all-powerful hand
Should so direct my earthly fate
That I may seem unfortunate
To them who do not understand
That all things follow Thy decree,
Staunchly I'll bear what e'er's Thy will –
Praying Thee but to grant me still
That none shall come to harm through me;
For, God, although Thou knowest all,
I am too young to comprehend
The windings to my journey's end;
I fear upon the road to fall
In the worst sin of all that be
And trust my brother in the sea.

CONAL O'RIORDAN

304. '*Mother, never mourn*'

'It was my own mother,' wrote Thomas Cantimpratanus about 1260, 'who told me the story which I am about to relate. My grandmother had a firstborn son of most excellent promise, comely beyond the wont of children, at whose death she mourned . . . with a grief that could not be consoled, until one day, as she went by the way, she saw in her vision a band of youths moving onwards, as it seemed to her, with exceeding great joy; and she, remembering her son and weeping that she saw him not in this joyful band, suddenly beheld him trailing weary footsteps after the rest. Then with a grievous cry the mother asked: "How comes it, my son, that thou goest alone, lagging thus behind the rest?" Then he opened the side of his cloak and showed her a heavy water-pot, saying: "Behold, dear mother, the tears which thou hast vainly shed for me, through the weight whereof I must needs linger behind the rest."'

But not all mourners are, in their dreams, so rebuked or so comforted. St Augustine, a loving son, pined in vain:

'If the dead could come in dreams,' he wrote, 'my pious mother would no night fail to visit me. Far be the thought that she should, by a happier life, have been made so cruel that, when aught vexes my heart, she should not even console in a dream the son whom she loved with an only love.'

307. '*Like stars upon some gloomy grove*'

> . . . Stars are of mighty use; The night
> Is dark, and long;
> The Rode foul, and where one goes right
> Six may go wrong.
> One twinkling ray
> Shot o'er some cloud,
> May clear much way
> And guide a croud.

> Gods Saints are shining lights: who stays
>   Here long must passe
> O'er dark hills, swift streams, and steep ways
>   As smooth as glasse;
>   But these all night
>   Like Candles, shed
>   Their beams, and light
>   Us into Bed . . .

HENRY VAUGHAN

310

This poem has been at hide-and-seek with the world for many years past. Mr Frank Sidgwick, having long played Seek, at last found it hidden away in the British Museum in a manuscript, No. 24665, inscribed 'Giles Earle – his book, 1615'. In this MS. the poem consists of eight stanzas of ten lines each, with a chorus of five lines. The version on page 529 is of twenty-five lines only, and has been taken from Alice Meynell's beautiful anthology *The Flower of the Mind*. They differ, says Mr Sidgwick, from their original not only in their order, but, here and there, in their words. The 'Moon' (l.1), for example, is in the MS. *morn;* 'lovely' (l.2) is *lonely,* and 'marrow' is *morrow;* 'rounded' (l.10) is *wounded;* 'heart' (l.16) is *host;* and 'with' (l.21) is *by.* It is a nice exercise of taste and judgement to choose between them and to find good reasons for one's choice. When and by whom 'Tom o' Bedlam' was written is as yet undiscovered. It remains for the present a shining jewel in the crown of the most modest of all men of genius, known only as *Anon.*

314

This far-carrying rhyme belongs to the ancient and famous game of Dump. 'He who speaks first in it,' says Dr Gregor, 'or laughs first, or lets his teeth be seen, gets nine nips, nine nobs, nine double douncornes, an' a gueed blow on the back o' the head.'

Faht and *fahr* are the pleasing Aberdonian way of saying *what* and *where*.

316

So may the omission of a few commas effect a wonder in the imagination. To the imagination indeed there is nothing absurd in, 'I saw the sun at twelve o'clock at night' – for in the 'little nowhere of the mind' it is possible to see both burning sun and black night *together*. Once in a dream I myself was enchanted by three moons in the sky, shining in their silver above waters as wide as those of Milton's curfew. Even the most commonplace objects (in waking life) will take to themselves a strangeness and beauty never seen or 'marked' before, if (like Marcus Aurelius in the presence of his loaf of bread) we give them a few moments' rapt, intense attention. The object, the eye, the memory, the insight, the spirit within: these are the Five in Council.

Here is another old nursery 'nonsense' rhyme that conjures up almost as lively and dreamlike pictures in the mind:

> There was a man of double deed
> Who sowed his garden full of seed;
> And when the seed began to grow,
> 'Twas like a garden full of snow;
> And when the snow began to fall,
> Like birds it was upon the wall;
> And when the birds began to fly,
> 'Twas like a shipwreck in the sky;
> And when the sky began to crack,
> 'Twas like a stick upon my back;
> And when my back began to smart,
> 'Twas like a pen-knife in my heart;
> And when my heart began to bleed,
> Then I was dead – and dead indeed.

319. '*It had become a glimmering girl*'

'The Tuatha De Danaan – the divine Children of Danu which forgotten centuries ago invaded Ireland – can take all shapes, and those that are in the waters take often the shape of fish. A woman of Burren, in Galway, says, "There are more of them in the sea than on the land . . .," and another Galway woman says, "Surely those things are in the sea as well as on land. My father was out fishing one night off Tyrone. And something came beside the boat that had eyes shining like candles. And then a wave came in, and a storm rose all in a minute, and whatever was in the wave, the weight of it had like to sink the boat. And then they saw that it was a woman in the sea that had the shining eyes. So my father went to the priest, and he bid him always to take a drop of holy water and a pinch of salt out in the boat with him, and nothing could harm him."'

WILLIAM BUTLER YEATS

321. '*One without*'

Was it the sound of a footfall I heard
On the cold flag stone?
Or the cry of a wandering far night bird,
On the sea-winds blown?
Was that a human shape that stood?
In the shadow below,
Or but the mist of the moonlit wood
As it hovered low?
Was it the voice of a child that called
From the hill side steep?
Or, oh, but the wind as it softly lulled
The world to sleep?

ELIZABETH RAMAL

325. 'Brome, brome on hill'

The story is of how a bright lady comes to keep her tryst with a knight-at-arms in the golden broom of Hive Hill. She finds him under a charm, an enchantment, asleep; and having left her ring on his finger for proof of her coming, she steals away. Presently after he awakes – her presence gone. To leave a quiet and happy room vacant at night is sometimes to have this experience, as it were, *reversed*. There comes a feeling that one's-self being gone, far gentler visitants may enter and share its solitude – while its earthly tenant sleeps overhead, and one by one the stars sink to their setting.

326

When larks gin sing
Away we fling,
And babes new-born steal as we go;
An elf instead
We leave in bed,
And wind out, laughing, Ho, ho, ho!

329

It is difficult to read this poem slowly and intently enough if one is to experience to the *full* the living things and sights and sounds that by its words are charmed into the mind – the hushed solitude, the desolation. Tennyson (like Coleridge) had senses of a fineness rare even in a poet, and few artists have spent themselves so unwearyingly in the effort to record the 'harvest' of those senses in words. It is said that the tone and timbre of a fine fiddle is improved by the music of the master who plays upon it – that a Paganini or a Kreisler may charm into the throbbing wood some ghostly life and feeling of his own. However fantastic this may be, it is truth itself of language; and a writer like Tennyson, master artist that he was, leaves a personal impress on the language he uses that cannot be deleted. English is a marvellous fiddle, echoing almost in every sentence one says or writes with many tongues and a thousand individual craftsmen, doers, and thinkers, utterly dissimilar one from another, while the words of which it was made were rooted in the soil of the people, and were brought to ripeness by the dews and rains and suns of their nothern heavens. Take even, of all there is in 'Mariana', but the 'peering mouse' in the sixth stanza – his sharp nose sniffing the air beneath the small wooden arch of his dark-glimmering mousery, where gnaw and shriek and gambol his fellows behind the mouldering wainscot. Or stay for a moment looking down on the 'marish mosses' in the fourth stanza – of a hue as lively as a fairy's mantle in sunlight – greening the waters of the blackened sluice. So piece by piece the words of the poem build up in the imagination this solitary house with its forsaken Mariana, whom Tennyson himself had seen in the day-dream conferred on him by another poet, in *Measure for Measure*:

Isabella.   Can this be so? did *Angelo* so leave her?

Duke.   Left her in her teares, and dried not one of them with his comfort: swallowed his vowes whole, pretending in her discoveries of dishonour: in few, bestowed on her her owne lamentation, which she yet weares for his sake: and he, a marble to her teares, is washed with them, but relents not.

Isabella.   What a merit were it in death to take this poore maid from the world . . .

332. 'Yes Tor'

Turn your back on Okehampton and break away due South into the wilds of Dartmoor, and there, 'summering' together 'beneath the empty skies,' lie titanic Yes Tor and High Willes, rearing their bare vast shapes into the air.

333. '*To heare the madrake grone*'

Of the dangerous plant Mandrake ('its root in something the shape and appearance of man') is concocted Mandragora, one of the 'drowsy syrups'. 'The leaves and fruit be also dangerous, for they cause deadly sleep, and peevish drowsiness.' The fruit is 'of the bigness of a reasonable pippin, and as yellow as gold when it is thoroughly ripe: fair without, ashes within.' It is said that the mandrake's screams, when it is dragged out of the ground, will send the hearer mad. So anyone in need of it is advised first to seal his ears, then to tie the plant to a dog's tail and hike him on to haul it out of its haunt! 'Avicenna the Arabian physician asserts that a Jew at Metz had a mandragore with a human head, and the legs and body of a cock, which lived five weeks, and was fed on lavender and earthworms, and, when dead, was preserved in spirits.' Even up to the nineteenth century believers of witchcraft were wont to carry these monstrous little Erdmannikens in bosom or pocket for an amulet or charm.

The 'Basilisk,' old books maintain, is a fabulous beast whose icy glare petrifies with horror any human who meets her face to face. Approach her then with a mirror; and courage be your guide!

'*Hemlock, henbane, adders-tongue*'

Hemlock is that tall, dim-spotted plant of a sad green colour, and of a scent 'strong, heady and bad', which is 'very cold and dangerous', especially when 'digged in the dark'.

Clammy henbane is woolly-leafed, with hollow dark-eyed flowers of a purple-veined dingy yellow. 'It lusts to grow in rancid soil, To 'stil its deadly oil.'

Moonwort is the meek-looking little flowering fern that has the power to break locks, and to make any horse that chances to tread upon it cast his shoes.

The livid-flowered, cherry-like fruited Dwale, Enoron, Banewort, Nightshade or Naughty-man's-cherry is the most 'daunge-

rous' plant in England. While leopard's bane – though it bears a
bright-yellow daisy-like flower, and witches are said to fear sun-
colour – is venomous to animals.

I am uncertain of adder's tongue, for the fern of this name cures
sore eyes; and cuckoo-pint which is also so called, is 'a remedy for
poison and the plague'!

Of these six insidious plants only one is openly mentioned by
Shakespeare, and they have comparatively few country names;
unlike, for example, the purple orchis, 'which has so many', says
Nicholas Culpeper, 'that they would fill a sheet of paper': Long-
purples, Dead-men's fingers, Crake-feet, Giddy-gandy, Neat-legs,
Geese-and-goslings, and Gander-gooses, being a few choice specimens.

The gardener mentioned on page 314 would have called it
Orchis latifolia Lagotis, and the advantage of this name over that
of Deadmen's-fingers or Giddy-gandy is that if by any chance
you should be entertaining a pleasant company of botanists or
horticulturalists to tea – say, a Frenchman, a Spaniard, a German,
a Dutchman, a Russian, a Swiss, and a Swede – and you wished
to mention this particular variety of orchis, the mere gentle
murmuring of *Orchis latifolia Lagotis* would set every face shining,
and brighten every eye.

The Vegetable World, that is, has been classified, and also
indexed in (mostly low) Latin; and living men of Science, in this as
in much else, use in common a dead language. This vast and
valuable achievement – when one considers for how many centuries Man has shared the world with its flowers – took an uncons-
cionably long time, for in a book on Botany, published in Germany
in 1547, only two hundred and forty species of plants were included. In a successor to it, published eighty-six years afterwards,
there were six thousand; and in a complete collection of today
there would be about a quarter of a million.

It would be a pretty courtesy, when the learned converse with
the vulgar, if they translated their Latin into intelligible English.
When even a botanist names a flower he mentions only its kind or
variety – and that only in reference to some, but by no means to all,
of its characteristics. It is important, then, to keep on reminding

oneself that every living thing is not merely something which belongs to a family, species, genus, but is unique – itself only, and no other.

At the risk of their being merely tedious, here are a few more country names of English wild-flowers – names always lively, often humorous and sometimes curiously beautiful – but in danger nowadays of dying of disuse. To discover *why* each of these flowers has been so named would be an enthralling but laborious adventure.

The *Cuckoo-pint* or *Lords-and-Ladies* is called also Aaron, Adam-and-Eve, Adder's Meat, Bloody-Man's-Finger, Bobbin-Joan, Bulls-and-Cows, Calf's-foot, Friar's-cowl, Lamb-in-a-pulpit, Lily Grass, Nightingales, and Wake-Robin.

The *Wild Mercury* is Goosefoot, All-good, Blithe, Flowery Docken, Good King Henry, and Wild Spinach.

The *Marsh-Marigold* is Boots, Golds, Goldins, May-blobs, Meadow Bout, Water Buttercup, and Yellow Gowan.

The *Foxglove* is Dead-Men's-Bells, Finger Flower, Flap-Dock and Lusmore.

Goose-Grass is Bur-weed, Harif, Naritch, Cleavers, Geckdor, Love-man and Mutton-chops.

The common *Toad-flax* is Butter-and-Eggs, Gall-wort, Buttered Haycocks and Dragon-bushes.

Bird's-foot Trefoil is Cat-in-the-Clover, Crow's foot, Eggs-and-Bacon, Fingers-and-Thumbs, Ground Honey-suckle and Lamb's Toe.

The *Campion* is Flower of Constantinople, Flower of Bristowe, Gardener's-Eye, Jerusalem Cross and None-such.

Bog-myrtle is Candle-berry, Sweet Gale, Golden Osier, Sweet Willow.

Cat-mint is Ale-hoof, Blue-Runner, Devil's Candlesticks, Gill-go-by-ground, Robin-run-in-the-hedge and Tun-hoof.

Wood-Sorrel is Alleluia, Cuckoo-bread, Gowk-meat, Stubwort, and Wood-Sower.

Solomon's-Seal is David's Harp, Fraxinell, Ladder-to-Heaven and Lily-of-the-Mountain.

So, too, *Verbascum Thapsus* (the Wooly-beard), one of the

mulleins, has for folk-names, not only Duffle, Fluff-weed, Ag-leaf and Torches, but also Candle-wick, Hag's-taper, Jacob's-staff, Shepherd's-club, Beggar's-blanket, and Adam's-Flannel; while the *Wild Chervil* is not only three kinds of comb – Lady's, Shepherd's and Venus's, but at least eleven kinds of needle – Adam's, Beggar's, Shepherd's, Tailor's, Witches'; Clock, Crow, Crake, Pink, Puck and Poke.

Nowadays, our minds and their contents, like our clothes, seem to tend to be more and more alike; and most children are taught in school – what most children are taught in school. A lively and happy country girl, when I asked her the name of a star-clustering wildflower flourishing everywhere on her farmland, replied that she didn't know, and explained with a smile 'At school, you know, I never cared for Nature study.' The very phrase was like a knell. It was as if a child after politely listening to 'How many miles to Babylon?' or 'Ride-a-cockhorse,' or 'The Queen was in her parlour,' had muttered, 'I'm sorry, you know! but I can't abide that William Wordsworth.'

But while for the most part the meaning and reference of the names of wildflowers shines out of their faces, this is not usually so with the names of our English villages. They *have* a 'meaning' well worth the discovering, but meanwhile they are curious, romantic, echoing sounds merely to hear and utter. Take but a few from '*a Topographical Map* [Jan. 1, 1769] *of the County of* KENT . . . *in which are expressed all the Roads, Lanes, Churches, Towns, Villages, Noblemen and Gentlemen's Seats, Roman Roads, Hills, Rivers, Woods, Cottages, and everything Remarkable in the* COUNTY, *together with the Division of the Lathes and their Sub-divisions into Hundreds*': Allhollows, Mammonds, Drele, Welmm, Brodnyx, Sarr, Kemsyng, Buglus, Ripple, Molash, Lullingstone, Sutton Valance, Ewell, Binghton, Monchalsea. Listen to the *Shoals*, etc. [all Kent]: Columbine, the Culvery, Spreves, Spanyard, Cold Blow, Oase Edge, Knowle, Spile, Pann, Knockjohn and Girdler.

Then again, quite apart from cities, towns, villages, hamlets, streets, and houses, the vast majority even of our English fields and meadows have long had their own individual and proper names. The following are a few specimens from the village of

Hitcham, in Buckinghamshire, which I have borrowed from a pamphlet by the Rev. C. H. D. Grimes:

> Great and Little Cogmarthon.
> Upper and Lower Brissels.
> Homer Corner.
> Parliament Close.
> Hogg Hill.
> Lily Field.
> and Walnut Tree Close.

And these (by the kindness of Mr Henry Williamson) are from a patch of North Devonshire:

> Berber.
> Vineyard.
> Cunnycott
> Lunie Park.
> Monticroft.
> Hatchetty.
> Netherams.
> Zetheridge.
> Bewhayes.
> Flints, and
> Plain.

The village of Yarnton in Oxfordshire, Mr Leonard Rice-Oxley tells me, is divided into three districts – the *Clays*, the *Sands*, and the *Runtlings*, which is like saying, 'Yes, we have three children – *John*, *Mary*, and *Mahershalalhashbaz*.' But of all names, perhaps those which grammarians have given to the various species of words themselves are the most unalluring; *adjective, adverb, preposition, conjunction*, for example. And how many young heads are more meaningful than a parrot's when they repeat such terms as *vocative, ablative, conjunctive, infinitive, optative*, or even *person, mood, tense* and *voice*?

335. '*A thousand darling imps*'

'Aeriel spirits,' says Robert Burton, 'are such as keep quarter most part in the air, cause many tempests, thunder, and lightnings, tear oaks, fire steeples, houses, strike men and beasts, make it rain stones, . . . wool, frogs, etc., counterfeit armies in the air, strange noises, swords, etc.'

Nothing vexed Linnet Sara more than to be asked if there were any such darling imps or spectres or ghosts or blackamoors in Thrae. All such to her were nothing but idle fiddle-faddle. She believed little but in what she could touch or weigh or measure. She much preferred things to go on in a fashion she could be quite sure of, and had little patience with what may have happened to one person only (however gifted) until it could be made to happen to a good many more. But she was a wonderfully steady worker, keeping everything neat, orderly and ready for use as she toiled solemnly on. Still, there was much in Miss Taroone, excellent servant though Sara was, that remained and would probably always remain, a little beyond her faithful handmaid. When she was cleaning and tidying up Mr Nahum's room I doubt if she ever so much as opened the covers of that cumbersome old book of his called *The Other Worlde* – unless to beat the dust out of it.

'Now them jars up there is *fax!*' she would say, her large ruminating face close to mine, as we peered together into the quiet of her still-room. And yet, I am not so sure. Now and then when Sara was talking to me, I seemed to surprise, half-hidden in her features, and looking out at me, as if from the heart-shaped opening of a shutter, quite another face – and one as young and lovely as any that ever smiled out of the words of a poem.

Reginald Scot, who wrote *The Discoverie of Witchcraft* (1584), had a very different kind of kitchen company:

'. . . Our mothers maide,' he says, of his childhood, 'so terrified us with . . . bull beggars, spirits, witches, urchens, elves, hags, fairies, satyrs, pans, faunes, syrens, kit with cansticke, tritons, centaurs, dwarfes, giants, imps, calcars [astrologers], conjurors, nymphes, changlings, Incubus, Robin goodfellowe, the spoorne

[? a fiend], the mare, the man in the oke, the hellwaine [a night-sky wagon], the fierdrake [a dragon], the puckle [a spectre], Tom thombe, hob gobblin, Tom tumbler, boneles, and such other bugs, that we were afraid of our own shadowes: in so much as some never feare the divill, but in a dark night . . .'

There seems to be no mention here of the salamander – a creature at least as rarely seen by mortal eyes as the puckle, spoorne or fire-drake.

'When I was about five years old,' says Benvenuto Cellini, 'my father happened to be in a basement-chamber of our house, where they had been washing, and where a good fire of oak logs are still burning; he had a viol in his hand and was playing and singing alone beside the fire. The weather was very cold. Happening to look into the fire, he espied in the middle of the most burning flames a little creature like a lizard, which was sporting in the core of the intensest coals. Becoming aware of what the thing was, he had my sister and me called, and pointing it out to us children, gave me a great box on the ears, which caused me to cry with all my might. Then he pacified me by saying, "My dear little boy, I am not strik-ing you for anything that you have done, but only to make you remember that the lizard you see in the fire is a salamander, a creature which has never been seen before by any of whom we have credible information." So saying he gave me some pieces of money, and kissed me.'

'Bell and whip and horse's tail'

– such in old days was the Witch's vile punishment if she escaped drowning or the stake; to be whipped, tied to a horse's tail, and rung through the crowded streets.

'Agramie', I suppose, is agrimony, which, if worn by the wary, will enable the wearer to detect witches. Their eyes too will betray them, for *there* you will find no tiny reflected image of yourself as you will in the eyes of the honest. And if you would be rid of their company, pluck a sprig of scarlet pimpernel, and repeat this charm:

> Herbe pimpernell, I have thee found
> Growing upon Christ Jesus' ground:

> The same guift the Lord Jesus gave unto thee,
> When he shed his blood on the tree,
> Arise up, pimpernell, and goe with me.
>   And God bless me,
> And all that shall wear *thee*. AMEN.

'Say this fifteen dayes together, twice a day, morning earlye fasting, and in the evening full.'

Indeed, at last, whatever the peril, a quiet heart and heaven's courage, are charm enough:

> I say that we are wound
> With mercy round and round
> As if with air . . .

> GERARD MANLEY HOPKINS

But Charms have been used for many other purposes than fending off witches and their witch-craft.

'Last summer,' says John Aubrey, 'on the day of St John the Baptist, 1694, I accidentally was walking in the pasture behind Montague House, it was 12 o'clock. I saw there about two or three and twenty young women, most of them well habited, on their knees very busy, as if they had been weeding. I could not presently learn what the matter was; at last a young man told me, that they were looking for a coal under the root of a plantain, to put under their head that night, and they should dream who would be their husbands: It was to be sought for that day and hour.'

He gives another prescription – with the same blissful end in view:

'You must lie in another county, and knit the left garter about the right legged stocking (let the other garter and stocking alone) and as you rehearse the following verses, at every comma, knit a knot:

> This knot I knot,
> To know the thing, I know not yet,
> That I may see,

The man that shall my husband be,
How he goes, and what he wears,
And what he does, all days, and years.

Accordingly in your dream you will see him: if a musician, with a lute or other instrument; if a scholar, with a book or papers.

'A gentlewoman that I knew, confessed in my hearing, that she used this method, and dreamt of her husband whom she had never seen. About two or three years after, as she was one Sunday at church (at our Lady's church in Sarum), up pops a young Oxonian in the pulpit: she cries out presently to her sister, this is the very face of the man that I saw in my dream.

'Another way is, to charm the moon thus: at the first appearance of the new moon after new year's day, go out in the evening, and stand over the spars of a gate or stile, looking on the moon and say,

All haile to thee moon, all haile to thee;
I prithee, good moon, declare to me,
This night, who my husband – my husband – must be.

You must presently after go to bed.'

Or again:

Pluck the yarrow (*millefolium*, or Nose-bleed) growing on a young man's grave, repeating, as you do so, the words following:

Yarrow, sweet yarrow, the first I have found,
In the name of Christ Jesus, I pluck from the ground;
As Joseph loved sweet Mary, and took her for his dear,
So in a dream this night, I hope, my true love will appear.

And then go to sleep, with the yarrow under your pillow. In the morning you may awaken a little feverish. That being so, repeat:

Right cheek! Left cheek! Why do ye burn?
Cursed be she that doeth me harm!

If she be maid, let her be slayed;
If she be widow, long let her mourn;
But if my own true love – burn, cheek, *burn!*

But remember:

Those dressed in blue
Have lovers true;
In green and white,
Forsaken quite.

Or it may be apples rather than sweethearts that need the charming. That being so, it is the custom in Sussex to *worsle* (wassail) the orchard. The worslers, armed with a cow-horn, make a ring round the trees, then sing out at the top of their voices:

Stand fast root,
Bear well top,
Pray God send us
A howling crop.
Every twig
Apples big,
Every bough
Apples enow.
Hats full, caps full,
Full quarter sacks full,
Holla, boys, holla! *Huzzah!*

Or butter. If so, plunge or thump or grind away at the churn handle, keeping time with this incantation:

Come, butter, come,
Come, butter, come,
Peter stands at the gate,
Waiting for a buttered cake,
Come, butter, come!

If it fail, it is not because of its novelty for it is to be found in a book of 1655 with the tempting title, 'A Candle in the Dark'; and its author, Thomas Ady, heard it from a witch whose grandmother had learnt it in the days of Queen Mary.

The following charms are all in rhyme but are for miscellaneous purposes. Against a snakebite:

> Underneath this hazelin mote,
> There's a braggoty worm with a speckled throat;
> > Nine double is he:
> *Now* from nine double to eight double,
> And from eight double to seven double,
> And from seven double to six double,
> And from six double to five double,
> And from five double to four double,
> And from four double to three double,
> And from three double to two double,
> And from two double to one double,
> And from one double to no double,
> > *No* double hath *he!*

For before going to Court:

With a four-leaved clover, double-topp'd ash, and green-topp'd seave [rush],
You may go before the Queen's daughter without asking leave.

For a bad finger:

> Our Saviour was of Virgin born;
> His head was crowned with a crown of thorne;
> It never cankered nor festered at all,
> And I hope in Christ Jesus *this* never shaull.

For one's general (and permanent) health:

> He that would live for aye,
> He must eat *sage* in May.

For a burn or whitlow:

There came two Angels from the North,
One was Fire, and one was Frost.
Out *Fire!* in *Frost!*
In the name of the Father, the Son, and the Holy Ghost.

And for warts – which, like red hair and extremely stout gentlemen, seem to be far less common than they were some forty years ago:

'I had from my childhood,' says Francis Bacon, 'a wart on one of my fingers; afterwards, when I was about sixteen years old, being then at Paris, there grew upon both my hands a number of warts – at the least a hundred, in a month's space. The English Ambassador's lady, who was a woman far from superstition, told me one day she would help me away with my warts; whereupon she got a piece of lard with the skin on, and rubbed the warts all over with the fat side; and, amongst the rest, that wart which I had had from my childhood; then she nailed the piece of lard, with the fat towards the sun, upon a post of her chamber window, which was towards the south.

'The success was, that within five weeks' space all the warts went quite away: and that wart which I had so long endured for company. But at the rest I did little marvel, because they came in a short time and might go away in a short time again: but the going away of that which had stayed so long doth yet stick with me. They say the like is done by the rubbing of warts with a green alder stick, and then burying the stick to rot in the muck.'

He leaves the question at 'They say' – with the comment that further inquiry might be useful.

But things *worn* – magic rings, or gems, or roots, or stones – as well as things said, may act as charms or amulets:

'The best witnesses have it upon record how Charlemain's mistress enchanted him with a ring, which so long as she [being dead] had about her, he would not suffer her carcase to be carry'd out of his chamber; how a Bishop taking it out of her mouth, the Emperor grew to be as much bewitched with the Bishop; but he, being chyd with his excess of favour, threw it into a Pond, where the Emperor's chiefest pleasure was to walk to his dying day.'

336. *'The Water-Kelpy'*

is a fiend that haunts northern rivers and desolate waters. It is a horse-shape, and the sound of its neighings is a boding of death to the traveller.

But – if wits are set to work – he can be made not only harmless, but useful:

'A man carting home his peats for winter fuel was in the habit of seeing a big black horse grazing on the banks of the Ugie, at Inverugie Castle, near Peterhead, each morning as he passed to the "moss". He told some of his neighbours. They suspected what the horse was, and advised the man to get a "wraith-horse" bridle, approach the animal with all care and caution, and cast the bridle over his head. The man now knew the nature of the creature, and followed the advice. Kelpie was secured, and did good work in carrying stones to build the bridge over the Ugie at Inverugie. When his services were no longer needed he was set at liberty. As he left he said:

> "*Sehr back an sehr behns*
> *Cairryt a' the Brig o' Innerugie's stehns.*"

The old man, who handed down this story to his children, from one of whom I have now got it, used to say to any of them that complained of being tired after a hard day's work: "Oh, aye, ye're like the kelpie that cairryt the stehns to big the brig o' Innerugie – *Sehr back and sehr behns.*"'

Then again, 'a miller was annoyed by a kelpie entering his mill during the night and playing havoc among the grain and meal. One night he shut up in the mill his boar, for a miller generally kept a good many pigs and a breeding sow or two. As usual kelpie entered the mill. That boar stood on his defence, and fought the kelpie. Next night the creature appeared at the miller's window, and called to him:

' "Is there a chattie i' the mill the nicht?"

' "Aye, there is a chattie i' the mill, and will be for ever mair," was the answer.

'Kelpie returned no more to the mill.'

'Thus did the evil creatures often press me hard, but, as was meet, I served them well with my war-sword; they had no joyous fill by eating me, wicked destroyers, sitting round their feast nigh the bottom of the sea; but in the morning wounded by the sword, slain by the dagger, they lay up along the sea-strand, so that they could never more hinder sea-farers on their course in the deep channel.

'Light came from the east, the bright beacon of the Lord; the waves were stilled, and I could descry the sea-headlands, those windswept walls.'

Beowulf, translated by C. B. TINKER

341

'... THE USEWALL Method for a curious Person to get a transient Sight of this otherwise invisible Crew of Subterraneans, ... is to put his left Foot under the Wizard's right Foot, and the Seer's Hand is put on the Inquirer's Head, who is to look over the Wizard's right Shoulder ... then will he see a Multitude of Wights, like furious hardie Men, flocking to him haistily from all Quarters, as thick as Atoms in the Air ... Thes thorow Fear strick him breathless and speechless.'

So says 'Mr Robert Kirk, Minister at Aberfoill', in his *Secret Commonwealth* of 1691.

One needs but to find the wizard, and all is plain sailing – except, perhaps, that that 'right shoulder' is a little surprising. Is it not rather from over one's left shoulder that one expects to be warned of any such preternatural beings? But then what is this 'right' and 'left' of ours? I remember well, at any rate, when as a child I had to think hard before I could make sure which was which – and know not even now *how* I do it!

Of these invisible 'wights' the womenkind 'are said to Spin very fine, to Dy, to Tossue, and Embroyder, but whether only curious Cob-webs, impalpable Rainbows . . . I leave to conjecture.'

343. '*And Clootie's waur nor a woman was*'

A strip or patch of wild weedy uncropped ground (like the Sluggard's garden) that in England is called *No Man's Land*, the Scots country folk call *Clootie's Croft* (or Clootie's little field). They hand it over by name, as it were, to the Fiend, hoping that he may rest content with its harvest of nettle and bramble and burr, and not range elsewhere. It is an old belief that if, like Christian, the wayfarer meets Apollyon straddling across his path, he may have to withstand him not only with sword and staff, but with his wits. Just so, too, in old times, sovereign princes would test strangers with dark questions and riddles. In this ballad the Fiend disguised as a knight comes wooing at a Widow's door, in the next he is abroad on the high road. Jennifer and the wee boy kept up their hearts, their wits about them, their eyes open, and 'had the last word'; which, says Mr Sidgwick, is a mighty powerful charm against evil spirits – as against Witches are the herbs vervain, dill, basil, hyssop, periwinkle and rue. Iron, too; the sign of the Cross, and running water.

Here is another such encounter from Lady Grey's *The White Wallet* – packed with poems new and old. You can almost hear the voices of the two speakers standing together in the quiet and dust of the morning road:

Meet-on-the-Road

'Now, pray, where are you going, child?' said Meet-on-the-Road.
'To school, sir, to school, sir,' said Child-as-It-Stood.

'What have you in your basket, child?' said Meet-on-the-Road.
'My dinner, sir, my dinner, sir,' said Child-as-It-Stood.

'What have you for your dinner, child?' said Meet-on-the-Road.
'Some pudding, sir, some pudding, sir,' said Child-as-It-Stood.

'Oh, then I pray, give me a share,' said Meet-on-the-Road.
'I've little enough for myself, sir,' said Child-as-It-Stood.

'What have you got that cloak on for?' said Meet-on-the-Road.
'To keep the wind and cold from me,' said Child-as-It-Stood.

'I wish the wind would blow through you,' said Meet-on-the-Road.
'Oh, what a wish! Oh, what a wish!' said Child-as-It-Stood.

'Pray what are those bells ringing for?' said Meet-on-the-Road.
'To ring bad spirits home again,' said Child-as-It-Stood.

'Oh, then, I must be going, child!' said Meet-on-the-Road.
'So fare you well, so fare you well,' said Child-as-It-Stood.

And here, for titbits and *bonnes bouches* – and just in case – are Eight Ancient Riddles from *Popular Rhymes*, and a ninth which was sent in a letter by Lewis Carroll to the small friend he had in mind when he wrote *Alice in Wonderland*.

i.

The fiddler and his wife,
   The piper and his mother,
Ate three half-cakes, three whole cakes,
   And three quarters of another.

ii.

A house full, a yard full,
   And yet can't catch a bowl full.

iii.

As I was going o'er London Bridge,
   I heard something crack;
Not a man in all England
   Can mend that!

iv.

I had a little sister,
    They called her Pretty Peep;
She wades in the waters,
    Deep, deep, deep!
She climbs up the mountains,
    High, high, high;
My poor little sister,
    She has but one eye.

v.

As I was going o'er yon moor of moss,
I met a man on a gray horse;
He whipp'd and he wail'd,
I ask'd him what he ail'd;
He said he was going to his father's funeral,
Who died seven years before he was born!

vi.

As I looked out o' my chamber window,
    I heard something fall;
I sent my maid to pick it up,
    But she couldn't pick it all.

vii.

Black within, and red without,
Four corners round about.

viii.

Come a riddle, come a riddle,
Come a rot-tot-tot,
A wee, wee man, in a reid, reid coat,
A stauve in his hand an' an bane in his throat,
Come a riddle, come a riddle,
Come a rot-tot-tot.

ix.

Dreaming of apples on a wall,
    And dreaming often, dear,
I dreamed that, if I counted all,
    How many would appear?

Answers

i. 1¾ cakes each; since, if Mr Piper marries, his wife will be Mr and Mrs Fiddler's dear daughter-in-law. ii. Smoke; iii. Ice; iv. A Star; v. The poor soul in the coffin was by trade a dyer; vi. Snuff; vii. A Chimney (in Days of Yore); viii. A cherry; ix. Ten.

344. 'The fause knicht'

Such visitants, it would appear, have marvellous power even over faces or shapes in stone:

He's tied his steed to the kirk-stile,
    Syne wrang-gaites round the kirk gaed he;
When the Mer-Man entered the kirk-door,
    Away the sma' images turned their e'e . . .

Wrang-gaites must mean widdershins, right to left, West to East, the opposite to *deiseal* (deshal) – left to right, sunwise.

Here is another such visitor – one who considerately intrudes not all at once but little by little:

The Strange Visitor

A wife was sitting at her reel ae night;
    And aye she sat, and aye she reeled, and aye she wished for
    company.

In came a pair o' braid braid soles, and sat down at the fireside;
    And aye she sat, and aye she reeled, and aye she wished for
    company.

In came a pair o' sma legs, and sat down on the braid braid soles;
    And aye she sat, and aye she reeled, and aye she wished for company.

In came a pair o' muckle muckle knees, and sat down on the sma' sma' legs;
    And aye she sat, and aye she reeled, and aye she wished for company.

In came a pair o' sma' sma' thees, and sat down on the muckle muckle knees;
    And aye she sat, and aye she reeled, and aye she wished for company.

In came a pair o' muckle muckle hips, and sat down on the sma' sma' thees;
    And aye she sat, and aye she reeled, and aye she wished for company.

In came a sma' sma' waist, and sat down on the muckle muckle hips;
    And aye she sat, and aye she reeled, and aye she wished for company.

In came a pair o' braid braid shouthers, and sat down on the sma' sma' waist;
    And aye she sat, and aye she reeled, and aye she wished for company.

In came a pair o' sma' sma' arms, and sat down on the braid braid shouthers;
    And aye she sat, and aye she reeled, and aye she wished for company.

In came a pair o' muckle muckle hands, and sat down on the sma' sma' arms;
    And aye she sat, and aye she reeled, and aye she wished for company.

In came a sma' sma' neck, and sat down on the braid braid
    shouthers;
  And aye she sat, and aye she reeled, and aye she wished for
    company.

In came a great big head, and sat down on the sma' sma' neck;
  And aye she sat, and aye she reeled, and aye she wished for
    company.

'What way hae ye sic braid braid feet?' quo' the wife.
'Muckle ganging, muckle ganging.'
'What way hae ye sic sma' sma' legs?'
'*Aih-h-h!* – late – and *wee-e-e* moul.'
'What way hae ye sic muckle muckle knees?'
'Muckle praying, muckle praying.'
'What way hae ye sic sma' sma' thees?'
'*Aih-h-h!* – late – and *wee-e-e* moul.'
'What way hae ye sic big big hips?'
'Muckle sitting, muckle sitting.'
'What way hae ye sic a sma' sma' waist?'
'*Aih-h-h!* – late – and *wee-e-e* moul.'
'What way hae sic braid braid shouthers?'
'Wi' carrying broom, we' carrying broom.'
'What way hae ye sic sma' sma' arms?'
'*Aih-h-h!* – late – and *wee-e-e* moul.'
'What way hae ye sic muckle muckle hands?'
'Threshing wi' an iron flail, threshing wi' an iron flail.'
'What way hae ye sic a sma' sma' neck?'
'*Aih-h-h!* – late – and *wee-e-e* moul.'
'What way hae sic a muckle muckle head?'
'Muckle wit, muckle wit.'
'What do you come for?'
'For YOU!'

    But sometimes it is the monster who's at home:

The cat sits at the mill door spinnin', spinnin'.
Up comes a wee moose rinnin', rinnin'.

'What are ye doin' there my lady, my lady?'
'Spinnin' a sark for my son,' quo' Batty, quo' Batty.
'I'll tell a story, my lady, my lady,'
'We'll hae the mair company,' quo' Batty, quo' Batty.
'There was once a wee woman, my lady, my lady.'
'She tuk the less room,' quo' Batty, quo' Batty.
'She was sweepin' her hoose one day, my lady, my lady,'
'She had it the cleaner,' quo' Batty, quo' Batty.
'She found a penny, my lady, my lady.'
'She had the mair money,' quo' Batty, quo' Batty.
'She went to the market, my lady, my lady,'
'She didna stay at hame,' quo' Batty, quo' Batty.
'She bocht a wee bit o' beef, my lady, my lady.'
'She had the mair flesh meat,' quo' Batty, quo' Batty.
'She cam' home my lady, my lady.'
'She didna stay awa',' quo' Batty, quo' Batty.
'She put her beef on the coals to roast, my lady, my lady.'
'She didna eat it raw,' quo' Batty, quo' Batty.
'She put it on the window to cool, my lady, my lady.'
'She didna scaud her lips,' quo' Batty, quo' Batty.
'Up comes a wee moose an' ate it all up, my lady, my lady.'
'Ay, and that's the way I'll eat *you* up too,' quo' Batty, quo' Batty,

Quo' *Batty*, quo' BATTY,
Quo' BATTY.

345

I have included only these few stanzas of this familiar magical poem because a book is but one book, and to print everything as lovely or almost as lovely would need many.

In reading it as Coleridge explained, all that is necessary to ensure lilt and cadence is to remember that every line, however few or many its words or syllables, has four stresses or accents, and that these fall in accord with its 'meaning' as one reads it with clear eyes, attentive ear, and with all one's understanding. In his tale of Genevieve there is yet another false and lovely Fiend:

... But when I told the cruel scorn
That crazed that bold and lovely Knight,
And that he crossed the mountain-woods,
    Nor rested day or night;

That sometimes from the savage den,
And sometimes from the darksome shade,
And sometimes starting up at once
    In green and sunny glade, –

There came and looked him in the face
An angel beautiful and bright;
And that he knew it was a Fiend,
    This miserable Knight ...

'A toothless mastiff bitch'

This description of one *with* teeth – a dog seldom seen now – is taken from a German book on husbandry, translated by Barnabe Googe, and is quoted in *Animal Lore*:

'First the mastie that keepeth the house: for this purpose you must provide you such a one, as hath a large and a mightie body, a great and a shrill voyce, that both with his barking he may discover, and with his sight dismay the theefe, yea, being not seene, with the horror of his voice put him to flight; his stature must neither be long nor short, but well set, his head great, his eyes sharpe, and fiery, ... his countenance like a lion, his brest great and shaghayrd, his shoulders broad, his legges bigge, his tayle short, his feet very great; his disposition must neither be too gentle, nor too curst, that he neither fawne upon a theefe, nor flee [fly] upon his friends; very waking, no gadder abroad, not lavish of his mouth, barking without cause. Neither maketh it any matter though he be not swift: for he is but to fight at home, and to give warning of the enemie.'

347. 'Once a fair and stately palace'

The radiant, despoiled and spectral palace of this poem is indeed far away – the nether side of dream and night. Its monstrous word, *Porphyrogene*, means a prince, a child-Royal, one born in the Queen's chamber of an Eastern palace, walled with rare porphyry.

350. 'Sweet whispers are heard by the traveller'

> On a poet's lips I slept
> Dreaming like a love-adept
> In the sound his breathing kept;
> Nor seek nor finds he mortal blisses,
> But feeds on the aërial kisses
> Of shapes that haunt thought's wilderness.
> He will watch from dawn to gloom
> The lake-reflected sun illume
> The yellow bees in the ivy-bloom,
> Nor heed nor see, what things they be;
> But from these create he can
> Forms more real than living man,
> Nurslings of immortality! ...

PERCY BYSSHE SHELLEY

352. 'My a dildin'

This, and Nos 353, 355, and 356 are four Singing-Game Rhymes, worn down into almost nonsensical jingle by multitudinous tongues in long long usage. (See No. 41, page 62.)

And – since in my humble opinion it is not easy to get too much of this kind of good thing – here is another:

> Bobby Shafto's gone to sea,
> With silver buckles at his knee;
> When he'll come home he'll marry me,
> Pretty Bobby Shafto!

Bobby Shafto's fat and fair,
Combing down his yellow hair;
He's my love for evermair,
    Pretty Bobby Shafto!

When first my brave Johnnie lad
    Came to this town,
He had a blue bonnet
    That wanted the crown;
But now he has gotten
    A hat and a feather, –
Hey, brave Johnnie lad,
    Cock up your beaver!

ROBERT BURNS

King Edelbrode cam owre the sea,
    Fa la lilly.
All for to marry a gay ladye,
    Fa la lilly.

Her lilly hands, sae white and sma',
    Fa la lilly.
Wi' golden rings were buskit braw,
    Fa la lilly ...

And here is a Bride of Elizabeth's day whom I chanced on in that packed and inexhaustible book, *Shakespeare's England*. When 'buskit braw', she must have been as lovely to see as a hawthorn in May or a wax candle in a silver shrine:

'The bride being attired in a gown of sheeps russet, and a kirtle of fine worsted, her head attired with a billiment of gold, and her hair as yellow as gold hanging down behind her, which was curiously combed and pleated, according to the manner in those days: she was led to church between two sweet boys, with bride-laces and rosemary tied about their silken sleeves ... Then was there a fair bride-cup of silver and gilt carried before her wherein was a goodly branch of rosemary, gilded very fair, hung about with silken ribands of all colours: next was there a noise of musicians, that played all the way before her: after her came all the chiefest maidens of the country, some bearing great bride-cakes, and some garlands of wheat, finely gilded, and so she passed to the Church.'

As for the silken ribands they may have been of Drakes colour or Ladies blush or Gozelinge colour or Marigold or Isabel or Peas porridge tawny or Popingay blew or Lusty gallant, but they were certainly not Judas colour, Devil in the hedge, or Dead Spaniard.

355. *'And feed her wi' new milk and bread'*

The Yellow-haired Laddie sat down on yon brae,
Cries – Milk the ewes, Lassie! let nane o' them gae!
And ay she milked, and ay she sang –
The Yellow-haired Laddie shall be by gudeman!
And ay she milked, and ay she sang –
The Yellow-haired Laddie shall be my gudeman! ...

ALLAN RAMSAY

Apart from singing rhymes such as those actually used in the course of a game, there are the mere counting-out rhymes, for deciding on who is to be 'he' and so on. Some of them have been reduced to little more than gibberish, whatever they may once have been.

First, the rhyme we used when I was young:

Eena, deena, deina, duss,
Catala, weena, weina, wuss,
Spit, spot, must be done,
Twiddlum, twaddlum, twenty-one!

The next – with some of its 'sense' evidently gone astray – has fifty-four thumps in all:

Hinty, minty, cuty, corn,
Apple seed, and apple thorn,

Wire, briar, limber lock,
Three geese in a flock.
One flew east, and one flew west,
One flew over the cuckoo's nest.
Up on yonder hill.
That is where my father dwells;
He has jewels, he has rings,
He has many pretty things.
He has a hammer with two nails,
He has a cat with twenty tails.
Strike Jack, lick Tom!
Blow the bellows, old man!

This French set has six thumps to the line:

Un, deux, trois, j'irai dans les bois,
Quatre, cinq, six, chercher des cerises,
Sept, huit, neuf, dans mon panier neuf;
Dix, onze, douze, elles seront toutes rouges;
Treize, quatorze, quinze, pour mon petit Prince;
Seize, dix-sept, dix-huit, je les apporterai tout-de-suite.
Dix-neuf, vingt, pour qu'elles prennent leurs bains.

This German has eight in its first two lines, four in the rest —
total, thirty-two:

Eine kleine weisse Bohne, wollte gern nach Engelland,
Engelland war zugeschlossen, und der Schlüssel war zerbrochen.
Bauer, bind den Pudel an,
Dass er mich nicht beissen kann.
Beisst er mich, so kost es dich
Tausend Thaler sicherlich.

The next is a haunting Scots example, with hints in it of some
meddling to make it sense:

Eenity, feenity, fickety feg,
El, del, Dolmen eg;
Irky, birky, story, rock,
An, tan, toosh, Jock.

So, too, with this ancient one from Cornwall:

> Ena, mena, bora mi;
> Kisca, lara, mora di;
> Eggs, butter, cheese, bread;
> Stick, stock, stone dead.

The next is an ancient counting-out, or rather scoring rhyme, used in the very ancient game of Duck-and-Drake – played, of course, by so flinging across a sheet of water a flat stone or shell as to make it kiss the surface as many times as possible before it sink:

> A Duck and a Drake,
> And a half-penny cake,
> And a penny to pay the old baker;
> A hop and a scotch is another notch,
> Slitherum, slatherum, take her!

The next one is American (but see Note 24), a method of scoring (from one to twenty) that was current up to the fifties of the last century:

Een,	Een-dix,
Teen,	Teen-dix,
Tether,	Tether-dix,
Fether,	Fether-dix,
Fitz,	Bompey,
Sather,	Een-bompey,
Lather,	Teen-bompey,
Gother,	Tether-bompey,
Dather,	Fether-bompey,
Dix.	Giget.

And this gibberish (for groups of thirty) is from New York City:

> A knife and a razor,
> Spells Nebuchadnezzar,

A knife and a fork,
Spells Nebuchadnork.
A new pair of slippers,
And an old pair of shoes,
Spells Nebuchadnezzar,
The king of the Jews.

Old Dan Tucker
Came home to supper,
    And ate the hind leg of a frog;
He peeped o'er the steeple,
Saw many fine people,
    And looked at the mouth of a dog!

But there are dozens of similar rhymes in at least seventeen languages – all to be found in *Counting-out Rhymes*, by H. C. Bolton.

357

This old song, which was set to music in the reign of Henry VIII, comes (like Dallyaunce of No. 35), out of a Morality Play, *Lusty Juventus*, the author of which is said to have been one R. Wever.

'Oh, say, my Joan, will not that do?'

... The little maid replied, some say a little sighed,
    'But what shall we have for to eat, eat, eat?
Will the love that you're so rich in make a fire in the kitchen,
    Or the little god of love turn the spit, spit, spit?'

358. 'Milk-white fingers, cherry nose'

This is the only poem I have ever seen in which the midmost feature of a pretty face is compared to a cherry. And yet every frosty morning throughout the ages must have given many a dainty nose that fair bright coral colour.

There is indeed the widest of gaps between seeing a thing and noticing it; between merely noticing and realizing it, mind and heart; between realizing it and vividly conveying that realization. The unknown writer of 358 had a remarkably quick and ardent eye.

In *Notes on Noses*, a little brown book of a hundred and fifty-three pages published in 1859, the eloquent author (who omits his portrait) distinguishes six classes of 'simple noses': the *Roman*, undulating, rugose and coarse, but powerful; the *Greek*, straight, tasteful and astute; the *Cogitative*, wide-nostrilled and meditative; the *Hawk*, worldly and shrewd; the *Snub*, feeble, insolent and foxy; and last, the *Celestial*, or 'the snub turned up' – and for much the better. These, as he says, are the *simple* noses. They may be found combined and re-combined in a complex specimen to such a degree that it is difficult to say where each begins and ends.

But the nose in our poem is a feminine nose; and of feminine noses the Roman 'mars beauty'; the Greek (though Mrs Barbauld and Mrs Hemans, not to mention Hannah More, possessed specimens) is by no means, it seems, a sure sign of poetic gifts; while the Cogitative and the Hawk are rare in feminine faces – for 'it is the duty of men to relieve women from the cares of commercial life.' There remain, then, only the all-enticing coral-tipped *Celestial* and – but enough.

359. 'Or the bees their careful king'

In old times the 'Governor' of a Bee Hive was sometimes referred to as the King and sometimes as the Queen. The choice depended in part on which kind of monarch was on the throne. A curious bee-story of the middle ages is related by Mr Tickner Edwardes in his book on the Honey Bee.

A certain simple woman, on finding that her bees were storing little honey for her and were perishing of 'the murraine', stole one of the holy wafers from the priest, and for miraculous remedy concealed it in one of her hives. 'Whereupon the Murraine ceased and the Honie abounded. The Woman, therefore lifting up the hive at the due time to take out the Honie, saw there (most strange to be seene) a Chappell built by the Bees, with an altar to it, the wals adorned by marvellous skill of architecture, with windowes conveniently set in their places: also a doore and a steeple with bells. And the Host being laid upon the altar, the Bees making a sweet noise, flew around it.' Apart from 'the singing masons building roofs of gold', the gluttonous drones, the sentries, wax-makers, bread-kneaders, nurses in the hive, there are the Queen's Ladies-in-waiting: 'For difference from the rest they beare for their crest a tuft or tossell, in some coloured yellow, in some murrey, in manner of a plume; whereof some turne downward like an Ostrich-feather, others stand upright like a Hern-top.' But for truths even stranger than fantasy regarding bees and their kind, read Henri Fabre, M. Maeterlinck and Mr Edwardes.

> . . . There he arriving, round about doth flie,
> From bed to bed from one to other border,
> And takes survey, with curious busie eye,
> Of every flowre and herbe there set in order:
> Now this, now that he tasteth tenderly,
> Yet none of them he rudely doth disorder;
> Ne with his feete their silken leaves deface;
> But pastures on the pleasures of each place.
>
> And evermore, with most varietie,
> And change of sweetnesse, (for all change is sweete)
> He casts his glutton sense to satisfie,
> Now sucking of the sap of herbe most meete,
> Or of the dew which yet on them does lie,
> Now in the same bathing his tender feete:
> And then he pearcheth on some braunch thereby,
> To weather him, and his moist wings to dry . . .

EDMUND SPENSER

360. '*And here, and here!*'

As Flora slept and I lay waking,
I smiled to see a bird's mistaking,
For from a bough it down did skip
And for a cherry pecked her lip ...

362. '*My heart is gladder than all these*'

How many times do I love thee, dear?
Tell me how many thoughts there be
  In the atmosphere
  Of the new fall'n year,
Whose white and sable hours appear
  The latest flake of eternity:
So many times do I love thee, dear!

How many times do I love again?
Tell me how many beads there are
  In a silver chain
  Of evening rain
Unravelled from the tumbling main,
  And threading the eye of a yellow star:
So many times do I love again!

THOMAS LOVELL BEDDOES

363

The word 'screen' (line 4) means, I think, 'Hide and shelter those smiles away that in their beauty seem to burn in the air': for all beauty resembles radiance in its influence on the mind. And this recalls to memory Southwell's poem, 'The Burning Babe', No. 256.

364

The more closely one examines a fine *sonnet* – its way of rhyming, ascent, progress, poise, balance and cadences, the ease and exactitude with which what is said in it fills its mould or form – the more modestly one should hesitate before attempting to write or at least publish another. This particular sonnet (like No. 361), is of the English or Shakespearian kind, and is so lovely a thing that only a close attention would notice the carelessness of its rhymes. No. 342 is an example of the Petrarchan form of sonnet which our sixteenth-century poets borrowed from Italy. Comparison of them shows that, as with the old Chinese ginger jars, so in poetry: not only is the syrup delightful, but even the pot may be interesting.

Coleridge wrote few sonnets, and this is his explanation of the length one must be: 'It is confined to fourteen lines, because as some particular number is necessary, and that particular number must be a small one, it may as well be fourteen as any other number. When no reason can be adduced against a thing, Custom is a sufficient reason for it.'

The first sentence is no more and no less true also of a centipede's legs, a cat's claws or a paper of pins. But the second startles one's mind into instant attention, as one's body is when it collides with a stranger's in the street. There is a wide wisdom in it. How many natural, human and delightful things there are in this world, indeed, for which Custom is a sufficient reason: children, for instance, daisies in the grass, skylarks in the clouds, dreams in sleep, rhymes, gay clothes, friendship, laughter.

'The pale Queen'

There is the apparition of a lovely face in the Moon – proud and mute – to be discovered by careful eyes usually on the extreme right of the disc, her own eyes gazing towards the left.

> O lady Moon, your horns point to the East;
> Shine, be increased!

O Lady Moon, your horns point to the West;
    Wane, be at rest!

                    CHRISTINA ROSSETTI

368

This old Scottish song was a favourite of Oliver Goldsmith's in his childhood. 'The music of the finest singer,' he said, 'is dissonance to what I felt when our old dairy-maid sung me into tears with *Johnny Armstrong's Last Good-night*, or *The Cruelty of Barbara Allen*.'

As with the Scottish ballads so with this last poem – it is the brevity and bareness with which the story is told and is *not* told that sets it apart. Without one express word to prove it so, it is clear that Sir John had always loved the proud Barbara even if he had spoken lightly of her, and (as it seems to me) that she, without realizing it, had always loved him, though she refuses the word that would have saved his life.

'She heard the dead-bell ringing'

The jows of the Passing-bell in the 7th stanza are known as tolls or knocks or tellers in different parts of England, and the method of ringing differs according to the number of bells in the belfry. In general the tenor bell has been used – a bell often called Gabriel because it was wont to be rung morning and evening for the Angelus, summoning all who heard it to kneel and repeat the Angel Gabriel's Salutation in the first chapter of St Luke's Gospel. The most usual custom has been to sound thrice three tolls for a man, and thrice two for a woman – hence, it has been suggested, the old saying, 'Nine *tellers mark* a man' (rather than 'Nine *tailors make* a man').

In Leverton, Lincolnshire, twelve tolls were once (and may still be) sounded for a man, nine for a woman, seven for a boy under sixteen, and six for a girl under eighteen.

In the belfry of Marsham, Norfolk, the following was the rule:

Knocks for the Dead

iii for Girl	vii for Matron
iv for Boy	viii for Bachelor
vi for Spinster	ix for Husband

But Church bells were rung for many other purposes, and though their *lin-lan-lone* is to some hearts a melancholy cadence to hear even in the serenity of a summer evening, it is not 'surly' and 'sullen'. There was a ringing on St Thomas's Day – called 'Mumpsing'; and an all-night ringing on the Eve of All Saints. There was the Pancake Bell, the Gleaning Bell, the Harvest Bell and the Oven Bell, and a sudden jangling – the whole peal being rung out, or backwards, or confusedly and 'out of tune and harsh' – for a warning of fire. But for further and fuller information see *English Bells and Bell-Lore*, by J. North, and many another book on this subject.

371. '*I never had but one true love,*
In cold grave she was lain'

Yet another tragic and sorrowful poem is the story of the beautiful Princess Uillanita. She cared only for flowers white and colourless as dew in the first light of day. And one still evening, when she was in search of what she could not find, she came to a valley wherein a forest gloomed above a deep but placid river. Within the forest, refreshed by the mists of the river, grew none but flowers blue and dark and purple, and such was the young Princess's hatred of them that she covered her eyes with her hands, fled on, and so lost her way.

In the middle of the night and long after she had wept herself to sleep, the wailing of a bird pierced into her dreams, and she awoke to see one solitary star of the colourless radiance of Vega shining in a space of sky betwixt the branches above her head. Its thin ray

silvered down – spearlike in its straightness – and of a beam easily
sufficing to irradiate a tiny clustering flower which stood half-
hidden in the moss at her hand's side, and was drenching the air
with its fragrance. It was a flower utterly strange to her, whiter
than hoarfrost, fairer than foam.

The enravished Princess gazed spellbound. 'Why,' whispered
she to herself, in the quiet of the dark; 'if I had not hated the sad-
coloured flowers of this sombre forest, and so lost my way, if I
had not been moved in my sleep to awaken, I never should have
seen this crystal thing – that is lovelier than I deemed Paradise
itself could bring to bloom.' And she kissed the thin-spun petals,
and fell again happily asleep.

372

Only two stanzas out of six, and these, maybe, a little difficult in
the old Scots:

> Depart, depart, depart!
> Alas! I must depart
> From her that has my heart
>   With heart full sore;
> Against my will indeed
> And can find no remede –
> I wait the pains of death –
>   Can do no more . . .
>
> Adieu mine own sweet thing,
> My joy and comforting,
> My mirth and solacing
>   Of earthly gloir:
> Farewell, my lady bright,
> And my remembrance right,
> Farewell, and have good night –
>   I say no more.

373. '*Maidens, willow branches bear*'

Thou art to all lost love the best,
  The onely true plant found,
Wherewith young men and maids distrest,
  And left of love, are crown'd.

When once the Lovers Rose is dead,
  Or laid aside forlorne;
Then Willow-garlands, 'bout the head,
  Bedew'd with teares, are worne . . .

And underneath thy cooling shade,
  (When weary of the light)
The love-spent Youth, and love-sick Maid,
  Come to weep out the night.

ROBERT HERRICK

380

Who 'the wayworn wanderer' is, I am uncertain; but apart from its rare music, how long a journey awaits the imagination in this poem, and how closely inwoven is its imagery. Yet it is said to have been written when Poe was still a boy.

381

Mr Nahum's picture for this poem was of a little winged boy at evening, his quiver of arrows on his back, his bow the perch of a nightingale, and himself lying fast asleep under a hawthorn bush in full flower – a narrow green sun-dappled river near by, rosy clouds and birds in the air, and strange snow-peaked hills afar.

'*I did but see her*'

There be none of Beauty's daughters
    With a magic like thee;
And like music on the waters
    Is thy sweet voice to me:
When, as if its sound were causing
The charmed ocean's pausing,
The waves lie still and gleaming,
And the lull'd winds seem dreaming ...

LORD BYRON

'*Till I die*'

... Only our love hath no decay;
This no to-morrow hath, nor yesterday;
Running it never runs from us away,
But truly keeps his first, last, everlasting day.

JOHN DONNE

383. '*It is not so*'

Silly boy 'tis ful Moon yet, thy night as day shines clearly.
Had thy youth but wit to feare, thou couldst not love so dearely.
Shortly wilt thou mourne when all thy pleasures are bereavèd;
Little knows he how to love that never was deceivèd ...

Yet be just and constant still! Love may beget a wonder,
Not unlike a Summer's frost, or Winter's fatall thunder.
He that holds his Sweetheart true, unto his day of dying,
Lives, of all that ever breathed, most worthy the envýing.

THOMAS CAMPION

385

In this poem, as in all Christina Rossetti's work, there is a rhythm and poise, a serpentining of music, so delicate that on clumsy lips it will vanish as rapidly as the bloom from a plum. Indeed, each stanza is like a branch (with its twigs) of a wild damson-tree, its wavering line broken and beautiful with bud, flower and leaf. As fresh an air, and as clear a light, stirs and dwells in the poem as on the tree itself in April.

387

This is from Part II, Act II, Scene 1 of *Zapolya*. Glycine sings unseen in a cavern – her voice comforting her lover wandering forlorn by night 'in a savage wood'.

389. '*I'll overtake thee*'

I'll weave my love a garland,
    He shall be dressed so fine,
I'll set it round with roses,
    With lilies, pinks, and thyme;
And I'll present it to my love
    When he comes back from sea:
For I love my love, and I love my love
    Because my love loves me.

I wish I were an arrow
    That sped into the air,
To seek him as a sparrow,
    And if he be not there
Then quickly I'd become a fish
    To search the raging sea:
For I love my love, and I love my love
    Because my love loves me.

I would I were a reaper,
  I'd seek him in the corn;
I would I were a keeper,
  I'd hunt him with my horn;
I'd blow a blast, when found at last,
  Beneath the greenwood tree:
For I love my love, and I love my love,
  Because my love loves me.

And again:

For I'll cut my green coat a foot above my knee,
And I'll clip my yellow locks an inch below mine ee.
  Hey, nonny, nonny, nonny.

I'll buy me a white cut, forth for to ride,
And I'll go seek him through the world that is so wide.
  Hey, nonny, nonny, nonny.

But others stay at home:

Queen Mary, Queen Mary, my age is sixteen,
My father's a farmer on yonder green.
He's plenty of money to dress me, an' a',
An' there's *nae* bonnie laddie will tak' me awa'!

This morning I rose and I looked in the glass;
Says I to myself: 'What a handsome young lass!'
I tossed up my head and I gave a 'Ha! ha!
There's nae bonnie laddie will tak' *me* awa!'

Further south than where this lively rhyme comes from, the 'will' (lines 4 and 8) would be *shall*. The standard test is that of the unfortunate Scotsman who fell into the Thames (near Blackfriars) and each time his head appeared above the mirky flood cried piteously, 'I wull *droon! Nae*body shall save me!' And the Londoners looking down from above, being respecters of persons, didn't even try.

391. *'Chimborazo, Cotopaxi'*

In medieval days it seems that a traveller here and there, happily supposing the world to be a floating island of undiscoverable dimensions hung in the wilds of space, and not knowing that it was merely a rotating and 'oblate spheroid', would journey clear round it and so return to his amazement to the place from which he started. Here is such an experience from Sir John Mandeville – in our spelling: 'It was told that a certain worthy man departed some time from our Country for to go search the World ... He passed India and the Isles beyond it, where are more than 5000 Isles, and so long and for so many seasons he went by Sea and Land, and so environed the World, that he came at last to an Isle whereon he heard spoken his own language – a calling of oxen in the Plough – such Words in fact as men were wont to speak to Beasts in his own country. Whereof he greatly marvelled, knowing not how that might be.' For there – as if it were a picture in a dream – *there* was the chimney of his own house smoking up into the clear morning air! And what did he do? Maybe he stared; he sighed; he grew pale; he shuddered: and – turned back.

392

For the first sight of this poem I must gratefully thank my friend Mr Ivor Gurney. The poem was written by William Cleland while he was still at St Andrews. All else I know of him is that he was born about 1661, and fell at Dunkeld in 1689. There is nothing in English to my knowledge that resembles it. *Erra Pater* (stanza 4) was the name given to a busy astrologer and almanac-concocter, William Lilly, of the time. King Phalaris's monstrous bull was of brass: he perished in it.

By 'the tapers' (stanza 2) is meant, I fancy, those phosphoric fires that gather on the yard-arms of ships at sea when the air is electric with tempest. Sir Humphrey Gilbert's sailors were fearful at sight of this apparition, and of a hideous monster, too – which, to calm and cheer them, he said was *Bonum omen* – that had appeared

swimming in the waves beside their frigate, the *Squirrel*, a little
before she and her riding lights disappeared for ever. He himself
had remained serene, had spent some time in reading, had called
merrily over the water to his companion cockleshell, 'We are as
near Heaven by sea as by land.' And then –

'... Men which all their life time had occupied the Sea, never
was more outragious Seas. We had also upon our main yard, an
apparition of a little fire by night, which seamen doe call Castor
and Pollux. But we had onely one, which they take an evill signe of
more tempest ... The same Monday night, about twelve of the
clocke ... suddenly her lights were out ... and withall our watch
cryed, *the Generall was cast away*, which was too true. For in that
moment, the Frigat was devoured and swallowed up of the Sea ...'

Ariel. I boarded the king's ship; now on the beak,
  Now in the waist, the deck, in every cabin,
  I flam'd amazement: sometimes I'd divide
  And burn in many places; on the topmast,
  The yards, and boresprit, would I flame distinctly,
  Then meet, and join ...

The Tempest

As for Cupid (stanza 5), he is said to be the slyest archer that
ever loosed arrow – and a dangerous child to entertain:

  Cupide abroade was 'lated in the night,
    His wings were wet with ranging in the raine;
  Harbour he sought, to mee hee took his flight,
      To dry his plumes I heard the boy – complaine.
      I opte the doore and graunted his desire,
      I rose my selfe, and made the wagge a fire ...

or – as yet another poem goes on to tell – to take as a scholar:

      I dreamt by me I saw fair Venus stand,
      Holding young Cupid in her lovely hand,
      And said, kind Shepherd, I a scholar bring
      My little son, to learn of you to sing ...

And last, the pelican (in stanza 7). She was supposed in old days to be 'the lovingest bird that is', since at need she would pierce her breast with her bill to feed her young ones. The singing (stanza 7) of the dying swan I have never heard – except in Tennyson's words – packed with poetic observation:

> The plain was grassy, wild and bare,
> Wide, wild, and open to the air,
> Which had built up everywhere
>   An under-roof of doleful gray.

> With an inner voice the river ran,
> Adown it floated a dying swan,
>   And loudly did lament.
>   It was the middle of the day.
> Ever the weary wind went on,
>   And took the reed-tops as it went . . .
> Some blue peaks in the distance rose,
> And white against the cold-white sky,
> Shone out their crowning snows.

>   One willow over the river wept,
> And shook the wave as the wind did sigh;
> Above in the wind was the swallow,
>   Chasing itself at its own wild will,
>   And far thro' the marish green and still
>   The tangled water-courses slept,
> Shot over with purple, and green, and yellow.

393. 'Columbus's doom-burdened caravels'

'. . . The next day, Thursday, October 11, 1492, was destined to be for ever memorable in the history of the world . . . The people on the *Santa Maria* saw some petrels and a green branch in the water; the *Pinta* saw a reed and two small sticks carved with iron, and one or two other pieces of reeds and grasses that had been grown on shore, as well as a small board. Most wonderful of all, the people of the *Nina* saw "a little branch full of dog roses"; ... The day drew to its close; and after nightfall, according to their custom, the crews of the ships repeated the *Salve Regina*. Afterwards the Admiral addressed the people and sailors of his ship, "very merry and pleasant," ... The moon was in its third quarter, and did not rise until eleven o'clock. The first part of the night was dark, and there was only a faint starlight into which the anxious eyes of the look-out men peered from the forecastles of the three ships. At ten o'clock Columbus was walking on the poop of his vessel, when he suddenly saw a light right ahead. The light seemed to rise and fall as though it were a candle or a lantern held in some one's hand and waved up and down. The Admiral called Pedro Gutierrez to him and asked him whether he saw anything; and he also saw the light. Then he sent for Rodrigo Sanchez and asked him if he saw the light; but he did not ... Dawn came at last, flooding the sky with lemon and saffron and scarlet and orange, until at last the pure gold of the sun glittered on the water. And when it rose it showed the sea-weary mariners an island lying in the blue sea ahead of them: the island of Guanahani; San Salvador ...'

Christopher Columbus, FILSON YOUNG

The appearance of the petrels, and that saffron and scarlet in the sunrise must have made the sight of land the more welcome: and it was only a week or two after the autumnal equinox:

> When descends on the Atlantic
>   The gigantic
> Storm-wind of the equinox,
>   Landward in his wrath he scourges
>   The toiling surges,
> Laden with seaweed from the rocks:
>
> From Bermuda's reefs; from edges
>   Of sunken ledges,
> In some far-off, bright Azore;
> From Bahama, and the dashing,
>   Silver-flashing
> Surges of San Salvador;

From the tumbling surf, that buries
  The Orkneyan skerries,
Answering the hoarse Hebrides;
And from wrecks of ships, and drifting
  Soars, uplifting
On the desolate, rainy seas ...

HENRY WADSWORTH LONGFELLOW

395

... To the ocean now I fly,
And those happy climes that lie
Where day never shuts his eye.
Up in the broad fields of the sky;
There I suck the liquid air
All amidst the gardens fair
Of Hesperus, and his daughters three
That sing about the golden tree:
Along the crispèd shades and bowers
Revels the spruce and jocund Spring;
The Graces, and the rosy bosomed Hours,
Thither all their bounties bring;
There eternal Summer dwells,
And west winds, with musky wing,
About the cedared alleys fling
Nard and Cassia's balmy smells ...
But now my task is smoothly done,
I can fly, or I can run,
Quickly to the green earth's end,
Where the bowed welkin slow doth bend;
And from thence can soar as soon
To the corners of the moon ...

JOHN MILTON

Master.   Steersman, how stands the wind?
Steersman.   Full north-north-east

Master.	What course?
Steersman.	Full south-south-west.
Master.	No worse, and blow so fair,
	Then sink despair,
	Come solace to the mind!
	Ere night, we shall the haven find.

'Caved Tritons' azure day'

Dark-fated Clarence in *King Richard III* dreamt of that 'azure day':

         ... As we paced along
Upon the giddy footing of the Hatches,
Me thought that Glouster stumbled, and in falling
Strooke me (that thought to stay him) over-board,
Into the tumbling billowes of the maine.
O Lord, methought what paine it was to drowne,
What dreadfull noise of water in mine eares,
What sightes of ugly death within mine eyes ...
Methought I saw a thousand fearful wrackes:
A thousand men that Fishes gnawed upon:
Wedges of Gold, great Anchors, heapes of Pearle,
Inestimable Stones, unvalewed Jewels,
All scattered in the bottome of the Sea.
Some lay in dead-men's Sculles; and in the holes
Where eyes did once inhabit, there were crept,
(As 'twere in scorne of eyes) reflecting Gemmes,
That wooed the slimy bottome of the deepe,
And mocked the dead bones that lay scattered by ...

396. 'Huge sea-monsters'

'It's appearance is like that of a rough rock. [It seems] as if it extended beside the shore of the channel like [an immense] reedy island surrounded by sand-dunes. For this reason it happens that seafarers imagine they are gazing with their eyes on some island, and so they fasten their high-stemmed ships with anchor ropes to this false land; they make fast their sea-horses as if they were at the sea's brink, and up they climb on the island, bold of heart; [while their] vessels stand, fast by the shore, surrounded by the stream. And then the voyagers, weary in mind, and without thought of danger, encamp on the isle. They produce a flame, they kindle a vast fire. Full of joy are the heroes, late so sad of spirit; they are longing for repose. But when the creature, long skilled in guile, feels that the sailors are securely resting upon him, and are keeping their abode there, in enjoyment of the weather, suddenly into the salt wave, together with his prey, down dives the Ocean-dweller and seeks the abyss; and thus, by drowning them, imprisons the ships, with all their men, in the hall of death.'

'Jewels more rich than Ormus shows'

Mr Nahum's picture to this was of a man clothed in rags. As though in a cloud of despair, he sits gnawing his nails upon a heap of what appears to be precious stones and lumps of gold. Around him stretch the sands of the seashore, and there is a little harbour with a decayed quay, its river-mouth silted up with ooze and flotsam, so that nothing but a row-boat could find entrance there. An immense sun burns in the sky; and, though a thread of fresh water flows near at hand, the man among the jewels seems to be tormented with thirst . . .

Ormus, or Hormuz, on its narrow island of wild-coloured rocks, date-palms, parrots and many birds, was once the rich mart and treasure-house between Persia and India – spices, pearls, ivory, gold, precious stones, and, in particular, the diamond, being its merchandise. In 1507 the Portuguese Conqueror Alfonso Albuquerque stole it from its dark princes. In 1622 Shah Abbas the Great razed it to the ground. Today it is but a waste, inhabited by a few fishermen and diggers, its only commodities – that once were gems – salt and sulphur; while still in the height of its Summer blows Julot, Harmatan, Il Sirocco, the Flame-Wind, so deadly in its breath that the troops of an army of 1,600 horsemen and 6,000 foot, says Marco Polo, marching to punish the city for neglecting to pay tribute to the King of Kîrman, and camping overnight without its walls, were baked next noon as dry as pumice, and not a voice among them to tell the tale, though their bodily shape and colour seemed to appear unchanged. To protect themselves against this Julot, the citizens of Ormus used to build huts of sheltering osier-work over the water, and in the heat of the morning would stand immersed in its coolness up to the chin.

'Apples'

– these are pineapples, the 'price' of the next line meaning excellence. 'Ambergris' (line 28), is a rare and costly stuff which, as its name tells, resembles grey amber. It has a wondrously sweet smell, was once used in cooking, and is disgorged by the whale that supplies the world with the comforting ointment of childhood called spermaceti.

In Shakespeare's day, Marvell's 'remote Bermudas' were known as the 'Isle of Divels' – because of the nocturnal yellings, cries and yelpings that were reported to haunt them. English sailors, wrecked and cast away on Great Bermuda in 1709, however, brought home in their boats of cedar-wood the news that this mild music was caused (at least in part) by descendants of the hogs that had been left there by the long-gone Spaniard, Juan Bermudez and his men. They told, too, that it was an island fair and commodious, of a gentle climate, and a sweet-smelling air; and Shakespeare almost certainly had its enchantments in mind when he wrote of Ariel, Caliban and Miranda. Was not Ariel in Prospero's more solitary days called up at midnight 'to fetch dewe From the still-vext Bermoothes'?

To the Puritan voyagers of Andrew Marvell's poem the Islands were as welcome and angelic as the Hesperides. And no poet could better tell of them than he. For in Marvell's verse dwells a curious happiness, like sunshine on a pool of water-lilies. Yet he, too, like other dreamers, was a man of affairs, and of endless industry and zeal. He was thrice Member of Parliament for his birthplace, Kingston-on-Hull, and, with Milton, was one of Oliver Cromwell's Latin Secretaries. John Aubrey describes him as 'of a middling stature, pretty strong sett, roundish face, cherry-cheek't, hazell eie, brown hair. He was in his conversation very modest, and of very few words. And though he loved wine, he would never drink heartilie in company, and was wont to say, that, *he would not play the good fellow in any man's company in whose hands he would not trust his life.*' ... He was drowned on 23 January 1674, crossing the Humber 'in a barrow-boat; the same was sand-warpt', and he 'lies interred under the pews in the south side of St Giles' church-in-the-Fields, under the window wherein is painted in glass a red lyon'. But as his epitaph says (rather pompously): 'A tomb can neither contain his character nor is marble necessary to transmit it to posterity; it will be always legible in his imitable writings.' And there, under the same roof, St Giles's, share his rest vehement George Chapman, the dramatist and translator of Homer; James Shirley, the poet of 'The glories of our blood and state'; Sir Roger L'Estrange, who into the pithiest of English translated Æsop's Fables, and was a staunch Royalist; and Richard Pendrell, who 'preserved ... his sacred Majesty King Charles ii. after his escape from Worcester fight.'

> O, fly, my soul! What hangs upon
> Thy drooping wings,
> And weighs them down
> With love of gaudy mortal things?
> The Sun is now i' the east: each shade,
> As he doth rise,
> Is shorter made,
> That earth may lessen to our eyes.
> O, be not careless then and play
> Until the star of peace
> Hide all his beams in dark recess!
> Poor pilgrims needs must lose their way,
> When all the shadows do increase.

JAMES SHIRLEY

397. 'That talkative, bald-headed seaman came'

... And now my name; which way shall lead to all
My miseries after, that their sounds may fall
Through your ears also, and shew (having fled
So much affliction) first, who rests his head
In your embraces, when, so far from home,
I knew not where t' obtain it resting room:
    I am Ulysses Laertiades,
The fear of all the world ...

The Odyssey, GEORGE CHAPMAN

398

The prose 'argument' to the 'Ancient Mariner', which is almost as rare an experience to read as the Rime itself, has been omitted. But here is a fragment of it relating to the passage on pages 640–44: '... The Wedding-Guest feareth that a Spirit is talking to him; but the ancient Mariner assureth him of his bodily life, and proceedeth to relate his horrible penance. He despiseth the creatures of the calm, and envieth that *they* should live, and so many lie dead. But the curse liveth for him in the eye of the dead men. In his loneliness and fixedness he yearneth towards the journeying Moon, and the stars that still sojourn, yet still move onward; and every where the blue sky belongs to them, and is their appointed rest, and their native country and their own natural homes, which they enter unannounced, as lords that are certainly expected and yet there is a silent joy at their arrival.

'By the light of the Moon he beholdeth God's creatures of the great calm – their beauty and their happiness. He blesseth them in his heart. The spell begins to break. By grace of the holy Mother, the ancient Mariner is refreshed with rain. He heareth sounds and seeth strange sights and commotions in the sky and the element. The bodies of the ship's crew are inspired and inspirited, and the ship moves on; but not by the souls of the men, nor by dæmons of earth or middle air, but by a blessed troop of angelic spirits, sent down by the invocation of the guardian saint . . .'

'Daemons of earth or middle air' have been told of also by land travellers – by Friar Odoric, for example, in the account of his journey through Cathay during the years 1316–1330:

'Another great and terrible thing I saw. For, as I went through a certain valley which lieth by the River of Delights, I saw therein many dead corpses lying. And I heard also therein sundry kinds of music, but chiefly nakers, which were marvellously played upon. And so great was the noise thereof that very great fear came upon me. Now, this valley is seven or eight miles long; and if any unbeliever enter therein he quitteth it never again, but perisheth incontinently. Yet I hesitated not to go in that I might see once for all what the matter was. And when I had gone in I saw there, as I have said, such numbers of corpses as no one without seeing it could deem credible. And at one side of the valley, in the very rock, I beheld as it were the face of a man very great and terrible, so very terrible indeed that for my exceeding great fear my spirit seemed to die in me. Wherefore I made the sign of the cross, and began continually to repeat VERBUM CARO FACTUM, but I dared not at all to come nigh that face, but kept at seven or eight paces from it. And so I came at length to the other end of the valley, and there I ascended a hill of sand and looked around me. But nothing could I descry, only I still heard those nakers to play which were played so marvellously. And when I got to the top of that hill I found there a great quantity of silver heaped up as it had been fishes' scales, and some of this I put into my bosom. But as I cared nought for it, and was at the same time in fear lest it should be a snare to hinder my escape, I cast it all down again to the ground. And so by God's grace I came forth scathless. Then all the Saracens, when they heard of this, showed me great worship, saying that I was a baptised and holy man. But those who had perished in that valley they said belonged to the devil.'

> As an Arab journeyeth
> Through a sand of Ayaman,
> Lean Thirst, lolling its cracked tongue,

Lagging by his side along;
And a rusty wingèd Death
Grating its low flight before,
Casting ribbèd shadows o'er
The blank desert, blank and tan:
He lifts by hap to'rd where the morning's roots are
    His weary stare, –
      See although they plashless mutes are,
       Set in a silver air
    Fountains of gelid shoots are,
    Making the daylight fairest fair;
    Sees the palm and tamarind
Tangle the tresses of a phantom wind; –
A sight like innocence when one has sinned
A green and maiden freshness smiling there,
    While with unblinking glare
The tawny-hided desert crouches watching her . . .

The Mirage, FRANCIS THOMPSON

Thou to me art such a spring
As the Arab seeks at eve,
Thirsty from the shining sands;
There to bathe his face and hands,
While the sun is taking leave,
And dewy sleep is a delicious thing.

Thou to me art such a dream
As he dreams upon the grass,
While the bubbling coolness near
Makes sweet music in his ear;
And the stars that slowly pass
In solitary grandeur o'er him gleam.

Thou to me art such a dawn
As the dawn whose ruddy kiss
Wakes him to his darling steed;

And again the desert speed,
And again the desert bliss,
Lightens thro' his veins, and he is gone!

GEORGE MEREDITH

Part I. 'At length did cross an Albatross'

'I remember the first albatross I ever saw,' says Herman Melville in a footnote to *Moby Dick*. 'It was during a prolonged gale, in waters hard upon the Antarctic seas. From my forenoon watch below, I ascended to the overclouded deck; and there, dashed upon the main hatches, I saw a regal, feathery thing of unspotted whiteness, and with a hooked, Roman bill sublime. At intervals, it arched forth its vast archangel wings, as if to embrace some holy ark. Wonderous flutterings and throbbings shook it. Though bodily unharmed, it uttered cries, as some king's ghost in supernatural distress. Through its inexpressible, strange eyes, methought I peeped to secrets which took hold of God. As Abraham before the angels, I bowed myself; the white thing was so white, its wings so wide, and in those for ever exiled waters, I had lost the miserable warping memories of traditions and of towns. Long I gazed at that prodigy of plumage. I cannot tell, can only hint, the things that darted through me then ... By no possibility could Coleridge's wild Rhyme have had aught to do with those mystical impressions which were mine, when I saw that bird upon our deck. For neither had I then read the Rhyme, nor knew the bird to be an albatross. Yet, in saying this, I do but indirectly burnish a little brighter the noble merit of the poem and the poet.'

'In flight,' says Froude, 'the albatross wheels in circles round and round and for ever round the ship – now far behind, now sweeping past in a long, rapid curve, like a perfect skater on an untouched field of ice. There is no effort; watch as closely as you will, you rarely or never see a stroke of the mighty pinion.'

The greater part of the extract from Herman Melville is cited in the Notes to *The Road to Xanadu* by Professor Lowes, a packed and vivid book devoted to the revelation of what Coleridge was doing, thinking and seeing, and most particularly what he was reading a little before he wrote the 'Ancient Mariner' and 'Kubla Khan' and how all this was transmuted by his genius into this supremely original poetry. Collected from books that Coleridge without question had read and pondered on, Professor Lowes shows you, as it were, a handful of rich leaf-mould, then bids you glance again at the flower of poetry – like that telling of the ship becalmed – which sprang out of it. The miracle takes place before your very eyes – and remains a miracle.

Part V. '*The mariners all 'gan work the ropes*'

Of Sea Shanties or Chanties, capstan and halliard, to whose haunting strains the sea-men of the old sailing ships used to set about every job of work – 'the long haul', 'the sweat-up', 'the hand-over-hand', 'the stamp-and-go', – there is only space for one example – 'Storm Along', but it is one of the finest of all. In old days the shanty-men sang the first and third lines, and the rest joined in the refrain.

> Stormey's dead, that good old man –
> > *To my ay, Stormalong!*
> Stormey he is dead and gone
> > *Ay, ay, ay, Mister Stormalong!*
>
> Stormey's dead and gone to rest –
> > *To my ay, Stormalong!*
> Of all the skippers he was best –
> > *Ay, ay, ay, Mister Stormalong!*
>
> We dug his grave with a silver spade –
> > *To my ay, Stormalong!*
> His shroud of softest silk was made –
> > *Ay, ay, ay, Mister Stormalong!*
>
> I wish I was old Stormey' son–
> > *To my ay, Stormalong!*
> I'd build a ship a thousand ton –
> > *Ay, ay, ay, Mister Stormalong!*

I'd load her deep with wine and rum –
To my ay, Stormalong!
And all my shellbacks should have some –
Ay, ay, ay, Mister Stormalong!

'Without the chanties,' says Mr Masefield, 'you would never get the work done. "A song is ten men on the rope." In foul weather ... it is as comforting as a pot of hot drink.' He himself says of one of them: 'Another strangely beautiful chanty is that known as 'Hanging Johnny'. It has a melancholy tune that is one of the saddest things I have ever heard. I heard it for the first time off the Horn, in a snowstorm, when we were hoisting topsails after heavy weather. There was a heavy grey sea running and the decks were awash. The skies were sodden and oily, shutting in the sea about a quarter of a mile away. Some birds were flying about us, screaming.

They call me Hanging Johnny,
Away-i-oh;
They call me Hanging Johnny,
So hang, boys, hang!

I thought at the time that it was the whole scene set to music. I cannot repeat those words to their melancholy wavering music without seeing the line of yellow oilskins, the wet deck, the frozen ropes, and the great grey seas running up into the sky.'

AND NOW 'TWAS LIKE ALL INSTRUMENTS,
NOW LIKE A LONELY FLUTE,
AND NOW IT IS AN ANGEL'S SONG ...

In Hampstead there is a Children's Orchestra, and a friend, Miss M. M. Johnson, has very kindly permitted me to print for the first time a poem which she has written on this theme:

The Children's Orchestra

Like archangels in infancy
They sit, and play on wry, sweet strings,
With sober shoulders quaintly drooped:
But who has shorn their tender wings?

Half-circle-wise, celestially
The sprightly violins are ranged:
Behind them sombre 'cellists ply
Harmonious bows, – but half estranged.

Anon and ever each uplifts
To One a clear, obedient eye,
Who, armed with shining baton, stands
Enthroned, – their awful Deity ...

Their inexpressive brows, still eyes,
And carven lips no rapture paints,
But she, who holds their hearts, can read
The ecstasies of infant saints.

And when the royal word goes forth
'Let strings be tuned,' then all contend
With tangled notes and discords wild
Of sudden zeal, the air to rend.

Like archangels in infancy
They sit, and play on wry, sweet strings:
I think my earth-dimmed sight, alone,
Has quenched their crowns and shorn their wings.

399. *'He told of waves'*

So, too, does the Ship's Captain in yet another ore-laden poem of
the marvellous, 'The Sale of St Thomas', telling how the saint in
terror of the unknown would turn back from his mission, is
rebuked by his Master, and sold by him for twenty pieces of silver
to the Captain of a slant-sailed vessel bound for the barbarous
Indies. Here is but a fragment of the poem:

... *A Ship's Captain.*   You are my man, my passenger?
Thomas. I go to India with you.

Captain.   Well, I hope so.
          There's threatening in the weather. Have you a mind
          To hug your belly to the slanted deck,
          Like a louse on a whip-top, when the boat
          Spins on an axle in the hissing gales?
Thomas. Fear not. 'Tis likely indeed that storms are now
          Plotting against our voyage; ay, no doubt
          The very bottom of the sea prepares
          To stand up mountainous or reach a limb
          Out of his night of water and huge shingles,
          That he and the waves may break our keel. Fear not;
          Like those who manage horses, I've a word
          Will fasten up within their evil natures
          The meanings of the winds and waves and reefs.
Captain. You have a talisman? I have one too;
          I know not if the storms think much of it.
          I may be shark's meat yet. And would your spell
          Be daunting to a cuttle, think you now?
          We had a bout with one on our way here;
          It had green lidless eyes like lanterns, arms
          As many as the branches of a tree,
          But limber, and each one of them wise as a snake.
          It laid hold of our bulworks, and with three
          Long knowing arms, slimy, and of a flesh
          So tough they'ld fool a hatchet, searcht the ship,
          And stole out of the midst of us all a man;
          Yes, and he the proudest man upon the seas
          For the rare powerful talisman he'd got.
          And would yours have done better?
Thomas.   I am one
          Not easily frightened. I'm for India . . .

                    LASCELLES ABERCROMBIE

. . . In what torne ship soever I embarke,
          That ship shall be my embleme of thy Arke;
     What sea soever swallow mee, that flood
     Shall be to mee an embleme of thy blood;

Though thou with clouds of anger do disguise
Thy face; yet through that maske I know those eyes,
Which, though they turne away sometimes,
They never will despise . . .

JOHN DONNE

400. 'Parrots of shrilly green'

– this gaudy and longevous bird, that seems to contain all the wisdom of Solomon and more than the craft of Cleopatra in his eye, perched first upon England many centuries ago. Skelton speaks of him:

My name is parrot, a bird of Paradise . . .
With my becke bent, my little wanton eye,
My fethers fresh, as is the emrawde grene,
About my neck a circulet, lyke the ryche rubye,
My little legges, my fete both nete and cleane . . .

And so, too, John Maplet, a 'naturalist' who in 1567 wrote *A Greene Forest*:

'The Parret hath all hir whole bodie greene, saving that onely about his necke she hath a Coller or Chaine naturally wrought like to Sinople or Vermelon. Indie hath of this kinde such as will counterfaite redily a mans speach: what wordes they heare, those commonly they pronounce. There have bene found of these that have saluted Emperours . . .'

But which Emperors, and when and to what end he does not relate. A parrot of price would be she that had thus held converse with 'Ozymandias, king of kings'.

402

'The march of Time'

Say, is there aught that can convey
An image of its transient stay?

'Tis an hand's breadth; 'tis a tale;
'Tis a vessel under sail:
'Tis a courser's straining steed;
'Tis a shuttle in its speed;
'Tis an eagle in its way,
Darting down upon its prey;
'Tis an arrow in its flight,
Mocking the pursuing sight;
'Tis a vapour in the air;
'Tis a whirlwind rushing there;
'Tis a short-lived fading flower;
'Tis a rainbow on a shower;
'Tis a momentary ray
Smiling in a winter's day;
'Tis a torrent's rapid stream;
'Tis a shadow; 'tis a dream;
'Tis the closing watch of night,
Dying at approaching light;
'Tis a landscape vainly gay,
Painted upon crumbling clay;
'Tis a lamp that wastes its fires,
'Tis a smoke that quick expires;
'Tis a bubble, 'tis a sigh:
Be prepared – O Man! to die.

They are like strings of precious stones, rosaries, these Tudor laments, one image following another, and however sad in colour, all making beauty:

... As withereth the primrose by the river,
As fadeth summer's sun from gliding fountains,
As vanisheth the light-blown bubble ever,
As melteth snow upon the mossy mountains:
So melts, so vanisheth, so fades, so withers,
The rose, the shine, the bubble, and the snow,
Of praise, pomp, glory, joy, which short life gathers,
Fair praise, vain pomp, sweet glory, brittle joy.

The withered primrose by the mourning river,
The faded summer's sun from weeping fountains,
The light-blown bubble vanishèd for ever,
The molten snow upon the naked mountains,
Are emblems that the treasures we uplay,
Soon wither, vanish, fade, and melt away ...

403

'But in green ruins, in the desolate walls
Of antique palaces'

Through torrid tracts, with fainting steps they go,
Where wild Altama murmurs to their woe.
Far different these from all that charmed before,
The various terrours of that horrid shore;
Those blazing suns, that dart a downward ray,
And fiercely shed intolerable day;
Those matted woods, where birds forget to sing,
But silent bats in drowsy clusters cling;
Those poisonous fields, with rank luxuriance crown'd,
Where the dark scorpion gathers death around;
Where, at each step, the stranger fears to wake
The rattling terrours of the vengeful snake;
Where, crouching tigers wait their hapless prey,
And savage men, more murderous still than they;
While oft in whirls the mad tornado flies.
Mingling the ravaged landscape with the skies.
Far different these ...

OLIVER GOLDSMITH

'Wild hyaena'

In old times it was believed that if a hungry hyaena or jaccatray —
which cannot wry his neck 'because his backbone stretches itself
out to the head' — dreams, he dreams so vividly that he calls into

his sleeping brain a vision of the beasts he covets for prey. And this vision is so lifelike that he howls out of his sleep in mockery of the beasts – and thus decoys them to his den! He is a nocturnal scavenger, haunting graveyards, and 'when' says Lyly, he 'speaketh lyke a man', he 'deviseth most mischief'.

404. '*In Xanadu did Kubla Khan*'

'Now, this lord [the Great Caan],' says Friar Odoric in his *Cathay*, 'passeth the summer at a certain place which is called SANDU, situated toward the north, and the coolest habitation in the world. But in the winter season he abideth in Cambalech. And when he will ride from the one place to the other this is the order thereof. He hath four armies of horsemen, one of which goeth a day's march in front of him, one at each side, and one a day's march in rear, so that he goeth always as it were, in the middle of a cross. And marching thus, each army hath its route laid down for it day by day, and findeth at its halts all necessary provender. But his own immediate company hath its order of march thus. The king travelleth in a two-wheeled carriage, in which is formed a very goodly chamber, all of lign-aloes and gold, and covered over with great and fine skins, and set with many precious stones. And the carriage is drawn by four elephants, well broken in and harnessed, and also by four splendid horses, richly caparisoned. And alongside go four barons, who are called CUTHE, keeping watch and ward over the chariot that no hurt come to the king. Moreover, he carrieth with him in his chariot twelve gerfalcons; so that even as he sits therein upon his chair of state or other seat, if he sees any birds pass he lets fly his hawks at them. And none may dare to approach within a stone's throw of the carriage, unless those whose duty brings them there. And thus it is that the king travelleth.'

'*A sunless sea*'

Our English eyes, loving light, weary a little of the short cold days in our country, when the sun makes 'winter arches'. Gloomier still would be our state in the regions told of by Marco Polo in the following passage:

'Beyond the most distant part of the territory of the Tartars, . . . there is another region (thick set with dark impenetrable woods) which extends to the utmost bounds of the north, and is called the Region of Darkness, because during most part of the winter months the sun is invisible, and the atmosphere is obscured to the same degree as that in which we find it just about the dawn of day, when we may be said to see and not to see. The men of this country are well made and tall, but of a vary pallid complexion. They are not united under the government of a king or prince, and they live without any established laws or usages, in the manner of the brute creation. Their intellects also are dull, and they have an air of stupidity. The Tartars often proceed on plundering expeditions against these people, to rob them of their cattle and goods. For this purpose they avail themselves of those months in which the darkness prevails, in order that their approach may be unobserved; but, being unable to ascertain the direction in which they should return homeward with their booty, they provide against the chance of going astray by riding mares that have young foals at the time, which latter they suffer to accompany the dams as far as the confines of their own territory, but leave them, under proper care, at the commencement of the gloomy region. When their works of darkness have been accomplished, and they are desirous of revisiting the region of light, they lay the bridles on the necks of their mares, and suffer them freely to take their own course. Guided by maternal instinct, they make their way directly to the spot where they had quitted their foals; and by these means the riders are enabled to regain in safety the places of their residence.'

406. 'One held a shell unto his shell-like ear'

> . . . Gather a shell from the strown beach
> And listen at its lips: they sigh
> The same desire and mystery,
> The echo of the whole sea's speech.

And all mankind is thus at heart
Not anything but what thou art:
And Earth, Sea, Man, are all in each.

DANTE GABRIEL ROSSETTI

407

This is, to me, a singularly beautiful fragment of poetry, and its loveliest lines are its simplest – the eighth and the last. This power so to use even commonplace or over-worn words – *innocence, dark, dial* – that, like Cinderella, they are not only transformed as at touch of magic wand, but seem to shed light on all around them, is the sovran mark of a poet. Set in this unique order, obedient to this rhythm, they resemble the sounding of a decoy in a haunt of wild birds, stir far echoes in the mind, arousing an inner and secret self.

For another simple example take these few lines from a sonnet by Keats:

Keen, fitful gusts are whispering here and there
Among the bushes, half leafless and dry;
The stars look very cold about the sky,
And I have many miles on foot to fare . . .

Of fair-haired Milton's eloquent distress,
And all his love for gentle Lycid' drowned;
Of lovely Laura in her light green dress
And faithful Petrarch gloriously crowned.

What are the decoys here? Surely – apart from the broken rhythm of the second line – that *very cold about*, that *fair-haired* and that *light green dress*. Yet they are phrases such as might be used in mere talk. But what life and reality they give; while the more 'poetical' words, *fare* and *gloriously* and even *eloquent* are rather a hindrance than a help.

Not, of course, that the words of a poem *are* its poetry. They are this no more than the paint and canvas of Piero della Francesca's *Resurrection*, or the time-worn stone of one of the figures in the façade at Chartres, are their beauty and supreme meaning. Words are but a *means* of conveying poetry from one imagination to another. So may a smile make lovely a plain face; or sunbeams weave a rainbow in the air. Even words themselves may be needless; for two human spirits may hold close converse together (of which only the rarest poetry in words or music, paint or stone could *tell*) without one syllable of speech between them:

'St Louis, King of France, went on pilgrimage to visit the holy places all over the world; and hearing the exceeding great fame of the sanctity of Brother Giles, who was one of the first companions of St Francis, he proposed in his heart, and determined at all cost, to visit him personally; for which reason he came to Perugia, where the said Brother Giles lived at that time.

'And coming to the door of the Community house, as a poor unknown pilgrim, with but few companions, he asked with great instance for Brother Giles, not telling the porter who he was that asked. The porter therefore went to Brother Giles, and told him there was a pilgrim at the door asking for him: and God inspired him and revealed to him that it was the King of France: wherefore, immediately, with great fervour of spirit, he came out of his cell and ran to the door and without further questioning, and without even having seen each other before, with the greatest devotion, inclining themselves, they embraced, and kissed one another, with as much familiarity as though for a long while they had been together in intimate friendship: but with all this, neither one nor the other spoke. But they stood thus embracing each other, with this sign of the love of charity between them, in silence.

'And after they had stood thus a great space, without either speaking a word to the other, they departed from each other, and St Louis went his way on his journey, and Brother Giles returned to his cell.'

Little Flowers of St Francis

'*Like solemn apparitions lulled sublime
To everlasting rest*'

... In the caves of the deep – lost Youth! lost Youth! –
O'er and o'er, fleeting billows; fleeting billows! –
Rung to his restless everlasting sleep
By the heavy death-bells of the deep,
Under the slimy-drooping sea-green willows,
          Poor Youth! lost Youth!
    Laying his dolorous head, forsooth,
        On Carian reefs uncouth –
          Poor Youth!
On the wild sand's ever-shifting pillows! ...

O could my Spirit wing
Hills over, where salt Ocean hath his fresh headspring
    And snowy curls bedeck the Blue-haired King,
      Up where sweet oral birds articulate sing
        Within the desert ring –
Their mighty shadows o'er broad Earth the Lunar Mountains fling,
Where the Sun's chariot bathes in Ocean's fresh headspring –
        O could my spirit wing! ...

                    GEORGE DARLEY

    Full fathom five thy Father lies,
    Of his bones are Corrall made:
    Those are Pearles that were his eies,
    Nothing of him that doth fade,
    But doth suffer a Sea-change
    Into something rich, and strange:
    Sea-Nimphs hourly ring his knell –
          Ding dong.
Harke now I heare them, *ding-dong bell.*

           WILLIAM SHAKESPEARE

411

This is a patchwork of stanzas from three versions of the old ballad. In one version the 'Golden Vanity' is said to be the 'Sweet Trinity', and to have been built by Sir Walter Raleigh in the Netherlands. According to another, the Cabin-boy, after threatening to sink the 'Goulden Vanite' as he had 'sunk the French gallee', is taken on board and the Captain and merchant adventurers proved 'far better than their word'. But if stanza 12 is any witness, this seems unlikely. Can one not actually *see* the cold faces mocking down upon the water?

412

To an eye and ear new to them, these old Scottish ballads may seem a little difficult and forbidding. But read on, and their enchantment has no match – the very strangeness of the words, their rare music, the colour and light and clearness and vehemence, and, besides these, a wildness and ancientness like that of a folk-tune which seems to carry with its burden as many lost memories as an old churchyard has gravestones. The stories they tell are world wide. How they first came into being (for of some of them there are as many as twenty to thirty different versions), how they have fared in their long journey in time, and even when and by whom they were made, are questions on which even scholars are not yet agreed.

'Kevels' in line 5 of 'Brown Robyn', means *lots*, and recalls a far older story:

'Now the word of the Lord came unto Jonah the son of Amittai, saying, arise, go to Nineveh, that great city, and cry against it; for their wickedness is come up before me. But Jonah rose up to flee unto Tarshish from the presence of the Lord, and went down to Joppa; and he found a ship going to Tarshish, so he paid the fare thereof, and went down into it, to go with them unto Tarshish from the presence of the Lord. But the Lord sent out a great wind into the sea, and there was a mighty tempest in the sea, so that the ship was like to be broken. Then the mariners were afraid, and cried every man unto his god, and cast forth the wares that were in the ship into the sea, to lighten it of them. But Jonah was gone down into the sides of the ship; and he lay, and was fast asleep . . . And they said every one to his fellow, Come, and let us cast lots, that we may know for whose cause this evil is upon us. So they cast lots, and the lot fell upon Jonah . . . Then said they unto him, What shall we do unto thee, that the sea may be calm unto us? for the sea wrought, and was tempestuous. And he said unto them, Take me up, and cast me forth into the sea; so shall the sea be calm upon you: for I know that for my sake this great tempest is upon you . . . So they took up Jonah, and cast him forth into the sea; and the sea ceased from her raging.'

415. 'A seal my father was'

Notes of music for the enticement of seals, with other beautiful old Gaelic airs and poems and tales, collected by Mr Martin Freeman, will be found in Journals 23–5 of the Folk-Song Society.

417

The Dowie Dee
It rins its lane;
But every seven year,
It gets ane!

418

The longer version of the ballad into which the genius of Sir Walter Scott wove a few new stanzas is the better known. But his was perilous work. Indeed, the secret of the art of this naked and lovely poetry seems nowadays to be lost: the marvel is how much it tells by means of the little it says.

To show, by one slight example, how the words of the same old ballad may vary in different versions, here are five variants of one stanza of Sir Patrick's, the first being that chosen (and adapted) by Scott:

(a)   They hadna sailed a league, a league,
      A league but barely three,
    When the lift grew dark and the wind blew loud
      And gurly grew the sea.

(b)   They had not saild upon the sea
      A league but merely three
    When ugly, ugly were the jaws [waves]
      That rowd unto their knee.

(c)   They hadna sailed a league on sea,
      A league but barely ane,
    Till anchors brak, and tap-masts lap:
      There came a deadly storm.

(d)   He hadna gane a step, a step,
      A step but barely ane,
    When a bout [bolt] flew out of our goodly ship,
      And the salt sea it came in.

(e)   'Come down, come down, my pretty boy,
      I fear we here maun die;
    For thro and thro my goodly ship
      I see the green-waved sea.'

'Late, late yestreen'

With money in his pocket and bewaring of glass, the Man of Superstitions bows low and seven times to the new moon. If he sees a dim cindrous light filling in the circle of which this crescent is the edge, he 'looks out for squalls' – the new moon has 'the auld moone in hir arme'. That light is the earth-shine. The sun illumines the earth; the earth like a looking glass reflects his radiance upon the moon; and she thus melancholily returns it; whereas the silver blaze on her eastern edge is light direct: eyes looking upward *thence* into her black skies are lit with her prodigious mornings.

Precisely how much history is contained in 'Sir Patricke Spence' is doubtful. Little more can be said than that in 1281 Margaret, daughter of Alexander III of Scotland, was married to Eric, King of Norway, and that of the knights and nobles who accompanied her to Norway many were drowned on the voyage home. But just as in the *Plays* you may trace Shakespeare's footprints through the old tales and chronicles he read – *King Lear*, *Macbeth*, *Cymbeline* – so in many of the ballads you can watch as it were the maker stringing his spirited stanzas on a definite thread of history. Take, for example 'Sir Andrew Barton'.

What follows is an extract from Edward Hall's *Chronicle*:

'In June [1511] the kyng beyng at Leicester, tidynges were brought to him, that Andrew Barton a Scottish man, and a pirate of the sea, feigning that the king of Scots, had war with the Portingals, did rob every nation, and so stopped the king's streams that no merchants almost could pass, and when he took the englishmen's goods, he said they were Portingal's goods, and thus he haunted and robbed at every haven's mouth. The king moved greatly with this crafty pirate, sent Sir Edward Howard, lord Admiral of England, and Lord Thomas Howard, son and heir to the earl of Surrey, in all the haste to the sea, which hastily made ready two ships, and without any more abode, took the sea, and by chance of weather were severed. The lord Howard lying in the Downs, perceived where Andrew was making towards Scotland, and so fast the said lord chased him, that he overtook him, and there was a sore battle: the englishmen were fierce, and the Scots defended them manfully, and ever Andrew blew his whistle to encourage his men, yet for all that, the lord Howard and his men, by clean strength entered the main deck; then the Englishmen entered on all sides, and the Scots fought sore on the hatches, but in conclusion, Andrew was taken, which was so sore wounded, that he died there: then all the remnant of the Scots' were taken, with their ship called the *Lion*.

'All this while, was the Lord Admiral in chase of the Barque of

Scotland, called *Jenny Pirwyn*, which was wont to sail with the *Lion* in company, and . . . he laid him on board, and fiercely assailed him, and the Scots as hardy and well-stomached men them defended, but the lord Admiral so encouraged his men, that they entered the Barque and slew many, and took all the other.

'Thus were these two ships taken, and brought to Black Wall, the second day of August; and all the Scots were sent to the Bishop's place of York, and there remained at the king's charge, till other direction was taken for them.'

So far the Chronicle: and now the ballad, or rather, the second half of it, the first having told how Henry sent out the English ships, how they chased out Sir Andrew Barton in the *Lion*, sunk his pinnace, shot down his fore-mast, and killed, one after the other, the men he sent up the main-mast in order to let 'its beams down fall' – that is (?), to cut away the wreckage of the fore-mast. They having failed, he goes himself:

> . . . But when hee saw his sisters sonne slâine,
>   Lord! in his heart hee was not well:
>   'Goe ffeitch me downe my armour of proofe,
>   For I will to the topcastle my-selfe.
>
> 'Goe ffeitch me downe my armour of prooffe,
>   For itt is guilded with gold soe cleere;
>   God be with my brother, Iohn of Bartton!
>   Amongst the Portingalls hee did itt weare.'
>
> But when he had his armour of prooffe,
>   And on his body hee had itt on,
>   Every man that looked att him
>   Sayd, Gunn nor arrow hee neede feare none.
>
> 'Come hither, Horsley!' sayes my lord Howard,
>   'And looke your shaft that itt goe right;
>   Shoot a good shoote in the time of need,
>   And ffor thy shooting thoust be made a knight.'

'I'le doe my best,' sayes Horslay then,
   'Your Honor shall see before I goe;
If I should be hanged att your maine-mast,
   I have in my shipp but arrowes tow.'

But att Sir Andrew hee shott then;
   Hee made sure to hitt his marke;
Under the spole [shoulder] of his right arme
   Hee smote Sir Andrew quite throw the hart.

Yett from the tree hee wold not start,
   But hee clinged to itt with might and maine;
Under the coller then of his iacke [coat of mail],
   He stroke Sir Andrew thorrow the braine.

'Ffight on my men,' sayes Sir Andrew Bartton,
   'I am hurt, but I am not slaine;
I'le lay mee downe and bleed a-while,
   And then I'le rise and ffight againe.'

'Ffight on my men,' sayes Sir Andrew Bartton,
   'These English doggs they bite soe lowe;
Ffight on ffor Scottland and Saint Andrew
   Till you heare my whistle blowe!'

But when the[y] cold not heare his whistle blow,
   Sayes Harry Hunt, I'le lay my head
You may bord yonder noble shipp, my lord,
   For I know Sir Andrew hee is dead.

With that they borded this noble shipp,
   Soe did they itt with might and maine;
The[y] ffound eighteen score Scotts alive,
   Besides the rest were maimed and slaine.

My lord Haward tooke a sword in his hand,
   And smote of[f] Sir Andrews head;
The Scotts stood by did weepe and mourne,
   But neuer a word durst speake or say.

He caused his body to be taken downe,
    And ouer the hatch-bord cast into the sea,
And about his middle three hundred crowes:
    'Wheresoeuer thou lands, itt will bury thee.'

With his head they sayled into England again,
    With right good will and fforce and main,
And the day before Newyeeres even
    Into Thames mouth they came againe.

My lord Haward wrote to King Heneryes grace,
    With all the newes hee cold him bring:
'Such a Newyeeres gifft I haue brought to your Gr[ace]
    As neuer did subiect to any king.

'For merchandyes and manhood,
    The like is no[where] to be ffound;
The sight of these wold doe you good,
    Ffor you have not the like in your English ground.'

But when hee heard tell that they were come,
    Full royally hee welcomed them home;
Sir Andrews shipp was the kings Newyeeres guifft;
    A braver shipp you never saw none.

Now hath our king Sir Andrews shipp,
    Besett with pearles and precyous stones;
Now hath England two shipps of warr,
    Two shipps of warr, before but one.

'Who holpe to this?' says King Henerye,
    'That I may reward him ffor his paine':
'Harry Hunt, and Peeter Simon,
    William Horseley, and I the same.'

'Harry Hunt shall have his whistle and chaine,
    And all his jewells, whatsoever they bee,
And other riche giffts that I will not name,
    For his good service he hath done mee.

'Horslay, right thoust be a knight,
    Lands and livings thou shalt have store;
Howard shal be erle of Nottingham,
    And soe was never Howard before.

'Now, Peeter Simon, thou art old;
    I will maintaine thee and they sonne;
Thou shalt haue five hundred pound all in gold
    Ffor the good service that thou hast done.'

Then King Henerye shiffted his roome;
    In came the Queene and ladyes bright;
Other arrands they had none
    But to see Sir Andrew Bartton, knight.

But when they see his deadly fface,
    His eyes were hollow in his head;
'I wold give a hundred poun,' sais Kinge Henerye,
    'The man were alive as hee is dead!

'Yett ffor the manfull part hee hath playd,
    Both here and beyond the sea,
His men shall haue halfe a crowne a day
    To bring them to my brother, King Jamye.'

This ballad, then, whether or not its vivid and clean-cut details are at first or second hand, is packed with history. Sir Thomas Howard – who led the vanguard at the Battle of Flodden – was the father of Henry, Earl of Surrey, the poet, (see No. 46) and the uncle of Anne Boleyn. He was the Great-grandfather, too, of the Lord Thomas Howard (first Earl of Suffolk), to whom Sir Richard Grenville was second in command. (See 'The Last Fight of the *Revenge*.')

In the 8th stanza before the end are the lines:

Now hath England two shipps of warr,
    Two shipps of warr, before but one.

One of these being, of course, *The Lion*, Sir Andrew's ship and Howard's prize. The other was the *Great Harry*, which was built in 1504, and *the first ship in the English navy*. Before this date 'when the Prince wanted a fleet he had no other expedient but hiring ships from the merchants'. But what a rumour – like the sound of the great west wind on a pine-clad mountainside – sweeps through the mind at sight of those few words in italics.

419

I have changed two words of the original.

420

The monastic story behind this ballad is that while, on 31 July, 1255, Sir Hugh was playing, he was kidnapped by a Jew named Copin and crucified, and that eighteen of the principal Jews in England were hanged in consequence. Whether there be any truth in this, or it be wholly false, the ballad builds up a pellucid picture in the imagination – the ancient town; the boys at their game; the narrow, gabled, cobbled streets; the evening gold on roof and wall; night, lamentation; and the clanging of the bells.

421

The spelling of this ballad usually begins 'Why dois your brand sae dripp wie bluid,' and so on. This spelling Professor Child thought 'affectedly antique'. But since, as he says, mere antiquated 'spelling will not make an old ballad, so it will not *un*make one'. And 'Edward' in any guise is 'one of the noblest' of the popular ballads. Here it is, then, in our present spelling.

422

The king in the third line is James the Sixth of Scotland and the First of England, with the big head, slobbering tongue, quilted clothes and rickety legs, who delighted to speculate and write on such subjects as Fate, witchcraft and tobacco-smoking. The 'wanton laird of young Logie' is John Wemyss who plotted against him with the Earl of Bothwell in 1592. His bold, crafty and merry young wife, May Margaret, says Mr Sidgwick, had one or other of these four delectable maiden names – Vinstar, Weiksterne, Twynstoun, or Twinslace. It is dubious which.

All ladies in the days of the ballad carried knives at their girdles; the one in stanza 8 was clearly a wedding gift. Doughty uses they sometimes put them to.

423

In the margins of Mr Nahum's copy of this ballad, two exquisite damosels were painted in green, blue and amethyst on gold (as in a monk's work), and between their fingers hung a linen napkin seemingly broidered with pearls and in the midst of it a sleeping dove. Whatever he may have meant by this, I confess that at first reading I fell in love with both these ladies. My feelings for the 'noble knight' who ransomed fair Annie, then wearied of her, were different. It was strange to find a noble knight so *hard* a gentleman, not so much because he wearied of her (since to weary of one so true, intelligent and tender was even more of a punishment than a misfortune) but more particularly, with regard to his craving for 'gowd and gear'. He reminds me of a similar piece of humanity described in three short stanzas which were found by Mr Macmath written on the flyleaf of a little volume printed at Edinburgh about 1670, and which appear in Child's *Ballads*:

> He steps full statly on the street,
>   He hads the charters of him sell,
> In to his cloathing he is complete,
>   In Craford's mure he bears the bell . . .

> I wish I had died my own fair death,
>   In tender age, when I was young;
> I would never [then] have broke my heart
>   For the love of any churl's son.

Wo be to my parents all,
    That lives so farr beyond the sea!
I might have lived a noble life,
    And wedded in my own countrée.

425. *'But think na' ye me heart was sair . . . ?'*

Down in yon garden sweet and gay
    Where bonnie grows the lily,
I heard a fair maid sighing say,
    'My wish be wi' sweet Willie!'

'Willie's rare, and Willie's fair,
    And Willie's wondrous bonny;
And Willie hecht to marry me
    Gin e'er he married ony.

'O gentle wind, that bloweth south
    From where my Love repaireth,
Convey a kiss frae his dear mouth
    And tell me how he fareth!

'O tell sweet Willie to come doun
    And hear the mavis singing,
And see the birds on ilka bush
    And leaves around them hinging.

'The lav'rock there, wi' her white breast
    And gentle throat sae narrow;
There's sport eneuch for gentlemen
    On Leader haughs and Yarrow.

'O Leader haughs are wide and braid
    And Yarrow haughs are bonny;
There Willie hecht to marry me
    If e'er he married ony.

'But Willie's gone, whom I thought on,
    And does not hear the weeping
Draws many a tear frae's true love's e'e,
    When other maids are sleeping.

'Yestreen I made my bed fu' braid,
    The night I'll mak' it narrow,
For a' the lee-lang winter night
    I lie twined o' my marrow.

'O came ye by yon water-side?
    Pu'd you the rose or lily?
Or came you by yon meadow green,
    Or saw you my sweet Willie?'

She sought him up, she sought him down,
    She sought him braid and narrow;
Syne, in the cleaving of a crag,
    She found him drowned in Yarrow!

Hecht (line 7) means vowed; *haughs* are water-meadows; and to be twined o' one's marrow, is to be separated from one's loved one.

427

Here is another ballad – 'The Water o' Wearie's Well' – of a similar pattern. But in this the bewitched young princess not only beguiles her betrayer into his own snare, but adds a merry word at parting:

There came a bird out o a bush,
    On water for to dine,[1]
An sighing sair, says the king's daughter,
    'O wae's this heart o mine!'

He's taen a harp into his hand,
    He's harped them all asleep,
Except it was the king's daughter,
    Who one wink couldna get.

1. sup

He's luppen on his berry-brown steed,
 Taen 'er on behind himsell,
Then baith rede down to that water
 That they ca Wearie's Well.

'Wide[2] in, wide in, my lady fair,
 No harm shall thee befall;
Oft times I've watered my steed
 Wi the water o Wearie's well.'

The first step that she steppèd in,
 She stepped to the knee;
And sighend says this lady fair,
 'This water's nae for me.'

'Wide in, wide in, my lady fair,
 No harm shall thee befall;
Oft times I've waterèd my steed
 Wi the water o Wearie's Well.'

The next step that she steppèd in,
 She stepped to the middle;
'O,' sighend says this lady fair,
 'I've wat my gowden girdle.'

'Wide in, wide in, my lady fair,
 No harm shall thee befall;
Oft times I've watered my steed
 Wi the water o Wearie's Well.'

The next step that she steppèd in,
 She stepped to the chin;
'O,' sighend says this lady fair,
 'They sud gar twa loves twin!'[3]

2. wade
3. Alas, that death should take lover from loved one!

'Seven king's daughters I've drowned there,
    In the water o Wearie's Well,
And I'll make you the eight o them,
    And ring the common bell.'

'Since I am standing here,' she says,
    'This dowie[4] death to die,
One kiss o your comely mouth
    I'm sure was comfort me.'

He louted him oer his saddle bow,
    To kiss her cheek and chin;
She's taen him in her arms twa,
    And thrown him headlong in.

'Since seven king's daughters ye've drowned there,
    In the water o Wearie's Well,
I'll make you bridegroom to them a',
    An ring the bell mysell.'

And aye she warsled, and aye she swam,
    And she swam to dry lan;
She thankèd God most cheerfully
    The dangers she oercame.

428

Hermione.	Come Sir, now I am for you againe:
	Pray you sit by us, and tell's a Tale.
Mamillius (her small son).	Merry, or sad, shal't bee?
Hermione.	As merry as you will.
Mamillius.	A sad Tale's best for Winter:
	I have one of Sprights, and Goblins.
Hermione.	Let's have that, good Sir.
	Come-on, sit downe, come-on, and doe your best

4. Grievous

To fright me with your Sprights: you're powrefull at
it.
Mamillius. There was a man . . .
Hermione. Nay, come sit downe: then on.
Mamillius. Dwelt by a Churchyard:
I will tell it softly,
Yond Crickets shall not heare it.
Hermione. Come on then, and giv't me in mine eare . . .

The Winter's Tale

429. '*That birk grew fair enough*'

A strange feature of these ballads is that many of the stories they
tell, or the customs, beliefs, lore they refer to, may be found
scattered up and down throughout the world. In Russia, for one
small instance, the birk or birch tree is honoured in this fashion:
A little before Whitsuntide, says Sir James Fraser in *The Golden
Bough*, the young women, with dancing and feasting, cut down a
living birch-tree, deck it with bright clothes or hang it with ribbons;
then set it up as an honoured guest in one of the village houses.
On Whit Sunday itself they fling it, finery and all, into a stream
for a charm.

And now for England: 'Thirty years ago,' says Mrs Wright, 'it
was still customary in some west-Midland districts to decorate
village churches on Whit Sunday with sprigs of birch stuck in
holes bored in the tops of the pews. I can remember this being
done by an old village clerk in Herefordshire, but when he was
gathered to his fathers in the same profession, the custom died with
him.' How happy must he have been then – as for that one evening
was the Wife of Usher's Well herself – when he lifted his eyes
upon a silver birch brushing with its light, green tresses the very
gates of Paradise.

433. 'A spangle here'

Dew sate on Julia's haire,
    And spangled too,
Like leaves that laden are
    With trembling dew:
Or glittered to my sight,
    As when the Beames
Have their reflected light,
    Daunc't by the Streames.

ROBERT HERRICK

If the daisies are not to shut their eyes until Julia shut hers, should they not most assuredly wait also until 'dear love Isabella' shut *hers?* She was the bosom friend and aunt of Marjorie Fleming, Sir Walter Scott's little friend, who was born in 1803, and who, having written her few tim-tam-tot little rhymes, died in 1811. And here is Isabel:

Here lies sweet Isabell in bed,
With a night-cap on her head;
Her skin is soft, her face is fair,
And she has very pretty hair;
She and I in bed lie nice,
And undisturbed by rats or mice;
She is disgusted with Mr Worgan,
Though he plays upon the organ.
Her nails are neat, her teeth are white,
Her eyes are very, very bright;
In a conspicuous town she lives,
And to the poor her money gives;
Here ends sweet Isabella's story,
And may it be much to her glory.

434

Bunyan's 'Comparison' for this poem (almost as though he had *this* year of grace in mind) runs thus:

> Our Gospel has had here a Summers day;
> But in its Sun-shine we, like Fools, did play,
> Or else fall out, and with each other wrangle,
> And did instead of work not much but jangle.
>   And if our Sun seems angry, hides his face,
> Shall it go down, shall Night possess this place?
> Let not the voice of night-Birds us afflict,
> And of our mis-spent Summer us convict.

435. *'Sweet rose, whose hue angry and brave'*

– that is, *red and resplendent*, though nowadays it might seem affected to use these words in this sense. Like most things in the world, words seldom remain exactly the same – either in sound or in sense. To Chaucer's ear, or even Shakespeare's, we should seem to be talking a curious dialect. A word comes into being, flourishes for a time, but may gradually fall out of common use, then out of literary use, and at last be clean forgotten. Another may remain in use, but steadily (though almost imperceptibly) change in meaning and effect. Take but this single stanza from Milton's 'Ode on the Morning of Christ's Nativity' (written when he was a boy of 21):

> The Shepherds on the Lawn,
> Or ere the point of dawn,
>   Sat simply chatting in a rustic row;
> Full little thought they than,
> That the mighty Pan
>   Was kindly come to live with them below;

Perhaps their loves, or else their sheep,
Was all that did their silly thoughts so busy keep.

Apart from 'or ere' which means *before*, and 'than', *then*; no fewer than five of the words in these eight lines have so changed in usage as to affect our minds in a way which Milton cannot have intended or foreseen. We should not nowadays use the word 'lawn' if we meant a pasture; 'chatting' has now for us a rather too indoorish effect to be appropriate for the talk of shepherds; *rustic*, because of town wags, or maybe of 'rustic furniture' is slightly belittling; *kindly* now means amiable or genial; and *silly*, a word that originally meant blessed, fortunate, prosperous ['silly Suffolk'] and then (and here) simple and artless, now means only foolish or weak-witted.

To some tastes it seems a barbarous pastime thus to pick a poem to pieces. For the moment, it is true, the poem – like a clock in similar conditions – ceases to 'go'. But only for the moment. At need it will at once put itself together again; and, as W. W. Skeat says, 'Why are we to be debarred from examining a poet's language because his words are sweet and his descriptions entrancing? That is only one more reason for weighing every word that he uses.'

And Ruskin too: 'You must get into the habit of looking intensely at words ... Never let a word escape you that looks suspicious. It is severe work; but you will find it, even at first interesting, and at last, endlessly amusing.'

And this is not merely advice, but a countersign and a *Sesame*. A word, too, is a symbol of four kinds: (*a*) of the meaning that has been given to it pure and simple – the dictionary meaning. (*b*) It is a graphic pattern, in print or in handwriting. Compare, for example the difference in graphic effect between 'grey' and *gray*; between 'errours' and *errorrs*. The latter is more pregnant with mistakes, so to speak – and mistakes not of the 'u' kind! (*c*) The sound of a word is yet another symbol, and a vital one. (*d*) The formation of that sound with the throat, tongue, vocal organs, is the fourth, and important, particularly in poetry. Say over:

O what can ail thee, knight at arms.

or

> Nothing is here for tears, nothing to wail ...
> Nothing but well and fair,
> And what may quiet us in a death so noble.

or

> What need a vermeil-tinctured lip for that,
> Love-darting eyes, or tresses like the Morn?

The very way of uttering such things is a delight – and therefore affects the mind and spirit within, and every word is like a fragment of honeycomb, its many cells filled with various nectars.

437

From *Songs of Innocence*; and this is from *Songs of Experience*:

> When the voices of children are heard on the green
> And whisp'rings are in the dale.
> The days of my youth rise fresh in my mind,
> My face turns green and pale.
> Then come home, my children, the sun is gone down,
> And the dews of night arise;
> Your spring and your day are wasted in play,
> And your winter and night in disguise.

For to grow old and look back to one's childhood, though in much it is a happy thing, may also be a thing chequered with dread and regret. The old poets never wearied of bidding youth gather its roses, seize its fleeting moments. But not all roses are sweet in the keeping and 'lilies that fester smell far worse than weeds'.

440

Every fine poem says much in little. It packs into the fewest possible words – by means of their sound, their sense, and their companionship – a wide or rare experience. So, in particular, with such a poem as this. It tells of a man thinking of the day when he shall have bidden goodbye to a world whose every living and lovely thing – spring, hawk, evening, wintry skies – he has dearly loved. And if what he relates is to be seen (and felt) as clearly and truly as if it were before one's very eyes, it must be read with a peculiar intensity – all one's imagination alert to gather up the full virtue of the words, and to picture in the mind each fleeting and living object in turn.

To compare the great and fine things of one age (the work in ours, for example, of Thomas Hardy, Charles Doughty, W. H. Hudson, Alice Meynell, Robert Bridges) with the great and fine things of another is an exceedingly difficult task (and to pit poet against poet, or imagination against imagination, a rather stupid one). But that in Elizabeth's day England was indeed a 'nest of singing birds' may be realized by the fact that when Shakespeare was finishing his last play, *The Tempest*, in the spring, apparently, of 1611 – when, that is, he himself was aged 47 (and she herself had been eight years dead), Sir Walter Raleigh was 59, George Chapman 52, Samuel Daniel 49, Michael Drayton 48, Thomas Campion 44, Thomas Dekker (?) 41, John Donne and Ben Jonson were 38, John Fletcher was 32, Francis Beaumont 27, William Drummond 26, John Ford 25, William Browne and Robert Herrick 20, Francis Quarles 19, George Herbert 18, Thomas Carew (?) 16, James Shirley 15. John Milton was 2 and John Webster was an infant. It was seven years before the birth of Richard Lovelace and of Abraham Cowley, ten before Marvell's, and eleven before Vaughan's. Edmund Spenser had been twelve years dead, Sir Philip Sidney twenty-five.

Two hundred and fifty years afterwards – in 1861 – another great queen was on the throne, Victoria. It was the year in which the Prince Consort died, and Edward, Prince of Wales, came of age. And the English imagination had come into its own again: William Barnes and Cardinal Newman were then 60, Edward Fitzgerald and Tennyson were 52, Robert Browning 49, Charles Kingsley 42, Matthew Arnold 39, Coventry Patmore 38, William Allingham 37, Dante Gabriel Rossetti and George Meredith were 33, Christina Rossetti was 31, William Morris 27, Algernon Swinburne 24, Thomas Hardy was 21, Mr Robert Bridges 17, Robert Louis

Stevenson 11, and Francis Thompson was 2. Other great writers, in English, then alive were Carlyle, Thackeray, Dickens, Ruskin, Darwin and Huxley; Emerson, Hawthorne, Longfellow and Walt Whitman. This is a clumsy catalogue, but *so* the strange flame of genius fitfully burns in this world. And 1611 knew as little of 1861 as 1861 knew of 2111. (But would that 1923 [or 1928] could leave to the future one-tenth part of such a legacy as did 1611 – the Authorized Version of the English Bible.)

But to return to Shakespeare. He was born in April 1564. About 1591 he wrote the first of his plays, *Love's Labour's Lost*. By 1611 he had finished the last of them; 34 in all as they appear in the first Folio, 37 as they now appear in the Canon. And apart from these, his Poems. There followed a strange silence. On the 25 March 1616, 'in perfect health and memory (God be praised!)', he made his will. On St George's Day, 1616, he died. To reflect for a moment on that brief lifetime, on that twenty years' work which is now a perennial fountain of happiness, light and wisdom to the whole world, is to marvel indeed. The life-giving secret of this supreme genius none can tell. We know not even what keeps our own small lamp alight. But Thomas Campbell recounts a parable: 'It was predicted of a young man lately belonging to one of our universities, that he would certainly became a prodigy because he read sixteen hours a day. "Ah, but," said somebody, "how many hours a day does he *think*?" It might have been added, "How many hours does he feel?" ' So of Shakespeare: What was *his* (and from his childhood) seeing, thinking, feeling, dreaming, working day? As said his old friends and fellow-players, John Heminge and Henry Condell in their Preface to the Folio: 'Reade him . . . and againe and againe: And if then you do not like him, surely you are in some manifest danger . . .'

441. *'With such a sky'*

> It is a beauteous Evening, calm and free,
> The holy time is quiet as a Nun
> Breathless with adoration; the broad sun

Is sinking down in its tranquility;
The gentleness of heaven broods o'er the Sea:
Listen! the mighty Being is awake,
And doth with his eternal motion make
A sound like thunder – everlastingly . . .

WILLIAM WORDSWORTH

442. 'Shepherds all, and Maidens fair, Fold your Flocks'

The curfew tolls the knell of parting day,
The lowing herd wind slowly o'er the lea,
The ploughman homeward plods his weary way,
And leaves the world to darkness and to me.

Now fades the glimmering landscape on the sight,
And all the air a solemn stillness holds,
Save where the beetle wheels his droning flight,
And drowsy tinklings lull the distant folds: . . .

These lines and the stanzas that follow them in the 'Elegy Wrote in a Country Churchyard' are as familiar as any in English. Here, 'a figure on paper' – from a letter to a friend written by Thomas Gray, on 19 November 1764, is a description – not of evening after the setting of the sun – but of a sun-*rise* as vivid as if one's own naked eye had watched its 'Levee':

'I must not close my letter without giving you one principal event of my history; which was, that (in the course of my late tour) I set out one morning before five o'clock, the moon shining through a dark and misty autumnal air, and got to the sea-coast time enough to be at the Sun's Levee. I saw the clouds and the dark vapours open gradually to right and left, rolling over one another in great smoky wreathes, and the tide (as it flowed gently in upon the sands) first whitening, then slightly tinged with gold and blue; and all at once a little line of unsufferable brightness that (before I can write these five words) was grown to half an orb, and now to a whole one, too glorious to be distinctly seen. It is very odd it makes no figure on paper; yet I shall remember it, as long as the sun, or at least as long as I endure. I wonder whether anybody ever saw it before? I hardly believe it.'

So each day and every day the sun rises, indeed is rising always above *some* watchful eye's horizon, and we come so to expect its rising, and so to be assured of it, as though it were no less certain than that twice two are four. But, in fact, it is only just certain enough to prevent night from being a dreadful apprehension, and life from becoming a mere routine. As Coleridge says in his *Table Talk*:

'Suppose Adam watching the sun sinking under the western horizon for the first time; he is seized with gloom and terror, relieved by scarce a ray of hope that he shall ever see the glorious light again. The next evening, when it declines, his hopes are stronger, but still mixed with fear; and even at the end of a thousand years, all that a man can feel is a hope and an expectation so strong as to preclude anxiety.'

> ... High among the lonely hills,
> While I lay beside my sheep,
> Rest came down and filled my soul,
> From the everlasting deep.
>
> Changeless march the stars above,
> Changeless morn succeeds to even;
> Still the everlasting hills
> Changeless watch the changeless heaven ...

CHARLES KINGSLEY

443. '*Swiftly walk o'er the western wave*'

So ran the first line of this poem by Shelley in the first edition of this book when it appeared. Whereupon a friend pointed out (more, I hope, in sorrow than in anger), that Shelley had written not 'o'er' but 'over' – at least, so the word appears in the Harvard MS. of the poem, though not in the edition of 1824. And this is not a trivial point.

'Swiftly walk o'er the western wave, Spirit of Night' brings into the mind a vast sea, the dusk of the heavens above darkening into night; and that sea is calm and without waves on its surface.

'Swiftly walk over', on the other hand, seems to conjure up into the imagination the very spectre of Night advancing over the wave-tossed darkness of the waters, as light and surely as the stormy petrel itself. And this is but a further proof that the rhythm of a poem is essential, not only to its sensuous, but to its imaginative and intellectual meaning.

444. *'Light the lamps up, Lamplighter'*

In towns and cities nowadays wayfarers in the streets are so much accustomed to seeing at fall of dusk their 'electric' lamps suddenly shine out, as if at the bidding of a sorcerer, that the feat is passed unnoticed. So with gas-lamps in my young days, though then, like Robert Louis Stevenson, most children watched the long-twinkling-poled lamplighter on his rounds, as if he might well be a wizard in disguise. Before gas there was oil, and before oil candles; and householders in cities were responsible for keeping this much at least of light burning in the moonless, narrow, dangerous and deserted streets – the horn-sided candle-lantern having been the invention of King Alfred himself.

Then Watchman and Bellman went their solitary rounds, calling the hours and weather, and knocking up those whose hanging lanterns burned dim or had gone out. The next three old rhymes refer to this practice:

> Maids in your smocks, look to your locks,
>   Your fire and candle-light!
> For well 'tis known much mischief's done
>   By both in dead of night;
> Your locks and fire do not neglect,
> And so you may good rest expect.

Maidens to bed, and cover coal!
Let the mouse out of her hole!
Crickets in the chimney sing,
While the little bell doth ring;
If fast asleep, who can tell
When the clapper hits the bell?

A light here, maids! Hang out your light,
And see your horns be clear and bright,
That so your candle clear may shine,
Continuing from six to nine;
That honest men that walk along,
May see to pass safe without wrong!

'On the Vigil of Saint John Baptist,' says John Stowe in his
Survey, of 1603, 'and on Saint Peter and Paule the Apostles, every
mans doore being shadowed with greene Birch, long Fennel,
Saint Johns wort, Orpin, white Lillies, and such like, garnished
upon with Garlands of beautiful flowers, had also Lampes of glasse,
with oyle burning in them all the night, some hung out braunches
of yron curiously wrought, contayning hundreds of Lampes light
at once, which made a goodly shew, namely in new Fishstreet,
Thames streete, etc. Then had ye besides the standing watches, all
in bright harnes in every ward and streete of this Citie and Suburbs,
a marching water, that passed through the principal streets thereof,
to wit, from the little Conduit by Paules gate, through west Cheape,
by ye Stocks, through Cornhill, by Leaden hall to Aldgate, then
backe downe Fenchurch streete, by Grasse church, aboute Grasse
church Conduite, and up Grass church streete into Cornhill, and
through it into west Chepe againe.'

'The children are going to bed'

Hush-a-ba, birdie, croon, croon,
    Hush-a-ba, birdie, croon.
The Sheep are gane to the siller wood,
    And the cows are gane to the broom, broom.

And its braw milking the kye, kye,
   It's braw milking the kye,
The birds are singing, the bells are ringing,
   And the wild deer come galloping by, by.

And hush-a-ba, birdie, croon, croon,
   Hush-a-ba birdie, croon.
The Gaits are gane to the mountain hie,
   And they'll no be hame till noon, noon.

This for the littlest ones, the cradle-creatures. But for the rest:

Boys and Girls, come out to play,
The Moon doth shine as bright as day;
Come with a whoop, come with a call,
Come with a goodwill or don't come at all;
Lose your supper and lose your sleep –
So come to your playmates in the street.

Snout.   Doth the Moone shine that night wee play our play?
Bottom. A Calendar, a Calendar, looke in the Almanack, finde
       out Moone-shine, finde out Moone-shine.
Quince. Yes, it doth shine that night.
Bottom. Why then may you leave a casement of the great chamber
       window (where we play) open, and the Moone may
       shine at the casement.
Quince. Ay, or else one must come in with a bush of thorns and
       a lanthorne, and say he comes to disfigure, or to
       present the person of Moone-shine ...
Lysander. Proceed, Moone.
Moone.   All that I have to say, is to tell you, that the Lanthorne is
       the Moone; I, the man in the Moone; this thorne bush,
       my thorne bush; and this dog, my dog ...

                          A Midsummer Night's Dream

Mon, in the monè, stond ant streit,
  On is bot-forke is burthen he bereth:
Hit is muche wonder that he na down slyt,
  For doute leste he valle he shoddreth ant shereth:

When the frost fresheth muche chele he byd,
The thornès beth kene is hattren to-tereth;
  Nis no wytht in the world that wot wen he syt,
Ne, bote hit bue the hegge, whet wedès he wereth.

And that, I gather, means that —

The Man in the Moon stands up there stark and still in her silver,
carrying his thornbush on his pitchfork. It's a marvel he doesn't slide
down; he's shuddering and shaking at the thought of it. When the
frost sharpens, he'll be frozen to the marrow. The prickles stick
out to tear his clothes; but nobody in the world has seen him sit
down, or knows, apart from his thornbush, what he has on.

I see the Moon,
The Moon sees me:
God bless the sailors,
And bless me.

449. 'That busy archer'

Though I am young and cannot tell
Either what Love or Death is well,
Yet I have heard they both bear darts
And both do aim at human hearts ...

BEN JONSON

'Are beauties there as proud as here they be?'

... The palace of her father the King, was on that side the Moon
no mortal sees, and of such an enchantment was her cold beauty
that on earth none resembles it. Yet all her folly and pride was but

to win the idolatrous love of far-travelling Princes, or even of wanderers of common blood; for the sake of that love and admiration only. And many perished in those rock-bound deserts and parched and icy lunar wildernesses on account of this proud damsel; before a strange fate befell her . . .

And this is a fragment (from a thirteenth-century MS.), to be found in *A Medieval Garner*:

'What shall we say of the ladies when they come to feasts? Each marks well the other's head; they wear bosses like horned beasts, and if any have no horns, she is a laughing stock for the rest. Their arms go merrily when they come into the room; they display their kerchiefs of silk and cambric, set on their buttons of coral and amber, and cease not their babble so long as they are in the bower. . . . But however well their attire be fashioned, when the feast is come, it pleases them nought; so great is their envy now and so high grows their pride, that the bailiff's daughter counterfeits the lady.'

But this was in the dark ages.

450. *'She hath no air'*

– and, that being so:

'. . . There will be no sounds on the moon . . . Even a meteor shattering itself to a violent end against the surface of the moon would make no noise. Nor would it herald its coming by glowing into a "shooting star", as it would on entering the earth's atmosphere. There will be no floating dust, no scent, no twilight, no-blue sky, no twinkling of the stars. The sky will be always black and the stars will be clearly visible by day as by night. The sun's wonderful corona, which no man on earth, even by seizing every opportunity during eclipses, can hope to see for more than two hours in all, in a long lifetime, will be visible all day. So will the great red flames of the sun . . . There will be no life (since) for fourteen days there is continuous night, when the temperature must sink away down towards the absolute cold of space. This will be followed without an instant of twilight by full daylight. For another fourteen days the sun's rays will bear straight down, with no diffusion or absorption of their heat, or light, on the way . . .'

This is a matter-of-fact fragment out of *The Outline of Science*, edited by Professor J. Arthur Thompson; but it would not be easy to say exactly how in its magical *effect* on the mind it differs from poetry. Indeed, there can hardly be a quicker journey to the comprehension of scientific fact than by way of the imagination. Moonless mountainous Hesper, the Evening Star, is an even lovelier thing to watch shining in the fading rose and green of sunset when we realize that at her most radiant – a radiance that casts an earthly shadow even – it is but a slim crescent of the planet that we see, a planet, too, almost sister in magnitude to the earth, but whose briefer year is of an ardour that might be happiness to fiery sprite and salamander, but would be unendurable to watery creatures like ourselves. Nor could language be used more scientifically (concisely, pregnantly and exactly), than in the words *moving, priestlike, human, mask*, in the following sonnet by John Keats – a sonnet written in mortal illness and in immortal sorrowfulness:

> Bright star, would I were stedfast as thou art –
>   Not in lone splendour hung aloft the night
> And watching, with eternal lids apart,
>   Like nature's patient, sleepless Eremite,
> The moving waters at their priestlike task
>   Of pure ablution round earth's human shores,
> Or gazing on the new soft-fallen mask
>   Of snow upon the mountains and the moors –
>
> No – yet still stedfast, still unchangeable,
>   Pillowed upon my fair love's ripening breast,
> To feel for ever its soft fall and swell,
>   Awake for ever in a sweet unrest,
> Still, still to hear her tender-taken breath,
> And so live ever – or else swoon to death.

JOHN KEATS

455. *'Right good is rest'*

Come, Sleep, and with thy sweet deceiving
Lock me in delight awhile;
Let some pleasing dreams beguile
All my fancies: that from thence
I may feel an influence
All my powers of care bereaving!

Though but a shadow, but a sliding,
Let me know some little joy!
We that suffer long annoy
Are contented with a thought
Through an idle fancy wrought:
O let my joys have some abiding!

JOHN FLETCHER

457

I have pieced this rhyme together from well-known versions and
fragments. But the Angels:

'Aftir these thingis I saigh [saw] foure *aungelis* stondinge on the
four corneris of the erthe, holdinge foure wyndis of the erthe that
thei blewen not on the erthe, neither on the see, neithir on ony tree.'

WICLIF, Apocalips, ch. 7

'And I beheld, and I heard the voice of many angels round about
the throne and the beasts and the elders: and the number of them
was ten thousand times ten thousand, and thousands of thousands.'

The Authorized Version (1611)

Of these Angels, having their fitting place among the hierarchies
– Seraphim, Cherubim, Thrones; Dominations, Virtues, Powers;
Principalities, Archangels, Angels – no names are given. But Michael

and Gabriel are archangels named in the Bible; and in the Apocrypha and elsewhere, Raphael, Zadkiel, Uriel, Chamuel, Jophiel. These too; steadfast or fallen: Samael, Semalion, Abdiel and gigantic Sandalphon, Rahab, Prince of the Sea; Ridia, Prince of the Rain; Yurkemi, Prince of the Hail; Af of Anger; Abaddona of Destruction; Lailah of Night. And the angelic sentinels of Eden (in *Paradise Lost*):

> Now had night measured with her shadowy cone
> Halfway up-hill this vast sublunar vault;
> And from their ivory port the Cherubim
> Forth issuing, at the accustomed hour, stood armed ...

Then speak together Gabriel, Uzziel, Ithuriel, Zephon. And last there is he whose trumpet will awaken the dead in the day of Resurrection – strangely-angelled Poe's shrill-tongued Israfel:

> In Heaven a spirit doth dwell
>   Whose heart-strings are a lute;
> None sing so wildly well
> As the angel Israfel,
> And the giddy stars (so legends tell),
> Ceasing their hymns, attend the spell
>   Of his voice, all mute ...
> Yes, Heaven is thine; but this
>   Is a world of sweets and sours;
>   Our flowers are merely – flowers,
> And the shadow of thy perfect bliss
>   Is the sunshine of ours.
>
> If I could dwell
> Where Israfel
>   Hath dwelt, and he were I,
> He might not sing so wildly well
>   A mortal melody,
> While a bolder note than this might swell
>   From my lyre within the sky.

'That there are distinct orders of Angels, assuredly I believe but what they are I cannot tell ... They are creatures that have not so much of a body as flesh is, as froth is, as a vapour is, as a sigh is; and yet with a touch they shall moulder a rock into less atoms than the sand that it stands upon, and a millstone into smaller flour than it grinds. They are creatures made, and yet not a minute older than when they were first made, if they were made before all measures of time begun; nor, if they were made in the beginning of time, and be now six thousand years old, have they one wrinkle of age in their face, one sob of weariness in their lungs. They are *primogeniti Dei*, God's eldest sons ...'

JOHN DONNE

Manoah, too, saw an angel, and Moses, and Gideon, and Nebuchadnezzar:

'"Be it known unto thee, O king, that we will not serve thy gods, nor worship the golden image which thou hast set up."

'Then was Nebuchadnezzar full of fury, and the form of his visage was changed against Shadrach, Meshach, and Abednego: therefore he spake, and commanded that they should heat the furnace one seven times more than it was wont to be heated. And he commanded the most mighty men that were in his army to bind Shadrach, Meshach, and Abednego, and to cast them into the burning fiery furnace. Then these men were bound in their coats, their hosen, and their hats, and their other garments, and were cast into the midst of the burning fiery furnace. Therefore because the king's commandment was urgent, and the furnace exceeding hot, the flame of the fire, slew those men that took up Shadrach, Meshach, and Abednego. And these three men, Shadrach, Meshach, and Abednego, fell down bound into the midst of the burning fiery furnace.

'Then Nebuchadnezzar the king was astonied, and rose up in haste, and spake, and said unto his counsellors, "Did not we cast three men bound into the midst of the fire?"

'They answered and said unto the king, "True, O king."

'He answered and said, "Lo, I see four men loose, walking in

the midst of the fire, and they have no hurt; and the form of the
fourth is like the son of God." '

Daniel iii. 18–25

458. 'Sleep Secure'

... The night is come, like to the day
Depart not Thou, great God, away.
Let not my sins, black as the night,
Eclipse the lustre of Thy light;
Keep still in my Horizon; for to me
The Sun makes not the day, but Thee.

Howere I rest, great God, let me
Awake again at last with Thee;
And thus assured, behold I lie
Securely, or to awake or die.
These are my drowsie days; in vain
I do now wake to sleep again:
O come that hour, when I shall never
Sleep again, but wake for ever.

SIR THOMAS BROWNE

459

This is the Song sung by his guardian Angel to a young sleeping
prince who has been cheated of his inheritance. It was printed by
Charles Lamb in his *English Dramatic Poets*, from a Tragedy
entitled *The Conspiracy*, written by Henry Killigrew when he was
seventeen.

460

The relics of this Saint, who for his miracles was thought to be a
sorcerer, and was murdered by a mob, were interred in Alexandria.

Hundreds of years afterwards these relics were coveted by the Venetians by reason of the story that the Saint had once visited their city and had heard speak to him an angel: *Pax tibi, Marce. Hic requiescet corpus tuum.* At length two Venetian merchants, having persuaded the Alexandrians that the sacred bones lay in danger of the raiding Saracens, travelled back with them to their own city, where they were reinterred with solemn ceremony in St Mark's. This church was in 976 burned to the ground, and the relics were lost. A century passed; a wondrously beautiful church had, Phoenix-like, arisen from the ashes of the old, and during the ceremony, held in the faith that it would be revealed where they lay hid, suddenly a light shone forth from one of the great piers, there was a sound of falling masonry, and, lo, the body of the Saint, with arm outstretched, as if at finger's touch he had revealed his secret resting-place.

'. . . Doves of Siam, Lima mice,
And legless birds of Paradise'

Why of Siam, why of Lima, I have as yet been unable to discover. But, according to Topsell, mice are of these kinds: the short, small, fearful, peaceable, ridiculous, rustik, or country mouse, the urbane or citty mouse, the greedy, wary, unhappy, harmefull, black, obscene, little, whiner, biter, and earthly mouse. Mice, too, he says, are 'sometimes blackish, sometimes white, sometimes yellow, sometimes broune and sometimes ashe colour. There are white mice amonge the people of Savoy, and Dolphin in France, called alaubroges, which the inhabitants of the country do beleev that they feede upon snow.' Then, again, 'the field mouse, the farie, with a long snout; and the sleeper – that is of a dun colour and will run on the edge of a sword and sleep on the point'.

What Topsell meant by 'whiner' I am uncertain, but it may be he refers to the mouse that sings. This is a habit quite distinct from the common squeaking, shrilling and shrieking. It resembles the slow low trill of a distant and sleepy canary, but sweeter and more domestic, and is as pleasant a thing to hear behind a wainscot, as it is to watch the creatures gambolling. Whatever mischief their ravagings may cause, may I never live under a roof wherein (Cat or no Cat) there isn't an inch of house-room (and an occasional crumb of cheese) for Mistress Mouse!

The fable that the Bird of Paradise is 'legless' was set abroad by travellers who had seen in old days its exquisite dismembered carcase prepared for merchandise. It is hard to explain how Man, capable of imagining a bird 'whose fixed abode is the region of the air', and that lives 'solely on dew', can also slaughter it and tie it up in bundles for feminine finery. But, as Iago says, 'if thou wilt needs damn thyself, do it a more delicate way than drowning. Make all the money thou canst . . .'

'At Venice'

So Keats left – unfinished – this, one of the happiest of his poems. There are others in this volume: but not the 'Eve of St Agnes', or 'Hyperion', or the odes: 'To a Nightingale', 'On a Grecian Urn', or the strange 'On Melancholy'. Nor are any of his Letters here – as full a revelation of the powers and understanding of that rare mind, as the poems are of his imagination.

466. 'Low in the south the "Cross"'

We peoples of the Northern hemisphere, from the Chinese and Chaldaeans until this last flitting hour, have the joy of so many brilliant and neighbouring stars in our night sky that for us it is now full of stories, and thronged with constellations of our own fantasy and naming. The Chair of Cassiopeia, for instance, is but a feigned passing picture. Nevertheless, what a delight it is to recognize it shining in the very midst of the firmament in the dusk of early June. For this reason the peoples of the Southern hemisphere, with their Crown and Net, their Phoenix and Peacock, hold dear the Southern Cross. It marks their very home.

And (for the last time) let me repeat what Miss Taroone once said to me: 'Learn the common names of every thing you see, Simon; and especially of those that please you most to remember: then give them names also of your own making and choosing – if you can. Mr Nahum has thousands upon thousands of words and names in his mind and yet he often fails to understand what I say to him. Nor does he always remember that though every snail is a snail and a Hoddydoddy, and every toad is a toad and a Joey, and every centipede is a centipede and a Maggie-monyfeet, each is just as much only its own self as you, Simon, are You.' For, 'be it ever so humble', a good name is a difficult thing to come by – a name that sounds well, sounds right, and whose meaning continues to fit it however far one chase it through its etymological origins. For apt sound alone only a flash of intuitive insight (especially in a child) can instantly suit word to sight; or maybe to hearing, (timbrel, trombone, bassoon); to touch (slimy, plush, velvet); to taste (syrop, caramel, myrrh, blancmange); to smell (bergamot, musk). These words, of course, happen to refer to these particular senses, but sounds that do *not* may be appropriate to them. Are not *crumpets, muffins, jumbles, parkin, candy, lollipops, comfits, humbugs, bulls'-eyes, brandy-snaps, ratafias, gob-stoppers* and *toffee* – are these not 'good' names for goodies? But children's fashions change, and names with them.

It is a poor name anyhow that means well but cannot prove it. A family of brothers, for example, consisting of a Cyril, an Edwin, a Walter, an Oscar, a Philip, a Cuthbert, a Eustace, an Adolphus and an Ambrose does not radiantly bring to mind (as it should) a group of all the manly virtues – a lord, a conqueror, a ruler of hosts, a bonny fighter, a lover of horses, the All-splendid, the Foursquare, a noble hero, and the Ever-happy One.

But to return to the stars. By strange good fortune – even apart from such honest homely terms as the Plough, the Pointers, the Guards, the Chair – the stars have been starrily named. These, for example: Merak, Megrez, Alcor, Alphacca, Alarneb, Dubhe, Markab, Murfrid, Almirzam, Alpheratz, Alphard, Zosma, Denebola, Fomalhaut. They are not only good names for stars, just as Kit Marlowe or Richard Lovelace or Geoffrey Chaucer is a good name for an English poet; or Tycho Brahe or Johannes Hevelius or Giovanni Donati is for an astronomer; or Vasco da Gama, Fernando Magellan or Francis Drake is for an adventurer; or Diego Rodriguez de Silva Velasquez is for a painter; but they mean as well as they sound. Nor can you ever be utterly alone, however dark the way, if you can see but one star shining and can hail it by name. To which divine end the following doggerel is intended:

> If to the heavens thou lift thine eyes
> When Winter rules o'er our northern skies,
> And snow-cloud none the zenith mars,
> At Yule-tide midnight these thy stars:

> Low in the south see bleak-blazing Sirius.
> O'er him hang Betelgeuse, Procyon wan.
> Wild-eyed to west of him, Rigel and Bellatrix,
> And rudd-red Aldebaran journeying on.
> High in night's roof-tree beams twinkling Capella,
> Vega and Deneb prowl low in the north,
> Far to the east, rovers the Lion-heart, Regulus;
> While the twin sons of Zeus toward the zenith gleam forth.

> But when Midsummer Eve in man's sleep-drowsed hours,
> Awaiteth the daybreak with dew-bright flowers,
> Though three of these Night Lights aloft remain,
> For nine thou may'st gaze, but wilt gaze in vain.
> Yet comfort find, for, far-shining there,
> See golden Arcturus, and cold Altaïr,
> Crystalline Spica, and, strange to scan,
> Blood-red Antares, foe to man.

Of these names, Regulus (the little Prince), Bellatrix (the She-Warrior), Capella (the little Goat), Arcturus (the Bearward) and Spica (the Wheatear), come from the Latin. Procyon (the Herald), Antares (the War-maker), and Sirius (the Fervent) are Greek. While Altair (the flying one), Deneb (the Hen's Tail), Rigel (Orion's Foot), prodigious Betelgeuse (his arm), Vega (the falling One), and Aldebaran (the Follower – of the Pleiads), are Arabian.

As for the precious stones, the mere recital of their names resembles an incantation, and may be of sovran use as a lullaby:

> Ruby, amethyst, emerald, diamond,
> Sapphire, sardonyx, fiery-eyed carbuncle,
>   Jacynth, jasper, crystal a-sheen;
> Topaz, turquoise, tourmaline, opal,
>   Beryl, onyx and aquamarine:
> Marvel, O mortal! – their hue, lustre, loveliness,
> Pure as a flower when its petals unfurl –
> Peach-red carnelian, apple-green chrysoprase,
>   Amber and coral and orient pearl!

469. 'Once a dream did weave a shade'

Full in the passage of the vale, above,
A sable, silent, solemn, forest stood,
Where nought but shadowy forms was seen to move,
As idless fancy'd in her dreaming mood;

And up the hills, on either side, a wood
Of blackening pines, ay waving to and fro,
Sent forth a sleepy horror thro' the blood;
And where this valley winded out, below,
The murmuring main was heard, and scarcely heard, to flow.

A pleasing land of drowsy-head it was,
Of Dreams that wave before the half-shut eye,
And of gay Castles in the clouds that pass,
For ever flushing round a summer sky ...

JAMES THOMSON

470. 'Awake, awake'

'I thank God for my happy dreams,' wrote Sir Thomas Browne in the *Religio Medici*, 'as I do for my good rest ... And surely it is not a melancholy conceit [or fancy] to think we are all asleep in this World, and that the conceits of this life are as meer dreams to those of the next as the Phantasms of the night to the conceits of the day. There is an equal delusion in both, and the one doth but seem to be the embleme or picture of the other; we are somewhat more than our selves in our sleeps, and the slumber of the body seems to be but the waking of the soul ...'

> The Door of Death is made of gold,
> That Mortal Eyes cannot behold;
> But, when the Mortal Eyes are closed,
> And cold and pale the Limbs reposed,
> The Soul awakes; and, wondering sees
>
> In her mild Hand the golden Keys:
> The Grave is Heaven's golden Gate,
> And rich and poor around it wait;
> O Shepherdess of England's Fold,
> Behold this Gate of Pearl and Gold! ...
>
> I give you the end of a golden string;
>   Only wind it into a ball,
> It will lead you in at Heaven's gate,
>   Built in Jerusalem's wall.

WILLIAM BLAKE

'Above the light of the Morning Star'

The morning star, Phosphor, beaming in the first crystal light of daybreak, and heralding the sun, is of an unearthly serenity and beauty – pure and lustrous as a dew-drop on a thorn. But the light in Blake's *poem* never was on sea or land; only in his imagination; though now, by what is little short of a miracle, we share it with him.

Blake was born in 1757, and died (in 1827) when he was 70. His *Songs of Innocence* were published in 1789 – songs which he hoped and intended 'every child' might '*joy* to hear'. Now from about 1750 to 1830 was the hey-day of the sampler; not, that is, the original 'exampler', which was a delicate slip of embroidery giving stitch patterns for grown-ups, but the show-pieces on canvas or linen of a little girl (aged six or upwards) to prove her skill and diligence with the needle.

In size these samplers range from that of a large bandanna handkerchief to a few inches square. The earlier ones are oblong in shape; and a few are heart-shaped, oval or circular. The vast majority of them must have taken months (of tedious days and hours) to finish – tongue-tip out, and fingers sore with needle-pricks, though the eyes that watched the stitches (as many little mistakes prove) must often have filled up with day-dreams.

Few samplers are very beautiful in design, pattern and colour; and as with so much else, alas, the earlier are the best. But even the coarsest of old samplers has that tinge of the romantic which the mere passing of time never fails to confer on anything made by man, and gives in abundance to anything made by a child. So it may be in due season with the 'decorative stitchery' of today! Over and over again in these mementos of young creatures who have long ago left the world we see around us, one finds an almost monotonous repetition of angular little Cupids and crowns and coronets; houses, birds, bees, and butterflies; trees, ships, flowers, and animals; since

> There's nothing near at hand or farthest sought
> But with the needle may be shaped or wrought.

Alphabets large and small, and a row of digits usually appear above, and a name and a date below. How much is lost by the absence of the last two particulars only an interested observer can say!

Ten years or so after Keats set aside unfinished the 'Eve of St Mark' (No. 460) with its

> Parrot's cage and panelled square,
> And the warm-angled winter screen,

Charlotte and Emily Brontë stitched in the last stitch of *their* samplers. Anne's (the youngest sister) was a year later. Remarkably crude specimens they are, but could any reader of *Villette*, *Wuthering Heights*, or *The Tenant of Wildfell Hall* even glance at such remembrances with a cold and unsympathetic eye?

But mention of samplers has appeared in these pages not merely for their own sake (though that is a happy one) but for the sake of their rhymes. And seven out of ten of them, at least, must be thus decorated. Far, however, from these rhymes being songs 'of pleasant glee' or 'happy cheer' they are 'nearly always in a moral, minor or miserable key'. The mothers and schoolmistresses of William Blake's day supposed that the best literary fare for young children was a sort of physic, sour with awful warnings; and all his life, for the world at large, Blake was like the sun in Winter, that cannot shed his light and warmth on the world because of the cold of the clouds in between. Surely, if little Tom Babington Macaulay had supped up with his bread and milk (or was it water-porridge and salt?) 'The Chimney Sweeper', 'The Laughing Song', 'Night', 'Spring', and 'A Dream', he couldn't, at the age of eight, have 'made up' such dismal stuff as this:

> Some men make Gods of red and blue
> And rob their Sovereign of his due:
> The good shall go to Heaven. The fell
> Blasts of thy wrath can bear to hell.

Young or old, male or female, the authors of sampler rhymes – and very few of them appear to be traceable – seem to have thoroughly enjoyed thinking of Hell and brimstone, death and children, all in the same breath. Yet for the most part they thought of these inexhaustible themes so meanly and shallowly that when they wrote verses about them they often failed even to find decent rhymes. Elizabeth Hicks, for example, at the ripe age of ten, when she might have been reading – well, any good book that calls to the young heart and mind, was made – stitch by stitch – to rhyme not only *youth* with *truth*, and *lips* with *keeps*, but *trust* with *first*, and *speak* with *lake*. Fortunately false and feeble sentiments are usually shown up by their style alone; the grammar is frail, the workmanship feeble, and the words have a dull and lumpy effect.

The examples that follow have (with very kind permission) been taken from two volumes, richly illustrated, entitled respectively *Samplers* and *Samplers and Tapestry Embroideries*, and from some specimens in my own possession. I have usually, but not always, followed the original spelling, but seldom the punctuation. First shall come a few in a wholly minor, moral and miserable key:

No. 1 is 'Against Lying'.

> O 'Tis a Lovely Thing for Youth
> To Walk betimes in wisdom's Way;
> To fear a Lie, to speak the Truth,
> That we may trust to all they say.
>
> But Liars we can never trust,
> Tho' they should speak the Thing that's true;
> And he that does one Fault at first,
> And lies to hide it, makes it two.
>
> The Lord delights in them that speak
> The Words of Truth, but ev'ry Liar
> Must have his portion in the Lake
> That burns with Brimstone and with Fire.
>
> Then let me always watch my Lips,
> Lest I be stuck to Death and Hell,
> Since God a Book of Reckoning keeps
> For ev'ry Lye that Children tell.

ELIZABETH HICKS, 1780

But that Book may be of many volumes, and in *Father and Son*
is a vivid and unforgettable account of the effect on a small boy
of detecting his best beloved grown-up in a lie.

The next few rhymes – like the last – are all of them haunted by
the horror of Death and of Time – the future that cannot be hin-
dered or delayed; the present that is but a passing breath; the past
that none can change, expunge or recall; and the nameless little
'soul' of No. 5 who sat, needle in hand, considering these mysteries
had just turned seven! They are reminders, too, first, that children
in the past had far less chance of evading an early death; and next,
that 'The Cry of the Children' was written as late as 1844. Whether
that little 'worldling' Mary Brewitt's 'she' [No. 6] was a slip or
an extremely unusual conception of the *Skulker* I cannot say.

(*2*)

Dear Child delay no time,
But with all speed amend
The longer thou dost live
The nearer to thy End.
Yesterday is gone
To-morrow is none of thine
Oh! [now this] day thy life
To vertuous acts incline.

SUSANNA INGRAM, 1700

(*3*)

Death at a Distance we but slightly fear,
He brings his Terrors as he draws more near.
Through Poverty, Pain, Slav'ry, we drudge on,
The worst of Beings better please than none;
No Price too dear to purchase Life and Breath,
The heaviest Burthen's easier borne than Death.

SUSANNA GELLETT, 1800

(4)

Swiftly, see, each Moment flies!
See and learn, be timely Wise!
Every moment shortens Day;
And every Pulse beats Time away;
Then seize the Minutes as they fly:
Know to Live, and learn to die.

ELIZABETH HEWITT, 1778

(5)

And now, my Soul, another year [the 6th]
Of thy short life is past;
I cannot long continue here,
And this may be my Last!

(6)

Worldling, beware betimes!
Death skulks behind thee!
And as She leaves thee
So will Judgment find thee.

MARY BREWITT, 1725

No. 7 (which is decked with a sprightly Lion and Unicorn above
and two floating cherubs carrying what appear to be bagpipes
below) is one stanza only (the last but one of six) on keeping the
Sabbath, and is well worth a moment's reflection. The last stanza
returns to hell.

(7)

... But O, ye thoughtless Sinners, know,
    If in your maker's courts below
No sweetness to your souls is given,
    'Twould be no Joy to be in Heaven ...

ELIZABETH CRESWELL, 1808 (*aged 11*)

893

No. 8 is unusual, not for the fleeting picture it gives of a horror-stricken little fugitive, but because it was the joint work of a brother and sister, Edward and Ruth Bachelor; in 1717.

(8)

O Thou to Whom Angels their Hymns address,
To whom all knees must bow, All Tongue confess;
I have offended God. Where shall I fly
To hide myself from his offended eye?

In No. 9 [probably of the seventeenth century] and in the last two lines of No. 10 there is a curious but vivid glint of imagination:

(9)

Youll mend your Life tomorrow Still you cry.
in what far Country does this morrow lie?
it Stays to long, tis fetch'd to far I fear:
Twill be both very old and Very dear.

(10)

Gay dainty flowers go swiftly to decay,
Poor wretched life's short portion flies away.
We eat: we drink: we sleep: but lo, anon
Old age steals on us, never thought upon.

MAY WAKELING, 1742 (aged 10)

And No. 11 – so matter-of-fact and yet so imaginative with its meals and its reckoning – comes from the *Emblems* of a true poet, Francis Quarles:

(11)

Our life is nothing but a winters day,
Some only break their fast and so away,
Others stay dinner, and depart full fed,
The deeper age but sups and goes to bed.

Hee's most in debt, that lingers out the day,
Who dys betimes, has lesse and lesse to pay.

MARG'T BURNELL, 1720

Emblems, however, was published in 1635, years before English
Poetry had turned to wit, artifice and common sense. But as early
as 1829, on a sampler worked at the age of 12 by Elizabeth Jane
Gates, is the thought Blake himself had in mind when he wrote
'The Little Black Boy'. But while Blake's poem cannot but in some
degree affect the heart and mind of its reader, the rhyme only
argues with his intellect:

(12)

There's mercy in each ray of light, that mortal eye e'er saw,
There's mercy in each breath of air, that mortal lips can draw,
There's mercy both for bird, and beast, in God's indulgent plan,
There's mercy for each creeping thing – But man has none for man.

The next few rhymes are still morally inclined, but there is less
of the minor and little of the downright miserable:

(13)

Look Well to that thou takest in Hand.
It's Better worth Than House or Land;
When Land is gone and Money is spent
Then learning is most Excelent.
Let [? glorious] vertue Be thy guide,
And it will keep the out of pride.

ELIZABETH CREASEY, 1686

Mary Green spelt better (or less persuasively) but must have
been rejoiced to get to her last stanza:

(14)

How shall the young secure their hearts
And guard their lives from sin?

Thy word the choicest rules imparts
to keep the conscience clean ...

'Tis like the Sun a heavenly light
That guides us all the day
And thro' the dangers of the night
A Lamp to lead our way.

Apart from a charming wreath round her rhyme (No. 15) Sarah Tracey's industry (she was 11 in 1823) is displayed in an unusually large sampler with a remarkably handsome house and dovecote at the foot of it, in front of which a complete family of children (with their mother) are at play among the haycocks:

(15)

Industry taught in early days
Not only give the teachers praise
But give us pleasure when we view
The work that innocence can do ...

The Parents with exulting joy
Survey it as no childish toy
But as prelude to [? what] :ich day
A greater genius will display.

Go on, dear Child, learn to excell
Improve in work and reading well
For books and work do both contend
To make the Housewife and the friend.

Rhyme No. 16 is enclosed in a frame of gold and green in the middle of a particularly fine piece of needlework, in colour, proportion and skill. It was the work of 'Cathrine Tweedall' (1775), John Ruskin's paternal grandmother. The sentiments it conveys might be the making of a successful pickpocket, of 'an entirely honest merchant', or of such genius as inspired Ruskin himself! But it banishes a good many 'wretches':

(16)

She who from Heaven expects to gain her end
Must by her own efforts her self befriend;
The wretch who ne'er exceeds a faint desire
Goes not half way to what she would acquire;
She that to virtues high rewards would rise
Must run ye race before she win ye prize.

Little Ann Maria Wiggins (and maybe with as 'fond' a mother) was only seven when she steadily stitched in similar sentiments (No. 17), but the delight of her sampler (as of her own eyes too, I hope), is the sprightly and lively goldfinch eyeing a butterfly that is perched on a spray above the rhyme, while both are surrounded by a wreath of rose, convolvulus and heartsease, with a bunch of white and red currants and cherries at the outside corners.

(17)

All Youth set right at first with Ease go on
And each new Task is with new Pleasure done.
But if neglected till they grow in years
And each fond Mother her dear Darling spares,
Error becomes habitual and you'll find
Tis then hard Labour to reform the Mind.

So again with Elizabeth Goss (1793) in a large sampler containing sixteen assorted birds, four butterflies, and eight animals, with a red house, a prodigious yellow lion (shaped like a fortipianer), two Chinamen, a kind of pagoda and flowers galore. And her warning steals a little further into the heart because it is half hidden in metaphor:

(18)

Sweet green leaves the rose Adorn,
Yet beneath it lurks a thorn.
Fair and flow'ry is the brake,
Yet it hides the vengeful snake.
Artless deeds and simple dress,
Mark the Chosen shepherdess.

So again with Jessie Maria Taylor (1831) who was evidently needling in a day-dream when she put in her second 'guide' instead of *guard*, and who had a hazy notion of the 'dart.'

(19)

>May Virtue point out wisdom's way,
>And ever Guide me when I stray;
>And ever Guide my youthful heart
>When vice and folly throws Adart.

More simple, and therefore nearer poetry, is the quatrain in Caroline Codling's sampler, a pretty and skilful piece of needle-work (enriched with flower-baskets, vases, small birds and large peacocks), apart from its clumsy lettering. But what did 'Amidre Sworld' mean for *her*?

(20)

>Assist Me While I wander Here
>Amidre Sworld of Cares
>Incline My Heart to Pray With Love
>And Then Accept My Prayers.

And in Mary Ann Enderwick's (1831), poetry itself smiles tenderly out of the frame. But she was a niece of Isaac Watts, and the author of 'The Sluggard' wrote her rhyme:

(21)

>Jesus permit thy gracious name to stand
>As the first efforts of a youthful hand,
>And as her fingers on the canvas move
>Inspire her tender heart to seek thy love;
>With thy dear children let her have a part,
>And write thy name thyself upon her heart.

But not even Isaac Watts could write as piercingly as the author of the lines on E. Wilmhurst's sampler (1786) – as delicate in design as it is in workmanship;

(22)

The loss of Gold is much;
The loss of Time is more;
The loss of Christ is such
As no Man can Restore.

And there is true poetry, too, in these lines on a sampler (in the Greg collection in Manchester) though I know not whose:

(23)

Child in age, child in heart,
Thy magnificent array
Could not joy or pride impart;
Thou hadst treasure more than they:
More than courtiers kneeling low,
More than flattery's ready [? ease],
More than conquest o'er the foe,
More, even more, than these –
Treasures in which the mind hath part,
Joys that teach the soul to rise,
Hopes that can sustain the heart
When the body droops and dies.
Therefore Star thou art; not shaded
In the darkness of the tomb:
Royal Rose thou art, not faded,
But in paradise dost bloom.

Actual glimpses of these long-gone young needle-imps, stooping over their frames, can only be imaginary, of course; but there *is* such a glimpse, prim and arch, in Frances Gray's sampler (1819):

(24)

With cheerful mind we yield to Men
The higher honours of the Pen,
    The Needle's our great Care:
In this we chiefly wish to shine,
How far the art's already mine,
    This Sampler will declare!

It is a little obscure in Tabitha Anon's:

(25)

Sweet it is to be a child
Tender merciful and mild
Ever ready to perform
Acts of kindness to a worm.

It grows clearer in Sarah Pelham's – who 'in the six year of her age' stitched in

(26)

When i was Young
and in my Prime
here you may see
how I spent my time:

and in Ann Woolfray's (1736):

(27)

When this you see remember me
And keep me in your mind
And be not like the Weathercock
That turns at every wind.

and in Frances Johnson's (1797):

(28)

In reading this if any faults you see
Mend them yourself and find no fault in me:

But it positively scintillates in:

(29)

This is my Work so
You may see. what
care my mother as
took of me. ann bell.

while as far back as 1712 Elizabeth Clements heaved a sigh of relief which (one trusts) continued to re-echo in innumerable small bosoms for scores of years afterwards:

(30)

THIS I HAVE DONE I THANK MY GOD
WITHOUT THE CORRECTION OF THE ROD.

But of all the samplers I have actually seen, or brooded over in books, or envied in shop-windows, there are two that come closest. One of them is unusually small – less than five inches square. It is nameless and dateless; it is worked on the finest of linen with the finest of stitches and the happiest of flowers; and I have a fancy its verses may have been written by the nameless one herself who must just have left childhood behind her:

(31)

The peace of Heaven attend thy shade,
My early friend, my favourite maid!
When life was new, companions gay,
We hail'd the morning of our day.
Untimely gone, for ever fled,
The roses of the cheek so red!
The affections warm, the temper mild
The sweetness that in sorrow smil'd!

And last the dearest:

(32)

Elizabeth Walters is my name
in Wales is my nation
ystradveltœ is my dwelling
and Christ is my salvation
When i am dead and in my grave
and all my bones are rotten
[if] this you see
Remember me
when i am quit forgoten.

Her lovely and remote mountain village lies about eleven miles north of the Porth-yr-Ogof, through the gloom of which foam the roaring waters of the Fellte. It is 'the last outpost of civilization on the way to Brecon' – where Henry Vaughan lived and died. In that last outpost, either in 1701 or in 1791 (the figures are uncertain) this ten-year-old at last finished her long, narrow, coarse, but deftly panelled sampler. Did she ever grow up? Did she ever venture out into the Civilization of Queen Anne or of George III? Not for me: she stays 10 – and unchanging.

473. '*Does the road wind up-hill all the way?*'

'Gentle herdsman, tell to me,
    Of courtesy I thee pray,
Unto the town of Walsingham
    Which is the right and ready way.'

'Unto the town of Walsingham
    The way is hard for to be gone;
And very crooked are those paths,
    For you to find out all alone . . .'

Tarry no longer: toward thine heritage
Haste on thy way, and be of right good cheer.
Go each day onward on thy pilgrimage;
Think how short time thou shalt abide here.
They place is bigged[1] above the starres clere,
None earthly palays[2] wrought in so stately wise,
Come on, my friend, my brother most entere[3]
For thee I offered my blood in sacrifice.

JOHN LYDGATE

1. Builded
2. Palace
3. In all and everything

475

Oh what a thing is man, how far from power,
    From settled peace and rest!
He is some twenty sev'ral men, at least,
    Each sev'ral hour.

476

Shee was brighter of her blee,[1]
    then was the bright sonn:
Her rudd[2] redder than the rose,
    that on the rise[3] hangeth:
Meekly smiling with her mouth,
    and merry in her lookes.
Ever laughing for love,
    as shee like would.
And as shee came by the bankes,
    The boughes eche one
They louted[4] to that ladye,
    and layd forth their branches;
Blossomes, and burgens
    breathèd full sweete;
Flowers flourished in the frith,[5]
    where shee forth stepped;
And the grasse, that was gray,
    greened believe.[6]

1. Hue
2. Complexion
3. Twig

4. Made obeisance
5. Woods
6. Instantly, at very sight of her

477

This poem for its full beauty must be read very slowly. Eve in long memory is musing within herself, hardly able to utter the words because of her grief and sorrow, and of the heavy sighs between them.

'Death is the fruit'

I am Eve, great Adam's wife,
'Tis I that outraged Jesus of old;
'Tis I that robbed my children of Heaven,
By rights 'tis I that should have gone upon the Cross ...

There would be no ice in any place,
There would be no glistening windy winter,
There would be no hell, there would be no sorrow,
There would be no fear, if it were not for me.

Tr. KUNO MEYER

'The kind hart's tears were falling'

To day my Lord of Amiens, and my selfe,
Did steale behinde him as he lay along
Under an oake, whose anticke roote peepes out
Upon the brooke that brawles along this wood.
To the which place a poore sequestred Stag
That from the Hunter's aime had tane a hurt,
Did come to languish; and indeed my Lord
The wretched annimall heaved forth such groanes
That their discharge did stretch his leatherne coat
Almost to bursting, and the big round teares
Coursed one another downe his innocent nose
In pitteous chase ...

As You Like It

479. ' " *Oh, what are you seeking . . . ?* " '

'In Persia there is a city which is called Saba, from whence were
the three magi who came to adore Christ in Bethlehem; and the
three are buried in that city in a fair sepulchre, and they are all
three entire with their beards and hair. One was called Baldasar,
the second Gaspar, and the third Melchior.

'Marco inquired often in that city concerning the three magi,
and nobody could tell him anything about them, except that
[they] were buried there in ancient times. After three days' journey
you come to a castle which is called Palasata, which means the
castle of the fire-worshippers; and it is true that the inhabitants of
that castle worship fire, and this is given as the reason.

'The men of that castle say, that anciently three kings of that
country went to adore a certain king who was newly born, and
carried with them three offerings, namely, gold, frankincense and
myrrh; gold, that they might know if he were an earthly king;
frankincense, that they might know if he were God; and myrrh,
that they might know if he were a mortal man. When these magi
were presented to Christ, the youngest of the three adored him
first, and it appeared to him that Christ was of his stature and age.
The middle one came next, and then the eldest, and to each he
seemed to be of their own stature and age. Having compared their
observations together, they agreed to go all to worship at once,
and then he appeared to them all of his true age.

'When they went away, the infant gave them a closed box, which
they carried with them for several days, and then becoming curious
to see what he had given them, they opened the box and found
in it a stone, which was intended for a sign that they should remain
as firm as a stone in the faith they had received from him. When,
however, they saw the stone, they marvelled, and thinking themselves deluded, they threw the stone into a certain pit, and instantly
fire burst forth in the pit. When they saw this, they repented
bitterly of what they had done, and taking some of the fire with
them they carried it home. And having placed it in one of their

churches, they keep it continually burning, and adore that fire as a god.'

MARCO POLO

480

This was found about 1855, copied out in an old MS. – the Commonplace-book of Richard Hill 'servant with Mr Wyngar, alderman of London' in 1493. The carol below is of the late fourteenth century, and these are the first two stanzas:

Jesus, sweete soṅe deare!
  On porful bed list thou here,

  And that me greueth sore;
For thi cradel is ase a bere,
Oxe and assè beeth thi fere:
  Weepe ich mai tharfore.

Jesu, swete, beo noth wroth,
  Thou ich nabbe clout ne cloth
    The on for to folde,
    The on to folde ne to wrappe

Jesus, sweetè soṅe deare!
  On wretched bed thou lyest
    here,
And that me grieveth sore;
For thy cradle is but a byre,

Only ox and ass are near,
  Weep I must therefore.

Jesu, sweete, be not wroth,
Though I've neither clout nor
    cloth,
    Thee in for to enfold –
    Thee to enfold unto thy rest
For ich nabbe clout ne
    lappe;
Bote ley thou thi fet to my
    pappe,
  And wite the from the
    colde . . .

Though I've neither clout nor
    vest,
Lay thy feet within my breast
  And guard thee from the
    cold . . .

483. '*This is the Key*'

And so – like the medieval traveller who had made a complete circuit of the world without knowing it – we have come back to the place which we started from.

'The Elephant,' says Topsell, in his *Historie of Foure-footed Beastes*, 'is delighted above measure with sweet savours, ointments, and smelling flowers, for which cause their Keeper will in the summer time lead them into the meadows of flowers, where they of themselves will by the quickness of their smelling, choose out and gather the sweetest flowers, and put them into a basket if their Keeper have any ...

'[Having sought] out water [wherewith] to wash themselves, [they will] of their own accord return back again to the basket of flowers, which, if they find not, they will bray and call for them. Afterward, being led into their stable, they will not eat meat until they take off their flowers and dress the brims of their manger therewith, and likewise strew their room or standing place, pleasing themselves with their meat, because of the savour of the flowers stuck about their cratch.'

'A *cratch*,' says Robert Nares – one of the most companionable of all writers on English words – 'a cratch was a manger, particularly that in which our Saviour was laid. This opens to us the meaning of a childish game, corruptly called scratch-cradle, which consists in winding packthread double round the hands, into a ... representation of a manger, which is taken off by the other player on his hands, so as to assume a new form, and thus alternately for several times, always changing the appearance. The art consists in making the right changes. But it clearly meant originally the *cratch-cradle*; the manger that held the Holy Infant as a cradle.

> If all things should be writ which erst was done
> By Jesus Christ (Gods everlasting sonne),
> From cratch to crosse, from cradle to his tombe,
> To hold the bookes, the world would not be roome.

Now Mr Nahum himself, it seems to me, might have written these four lines, and he would undoubtedly delight in Topsell's elephants and their pleasure in flowers. Was not that *Other Worlde* of his yet another 'Basket of Flowers': the forthshowing in formal beauty – in this world's soil, and beneath ministering rain, sunshine and dew – of the imaginations of men? Even Miss Taroone could have uttered a secret word or two in the great ear of the Elephants at their cratch: and were there not in her garden at Thrae flowers beyond telling?

First ere the morning breaks joy opens in the flowery bosoms,
Joy even to tears ... First the Wild Thyme
And Meadow-sweet downy and soft waving among the reeds
Light springing on the air lead the sweet Dance: they wake
The Honeysuckle sleeping on the Oak: the flaunting beauty
Revels along upon the wind: the White-thorn, lovely May,
Opens her many lovely eyes: listening the Rose still sleeps:
None dare to wake her: soon she bursts her crimson curtained bed,
And comes forth in the majesty of beauty: every Flower,
The Pink, the Jessamine, the Wall-flower, the Carnation,
The Jonquil, the mild Lilly opes her heavens: every Tree
And Flower and Herb soon fill the air with an innumerable Dance.
Wet all in order sweet and lovely ...

And so, Farewell.

AND SO FAREWELL

Index: Titles and First Lines of Poems

The numbers are page numbers—those in *italic* referring to the notes in
About and Roundabout.

Adam lay i-bowndyn, 747
Adieu! farewell earth's bliss!, 494, *760*
A dis, a dis, a green grass, 240
After the blast of lightning from the east, 207
Afterwards, 712, *868*
A Gyges Ring they beare, *342*
Ah! County Guy, the hour is nigh, 570
Ah! sad wer we as we did peäce, 507, *772*
Ah, what avails the sceptred race?, 611
Alas, the moon should ever beam, 534
Alice, dear, what ails you?, 269
A light here, maids, *874*
A little lonely child am I, 675, *851*
A little Saint best fits a little Shrine, *316*
All in this pleasant evening, together come are we, 37, *300*
Allison Gross, 679, *858*
All looks be pale, hearts cold as stone, 225, *430*
All my stars forsake me, 722
All the flowers of the spring, 503, *765*
All under the leaves and the leaves of life, 748, *905*
Amo, amas, *439*
A Mole-Catcher am I, *446*
An' Charlie he's my darling, 221
Ancient Mariner, The Rime of the, 632, *834*
And as for me, thogh that I can but lyte, 39, *300*
And in the midst of all, a fountaine stood, 187, *408*
And like a dying lady, lean and pale, 721
And now all nature seemed in love, 41, *306*
And then I pressed the shell, 89
And there were spring-faced cherubs that did sleep, 660, *847*
Angel spirits of sleep, 734
An idle Poet, here and there, *414*
Annabel Lee, 88, *342*
Annan Water's wading deep, 569, *798*
A piper in the streets to-day, 233
Are they shadows that we see?, 197
A Rose, as fair as ever saw the North, 185

Art thou gone in haste?, 622, *823*
Art thou poor, yet hast thou golden slumbers?, 485, *755*
As I in hoary winter's night, 282
As it fell upon a day, 137, *375*
As I walked out one night, *426*
As I was going by Charing Cross, 224
As I was walking all alane, 139
As I was walking all alone, 532
As I wer readen ov a stwone, 517, *773*
Ask me no more, 186, *405*
Asleep beneath this humble stone, *777*
A sparhawk proud did hold in wicked jail, 138, *376*
A sunny shaft did I behold, 621, *823*
As we dance round a-ring-a-ring, 36
At common dawn there is a voice of bird, 617
At the corner of Wood Street, 132, *371*
Auld Robin Gray, 608
Autumn, 261
A vision that appeared to me, 98, *350*
Awake, awake, my little Boy!, 736, *888*
A weary lot is thine, fair maid, 220
A widow bird sat mourning for her love, 484
A wife was sitting at her reel ae night, *803*
Ay me, alas, heigh ho, heigh ho!, 119, *361*

Before my face the picture hangs, 492, *759*
Behold her, single in the field, 259
Bells have wide mouths and tongues, 248, *449*
Beneath our feet, the shuddering bogs, 559, *785*
Bermudas, 630, *830*
Best and brightest, come away!, 189
Be thou at peace this night, 205
Bingo, 117, *359*
Birds, The, 143
Blow, blow, thou winter winde, 287, *469*
Blows the wind to-day, 82, *340*
Bobby Shaftoe's gone to sea, *808*
Bonny Barbara Allan, 601, *818*
Boys and Girls, come out to play, *875*
Break, break, break, 265
Brief, on a flying night, 252
Bright star, would I were stedfast, *878*
Bring us in good ale, 97, *350*
Bring us in no browne bred, 96, *350*
Brome, brome on hill, 548

Brown Robyn, 672
Buckee, Buckee, biddy Bene, 531
Burning Babe, The, 282
By Saint Mary, my lady, 62, *331*
By the Moone we sport and play, 149, *381*

Call for the robin-redbreast and the wren, 502
Call me no more, O gentle stream, 78
Cam' ye by the salmon fishers?, 60
Cauld blows the wind frae north to south, 272, *460*
Changeling, The, 549, *784*
Cherrie Ripe, Ripe, I cry, 183
Cherry and pear are white, 207
Child and the Mariner, The, 653, *840*
Chimney Sweeper, The, 69, *333*
Christabel, 577, *806*
Christmas at Sea, 56
Christ of His gentleness, 139
Cities drowned in olden time, 252
Close thine eyes and sleep secure, 724, *882*
Cold cold!, 271, *459*
Cold in the earth, 514
Come, Sleep, *879*
Come to me, grief, for ever, 504, *767*
Come to me in the silence of the night, 731
Come unto these yellow sands, 149, *380*
Come wary one, come slender feet, 141, *377*
Coronach, 208
Crystal Cabinet, The, 621
Cupid abroade was 'lated in the night, *826*

Dalyaunce, 53, *321*
Dark is the stair, and humid the old walls, 250, *450*
Dear, dear, dear, 133
Dear God, though Thy all-powerful hand, *779*
Death stands above me, *763*
Departe, departe, departe, 606, *820*
Dew sate on Julia's haire, *865*
Diaphenia, like the daffadowndilly, 596, *814*
Does the road wind up-hill all the way?, 741, *902*
Down in yonder meadow, 594
Down in yon garden, *860*
Do you remember an Inn, 237, *442*
Dreams, The Land of, 736
D'ye ken John Peel with his coat so gay?, 171, *393*

Eagle, The, 138
Earl of Mar's Daughter, The, 546
Earth has not anything to show more fair, *345*
Easter, 42, *311*
Edward, 684, *858*
Egypt's might is tumbled down, 614
Encinctured with a twine of leaves, 579
English Gentleman, The, 95, *346*
Even such is Time, *766*
Eve of Saint Mark, The, 726, *882*
Eve, with her basket, 743, *903*

Faht's in there?, 531, *781*
Fair Annie, 688, *859*
Fairies, 153, *383*
Fairies Feast, The, 164, *391*
Fall, leaves, fall; die, flowers, away, 263
Feare no more the heate o' th' Sun, 501, *764*
Fifty years and three, *355*
Fine knacks for ladies!, 103
Flowers of the Forest, The, 223, *429*
Follow thy fair sun, unhappy shadow, 740
For I'll cut my green, coat, *824*
Four and twenty bonny boys, 681, *858*
Four ducks on a pond, *338*
Four men stood by the grave of a man, 227, *431*
From noise of Scare-fires rest ye free, 253
Full fathom five, *849*
Full in the passage of the vale, *887*

Gane were but the winter cauld, 279, *460*
Garden, The, 182
Get up, our Anna dear, from the weary spinning, 155, *383*
Gilderoy was a bonnie boy, 111, *358*
Golden Slumbers kiss your eyes, 518, *779*
Golden Vanity, The, 670, *850*
Gone were but the Winter, 483
Good-Morrow to the Day so fair, 245
Green Broom, 180, *401*

Hallo My Fancy, 625, *825*
Hame, hame, hame, hame, fain wad I be, 215, *429*
Hark! now everything is still, 497, *763*
Haunted Palace, The, 580, *808*
Hay, nou the day dauis, 28, *293*

Hearke, hearke, the Larke at Heaven's gate sings, 30
Hear, sweet spirit, hear the spell, 572
He came and took me by the hand, 185, *405*
He clasps the crag with crooked hands, 138
He gave us all a good-bye cheerily, 212
He is gone on the mountain, 208
He is the lonely greatness of the world, 499, *764*
Helen of Kirkconnell, 693
Helen, thy beauty is to me, 612, *821*
Here a little child I stand, *312*
Here comes a lusty wooer, 590, *808*
Here lies a little bird, 131
Here lies sweet Isabell, *865*
Here she lies, a pretty bud, 507, *771*
Here she was wont to go, and here, and here!, 596, *816*
Here we bring new water, 28
Here we come a-piping, 36
Here where the fields lie lonely and untended, 80
Her Eyes the Glow-worme lend thee, 530
He sees them pass, 492, 758
He steps full stately on the street, *859*
He that lies at the stock, 724
He that spendeth much, *756*
Hey, nonny no!, 237, *442*
Hey! now the day dawns, 28, *293*
Hey, Wully wine, and How, Wully wine, 593, *810*
Hie upon Hielands, 70, *334*
His eyes are quickened so with grief, 658
His stature was not very tall, *303*
Hohenlinden, 214
Holy Thursday, 94
Home, home, from the horizon far and clear, 730
Home no more home to me, whither must I wander?, 52
Ho, sailor of the sea!, 58
How like an Angel came I down!, 195, *412*
How lovely is the sound of oars at night, 572
How many times do I love thee, dear?, *816*
How see you Echo?, 151, *382*
How should I your true love know, 607
How strange it is to wake, 731
How sweet I roamed from field to field!, 196
Hush-a-ba, birdie, croon, croon, *874*

I am Eve, Great Adam's wife, *904*
I and my white Pangur, 125, *366*

I'd a dream to-night, 518, *780*

I'd oft heard tell of this Sledburn fair, 104, *355*

I dreamed that, as I wandered by the way, 32, *296*

I dreamt a Dream! what can it mean?, *733*

I dug, beneath the cypress shade, 502

If I had but two little wings, 49, *318*

If I should ever by chance grow rich, *339*

I found her out there, 509, *772*

If souls should only shine as bright, *758*

If there were dreams to sell, 705

If to the heavens thou lift thine eyes, *886*

I got me flowers to straw thy way, 42, *311*

I had a dove and the sweet dove died, 137

I had a little bird, 70, *335*

I had a little nut tree, 234

I have a yong suster, 87

I have beene all day looking after, 560, *786*

I have seen old ships sail like swans asleep, 631, *834*

I have three presents from over the sea, 465

I have twelfè oxen that be faire and brown, 181, *402*

I have wished a bird would fly away, *370*

I hear a sudden cry of pain!, 124, *365*

I heard a soldier sing some trifle, 204, *420*

I hear the crane, if I mistake not, cry, *459*

I know a little garden-close, *739*

I know that all beneath the moon decays, *458*

I'll sing you a good old song, 95, *346*

I'll weave my love a garland, *823*

I loved a lass, a fair one, 239, *443*

I love to rise in a summer morn, 172

I met a traveller from an antique land, 654

I met the Love-Talker one eve in the glen, 553

Immortal Imogen crowned queen above, 538

In a drear-nighted December, 270, *458*

In Aprill, the Koocoo, *305*

I never shall love the snow again, 510

In March, and in April, *296*

In May, when sea-winds pierced our solitudes, *406*

In melancholy fancy, 625, *825*

In somer when the shawes be sheyne, 176, *393*

In the greenest of our valleys, 580, *808*

In the third-class seat sat the journeying boy, 50

In the wild October night-time, 211, *424*

Into the scented woods we'll go, 35

Invitation to Jane, The, 189

In Xanadu did Kubla Khan, 656, *845*
I remember, I remember, 49, *318*
Irish harper and his dog, The, 117
I saw a frieze on whitest marble drawn, 659, *846*
I saw a peacock with a fiery tail, 533
I saw with open eyes, 140
I see His blood upon the rose, *405*
I see in his last preached and printed Booke, 505, *769*
I see the moon, *876*
I sing of a maiden, 45, *316*
It fell upon a Wednesday, 672
I thee advise, *455*
It is a beauteous evening, *870*
It is an ancient Mariner, 632, *834*
It was a' for our rightfu' king, 222
It was a jolly bed in sooth, *299*
It was a Lover and his lasse, 236, *439*
It was in and about the Martinmas time, 601, *818*
It was intill a pleasant time, 546
It was many and many a year ago, 88, *342*
It was not in the winter, 607
I've heard them lilting at our ewe-milking, 223, *429*
I went out to the hazel wood, 535, *783*
I will sing, if ye will hearken, 686, *858*
I wish I were where Helen lies, 693
I would not be the Moon, the sickly thing, 720, *877*

Jarring the air with rumour cool, 188
Jesu, sweeté soné dere, *906*
John Peel, 171, *393*

Keith of Ravelston, 557
Kubla Khan, 656, *845*

La Belle Dame sans Merci, 160, *387*
Laid in my quiet bed, in study as I were, 730
Laird of Logie, The, 686, *858*
Lavender's blue, dilly dilly, lavender's green, 182, *403*
Lawne as white as driven Snow, 102, *354*
Lay a garland on my hearse, 606, *821*
Leave me, O Love, *763*
Leave Taking, A, 603
Let us go hence, my songs, 603
Let us walk in the white snow, 276, *460*
Life of Life, 598, *816*

Light the lamps up, Lamplighter, 776, *873*
Like archangels in infancy, *839*
Linen was her small camise, *387*
Little Black Boy, The, 46
Little Fly, *362*
Little Lamb, who made thee?, 121
Lo! Huddled up together lie, *777*
London Bridge is broken down, 93, *343*
London Snow, 274, *460*
London, thou art of townes *A per se*, *344*
Lonely, save for a few faint stars, the sky, 233, *433*
Long ago I went to Rome, *406*
Look how the pale Queen of the silent night, 599, *817*
Lord Rameses of Egypt sighed, 488, *757*
Love bade me welcome; yet my soul drew back, 741
Love not me for comely grace, 613
Lucy Gray, 276
Lullay, lullay, thou lytil child, *463*
Lully, lalley, lully, lulley, 749, *906*
Lydia is gone this many a year, 513
Lyke-Wake Dirge, A, 498, *763*

Mad Maid's Song, The, 245
Maidens to bed, and cover coal, *874*
Maids in your smocks, *873*
Mariana, 554, *784*
Mary's gone a-milking, 100, *353*
Matthew, Mark, Luke, and John, 724, *879*
May Song, 37
Mermaid, The, 676
Messmates, 212
Midnight was come, when every vital thing, 146
Mine eyes have seen the glory, 203, *419*
Mon, in the monè, *876*
Mortality, behold and fear!, 503, *766*
Most souls, 'tis true, but peep out once an age, 506, *770*
Much have I travelled in the realms of gold, 628
Music, when soft voices die, 247, *449*
My clothing was once of the linsey woolsey fine, 118, *361*
My dear, do you know, *370*
My heart is like a singing bird, 597, *816*
My love he built me a bonnie bower, 694, *860*
My love lies in the gates of foam, 610
My Luve's in Germany, 219
My master hath a garden, 751

My mistress frowns when she should play, 236, *434*

My mistress is as fair as fine, 595, *813*

My mother bore me in the southern wild, 47

My mother said, *357*

My name is Captain Kidd, *359*

My plaid awa', my plaid awa', 530

My true-love hath my heart, and I have his, 597

Nay, Ivy, nay, 285, *467*

Near to this Stone lies Archer (John), *778*

Night-Peace, The, 530

Not full twelve years, *761*

Not soon shall I forget, 77

Now gaze the stags, *453*

Now milkmaids' pails are deckt with flowers, 99, *351*

Now, pray where are you going, child, *800*

Now some may drink old vintage wine, 243, *447*

Now the bright morning Star, Dayes harbinger, 35, *298*

Now the hungry Lyon rores, 163, *389*

Now wolde I faine some merthes make, 613, *822*

Nurse's Song, The, 709, *868*

Nymph Complaining, The, 127

Nymph, nymph, what are your beads?, 154

O Allison Gross, that lives in yon towr, 679, *858*

O Bessie Bell and Mary Gray, *341*

O Blest unfabled incense-tree, *407*

Ode to the West Wind, 265, *457*

O'Driscoll drove with a song, 552

Of all the birds that I do know, 129, *369*

O fly, my soul!, *833*

O for a Booke and a shadie nooke, 180, *395*

Of this fair volume which we World do name, 197, *413*

Oft I had heard of Lucy Gray, 276

Oh! call my brother back to me, 75

Oh! dear! what can the matter be?, 103, *354*

Oh! poverty is a weary thing, 122, *364*

Oh, sweep chimney, sweep!, *333*

Oh, sweet content, 486

Oh the falling Snow!, 275

Oh, what a thing is man, how far from power, *903*

Oh, where are you going to, my pretty little dear?, 243, *447*

Oh, yes, my dear, *413*

O, I hae come from far away, 564, *810*

O Lady Moon, *817*

Old Mother Redcap, *350*
Old Ships, The, 631, *834*
O many a day have I made good ale in the glen, 599
O Mary, go and call the cattle home, 264
O Memory, thou strange deceiver, *404*
O mortal folk, you may behold and see, *766*
O Mother, lay your hand on my brow, 66
O my dark Rosaleen, 216, *429*
On a day when Jenkin, *305*
On a starred night Prince Lucifer uprose, 573
Once a dream did weave a shade, 735, *887*
Once I was a monarch's daughter, 135
Once musing as I sat, 119, *362*
Once upon a midnight dreary, 561
Once when the sun of the year was beginning to fall, 51, 320
One Friday morn when we set sail, 673
One king's daughter said to anither, 85, *341*
One without looks in to-night, 537, *783*
On first looking into Chapman's Homer, 628
On Linden, when the sun was low, 214
On the first day of Christmas, *463*
On the green banks of Shannon, 117
On Winter mornings, *402*
O sing unto my roundelay, *500*
O Sorrow, 489
O that those lips had language!, 67
O the evening's for the fair, bonny lassie O!, 244, *448*
O thou that swing'st upon the waving hair, *363*
O Thou, who plumed with strong desire, 583, *808*
O, to have a little house, 79
Our Gospel has had here a Summers day, *866*
Our King and Queen the Lord God Blesse, *419*
Our King went up upon a hill high, 227, *431*
Out in the dark over the snow, 732
Over the bleak and barren snow, 623
O whare are ye gaun?, 576, *803*
O, what can ail thee, knight at arms, 160, *387*
O what if the fowler my blackbird has taken?, 600
O wha will shoe my bonny foot?, *334*
O where were ye, my milk-white steed, 548, *784*
O, wild West Wind, thou breath of Autumn's being, 265, *457*

Pack, clouds, away, and welcome day!, 31, *295*
Pedlar's Song, The, 102, *354*
Pleasure it is, 42, *312*

Poor Old Horse, 118, *361*
Prayer unsaid, and Mass unsung, 571
Prepare, prepare the iron helm of War, 201
Proud Maisie is in the wood, 602

Queen and huntress, chaste and fair, 719
Queen Mary, Queen Mary, my age is sixteen, *824*
Queen of Elfland, The, 158, *385*
Question, The, 32
Quo' the Tweed to the Till, 678, *851*
Quoth John to Joan, 594, *813*

Rarely, rarely, comest thou, 487
Raven, The, 561
Recollection, The, 190, *409*
Remember me when I am gone away, 516
Remember us poor Mayers all, 38, *300*
Reverie of Poor Susan, The, 132, *371*
Rich in the waning light she sat, 65
Riding through Ruwu swamp, about sunrise, 120, *364*
Rock well, my cradle, *335*
Rosaleen, Dark, 216, *429*
Rose Aylmer, 611
Rosy apple, lemon, or pear 62, *330*
Round about, round about, 149
Ruby, amethyst, emerald, diamond, *887*

Sabrina fair, 162, *388*
Sands of Dee, The, 264
Say, is there aught that can convey, *842*
Schoolboy, The, 172
Seamen, three! What men be ye?, 242
Season of mists and mellow fruitfulness, 258, *454*
Secret was the garden, 522
See, with eyes shut, *357*
Seven lang years I hae served the King, 592
Seynt Stevene was a clerk, 280, *461*
Shed no tear – O shed no tear!, 520
Shee was brighter of her blee, *903*
She is so proper and so pure, 63, *332*
Shepherds all, and Maidens fair, 713, *871*
Shut not so soon; the dull-eyed night, 706, *865*
Shy in their herding dwell the fallow deer, 537
Sick Child, The, 66
Silent are the woods, 52

Silent is the house: all are laid asleep, 522
Silly Sweetheart, say not nay, 589
Sir Hugh, or the Jew's Daughter, 681, *858*
Sir Patrick Spence, 678, *851*
Sister, awake! close not your eyes, 36, *299*
Skip it and trip it, *433*
Sleep on, my Love, in thy cold bed, 508
Slow, slow, fresh fount, keep time with my salt tears, 484, *755*
Sluggard, The, 29, *293*
Soldiers, For, 202, *414*
Solitary Reaper, The, 259
Some folks as can afford, 193
Some say the Pilgrim's Progress is not mine, *450*
Somewhere, somewhen I've seen, 654, *842*
Sorrow, 489
So through the darkness and the cold we flew, 273
So, we'll go no more a-roving, 721
Spring, the sweet Spring, is the year's pleasant king, 40, *305*
Stepping Westward, 712
Stop, Christian passer-by!, 505, *770*
Stormey's dead, that good old man, *838*
Stupidity Street, 140
Sweet bird that shunn'st the noise of folly, 251
Sweet Content, 485, *755*
Sweet day, so cool, so calm, so bright, 707, *866*
Sweet Stay-at-Home, sweet Well-content, 64, *333*
Sweet Suffolk Owl, so trimly dight, 134, *372*
Sweet William and May Margaret, 698, *863*
Sweet wind that up the climbing road, *361*
Swiftly walk o'er the western wave, 715, *872*

Tales of my Nursery!, *399*
Tam o' the linn, *386*
Tell me not of joy, 130, *369*
Tell me where is fancie bred, 246
That houses forme within was rude and strong, 581
That wind, I used to hear it swelling, 268
The aïr to gi'e your cheäks a hue, *447*
The ample heaven of fabrik sure, 177, *394*
The captain stood on the carronade, 428
The cat sits at the mill door, *805*
The cheerful arn he blaws in the marn, 170
The cleanly rush of the mountain air, 84
The clouds have left the sky, 719
The crooked paths go every way, 192, *411*

The days are cold, the nights are long, 257, *453*
The Door of Death, *888*
The doubt of future woes, *393*
The Dragon that our Seas did raise his Crest, 224, *430*
The evening sun was sinking down, 705
The feathers of the willow, 263, *457*
The foddering boy, *468*
The fort over against the oak-wood, 229, *432*
The four sails of the mill, 176, *394*
The fresh air moves like water round a boat, 33
The gipsies lit their fires by the chalk-pit gate anew, 108
The heaving roses of the hedge are stirred, 260
The holly and the ivy, 283, *463*
The hunt is up, the hunt is up, 169, *392*
The King of China's daughter, 234
The king sits in Dumferling toune, 678, *851*
The king's young dochter, *433*
The lake lay blue below the hill, 136, *375*
The lark now leaves his watery nest, 30, *294*
The love that I hae chosen, 609
The maiden caught me in the wild, 621
The man of life upright, *759*
The miller's mill-dog lay at the mill-door, 117, *359*
The moon's my constant mistress, 529, *781*
The murmur of the mourning ghost, 557
The myrtle bush grew shady, 228
The night will never stay, 722
The North wind doth blow, *460*
The plain was grassy, wild and bare, *827*
The poplars are felled; farewell to the shade, 76, *337*
The unthrifty sun shot vital gold, *394*
There came a bird out o a bush, *861*
There came a ghost to Margret's door, 698, *863*
There cam' Seven Egyptians on a day, *356*
The red flame flowers bloom and die, 733, *884*
There grew a goodly tree him faire beside, *750*
There is a Garden in her face, 184, *404*
There is a Lady sweet and kind, 612, *821*
There is a silence where hath been no sound, 656, *844*
The reivers they stole Fair Annie, 688, *859*
There lived a wife at Usher's Well, 700, *864*
There's nane o' my ain to care, *335*
There's no smoke in the chimney, 79, *338*
There was a gallant ship and a gallant ship was she, 670, *850*
There was a knicht riding frae the east, 574, *800*

There was a man of double deed, *782*

There was an Indian, who had known no change, 628, *827*

There was an old man lived out in the wood, 180, *401*

There was a robber, *357*

There was a wee bit mousikie, *368*

There was no song nor shout of joy, 675

There were three gipsies a-come to my door, 108, *356*

There were twa brethren in the north, 83, *341*

There were twa sisters sat in a bowr, 696, *861*

The robin of the red breast, *371*

The sea would flow no longer, 660

These hearts were woven of human joys and cares, 206, *420*

The shadows flickering, the daylight dying, *321*

The sheets were frozen hard, 56

The smothering dark engulfs relentlessly, 279

The snow falls deep, the forest lies alone, 107

The snow had fallen many nights and days, 661

The splendour falls on castle walls, 152

The sun descending in the west, 708

The Sun does arise, 48

The trees of the elder lands, 655, *842*

The twilight is sad and cloudy, 57

The wanton Troopers riding by, 127, *369*

The warm sun is failing, the bleak wind is wailing, 261

The wind blows cold, *469*

The wind doth blow to-day, my love, 605, *819*

The wind's on the wold, 723, *879*

They are all gone into the world of light!, 521, *780*

They shut the road through the woods, 536

They stole her from the well, *383*

This ae nighte, this ae nighte, 498, *763*

This city and this country, 94, *344*

This is the Key of the Kingdom, 27, 292, 751, *907*

This is the sea, *458*

This is the weather the cuckoo likes, 34

This Life, which seems so fair, 485, *755*

This sailor knows of wondrous lands afar, 653, *840*

This was that yeere of wonder, *760*

Thomas Rymer, 158, *385*

Thou art to all lost love, *821*

Thou fair-haired angel of the evening, 706

Though three men dwell on Flannan Isle, 667

Thou hast come from the old city, 582

Thou simple Bird what mak'st thou here to play?, 142

Thou that desir'st to fish with line and hook, *306*

Thou to me art such a spring, *836*
Three things there be that prosper, *358*
Time you old gipsy man, 711
'Tis the middle of night, 577, *806*
'Tis the voice of a sluggard, I heard him complain, 29, *293*
To-day a rude brief recitative, 213, *426*
Toll no bell for me, dear Father, dear Mother, 549, *784*
Tom o' Bedlam, 529, *781*
Tom Pearse, Tom Pearse, lend me your gray mare, 105, *356*
To sea, to sea! The calm is o'er, 629, *829*
To yon fause stream, 676
Trafalgar, 211, *424*
True Thomas lay oer yond grassy bank, 158, *385*
Turnstile, The, 507, *772*
Twa Corbies, The, 139
Twa Sisters, The, 696, *861*
'Twas on a Holy Thursday, 94
Two Swans, The, 538
Tyger! Tyger! burning bright, 126, *368*

Under the after-sunset sky, 144
Under the greenwood tree, 176
Upon a dark ball spun in Time, 533
Upon a Sabbath-day it fell, 726, *882*
Upon my lap my sovereign sits, 46, *317*
Up the airy mountain, 153, *383*
Up, Timothy, up with your staff and away!, 512

Wae's me, wae's me, 573, *799*
Wake, all the dead!, *761*
War Song, A, 201
Was ever eie, did see that face, *769*
Was it the sound of a footfall I heard?, *783*
Water Lady, The, 534
We are three Brethren come from Spain, 590
We be the King's men, hale and hearty, 210, *422*
Weep no more, nor sigh, nor groan, 695
Weep, weep, ye woodmen!, 111, *358*
Weep you no more, sad fountains, 519
Wee Wee Man, The, 532
Welcome, fayre chylde, what is thy name?, 53, *321*
Well then; I now do plainly see, 345
We wandered to the Pine Forest, 190, *409*
We were young, we were merry, 558
Whar hae ye been a' day, my boy Tammy?, 60, *329*

What bird so sings, yet so does wail?, 40, *304*
What, hast thou run thy Race? Art going down?, 707, *866*
What if some little paine the passage have, 226, *431*
What is there hid in the heart of a rose, 184
What is this life if, full of care, 178
What noise of viols is so sweet, 110
What shall I your true-love tell, 496, *761*
What wondrous life is this I lead!, 182
What, you are stepping westward?, 712, *870*
When cats run home and light is come, 134, *373*
When from the world I should be ta'en, *773*
When I am dead, my dearest, 515, *773*
When I crept over the hill, broken with tears, 511
When I did wake this morn from sleep, 31
When I sailed out of Baltimore, 123
When Isicles hang by the wall, 286, *467*
When I was bound apprentice, 241, *446*
When I was but thirteen or so, 623, *825*
When larks gin sing, *784*
When men were all asleep the snow came flying, 274, *460*
When my mother died I was very young, 69, *333*
When night is o'er the wood, *373*
When once the sun sinks in the west, 710
When she sleeps, 497
When that I was and a little tinie boy, 262, *455*
When the cock begins to crow, *390*
When the green woods laugh with the voice of joy, 235, *434*
When the lamp is shattered, 490
When the Present has latched its postern, 712, *868*
When these old woods were young, 81, *338*
When the sheep are in the fauld, 608
When the voices of children are heard on the green, 709, *868*
When the words rustle no more, 66
When we lay where Budmouth Beach is, 210, *424*
Where are you going, Master mine?, 601
Where are your Oranges?, 209, *421*
Where do the gipsies come from?, 109, *357*
Where on the wrinkled stream the willows lean, 135, *374*
Where shall the lover rest, 515
Where's my lovely parsley, say?, *433*
Where the Bee sucks, there suck I, 151
Where the pools are bright and deep, 173
Where the remote Bermudas ride, 630, *830*
Where thou dwellest, in what Grove, 143
While I sit at the door, 733, *884*

While Morpheus thus does gently lay, 725, *882*
Whither, midst falling dew?, 144
Who calls? Who calls? Who?, 150, *382*
Who can live in heart so glad, 179
Who feasts tonight, 164, *391*
Who liveth so merry?, *401*
Who'll walk the fields with us to town?, 174
Who's at my window?, *762*
Whose Woods these are I think I know, *460*
Who – Who – the bride will be?, 134
Why does your brand so drop wi' blood, 684, *858*
Why do you lie with your legs ungainly huddled, 205
Widdecombe Fair, 105, *356*
Wife of Usher's Well, The, 700, *864*
Will you come?, 717
Witches' Ballad, The, 564, *791*
With blackest moss the flower-pots, 554, *784*
With deep affection and recollection, 247
With how sad steps, O Moon, 720, *876*
Wolcum be thu, hevene kyng, 284, *463*
World of Light, The, 521, *780*
Wraggle Taggle Gipsies, The, 108, *356*
Wull ye come in early Spring, 718

Ye banks and braes o' bonnie Doon, 77
Ye buds of Brutus' land, courageous youths, 202, *414*
Ye have been fresh and green, 257, *453*
Yes, I remember Adlestrop, 131
Yesterday returneth not, *300*
Yet if His Majesty our sovereign lord, 742, *903*
Young Love lies sleeping, 615, *823*

Index of Notes

All figures refer to the *number* of the note in *About and Roundabout*.

Albatross, 398
Ale, Good, 72
Alexander the Great, 203
Ambergris, 396
Angels, 457
Apes, 91

Bacon, Francis, 175
Ballads, 411, 418, 429
Barton, Sir Andrew, 418
Basilisk, 333
Bats, 111
'Beauties', 449
Bees, 359
Bellman, 444
Bells and bell-ringing, 226, 368
Bermudas, The Remote, 396
Birch, 35
Birds, 101, 102, 111, 115, 120, 255, 392; flights of, 115; names of, 167
Books, 153
Boxing Day, 255
Bride, A, 352
Brutus, 175
Bunyan, John, 225

Calls, Farmyard, 155
Campion, Thomas, 159
Castor and Pollux, 392
Cats, 98
Charms, 335
Chaucer, Geoffrey, 19
Children's books, 153
Christening, A, 175
Christmas Box, 255
Christmas Eve and Day, 258
Columbus, Christopher, 393

Commodities, County, 211
Cosmetics, 219
Counsel, Good, 237, 266
Counting, 24
Counting-out rhymes, 355
Cranes, 246
Cratch, 483
Cricket, 74
Cuckoo, 19
Cupid, 381

Daisies, 19
Dances, names of, 210
Dancing, 207
Dandling rhymes, 1, 24
Demons, etc., 133, 335, 343, 398
Demophon, 167
Dialect, 302
Dishes, names of, 22
Dogs, 88, 142, 345
Donne, John, 287
Dreams, 304, 470
Dump, 314
Dumplings, etc., 22

Easter Day, 13
Elephant, 483
Elizabeth I, 141, 175
Epitaphs, 265, 275, 285, 291, 302
Eton, 35
Evening Star, 450
Eyes, 185

Facts, 335
Fairies, 129, 133, 139, 319; charms for, 341
Familiar spirits, 135

Feasts, 71, 73
Fields, names of, 333
Fiend, The, 343
Fingers, names of, 24
Fireflies, 93
Fishing, 22
Fleas, 213
Flowers, 19, 30, 163, 284, 333; in Shakespeare's plays, 19; names of, 333
Folk-dancing, 210
Fools, Court, 237

Games, 74; *see also* Singing games
Gilbert, Sir Humphrey, 199, 392
Gilderoy, 87
Gilliflowers, 42
Glaucus, 138
Goodies, names of, 466
Gorse, 60
Grace before meat, 24, 176
Graves, 61
Griffins, 120

Halcyons, 112
Hawking, 115
Henry, Prince of Wales, 200
Henry VIII, 141
Herbs, 284
Hippocras, 261
Hobgoblins, etc., 335
Hopscotch, 41
Hornbooks, 153
Humming-birds, 111
Hunting, 97, 143
Hyena, 403

Imagination, 23, 316, 483
Inns, 210

Jonson, Ben, 176
July, 214

Keats, John, 233
Kelpie, Water, 336

Kent, 211
Knight, The False, 344
Kubla Khan, 404

Lairs, 119
Lampreys, 211
Language, 329, 407, 435
Letters, 35, 78, 285
London, 70
London Bridge, 68
Lyonnesse, 293

Madrigals, 210
Magi, The, 479
Mandrake, 333
Manners (table), 71
Marchpane, 22
Mariana, 329
Mark, St, 460
Marvell, Andrew, 100, 396
Masks, 76
May Day, 17, 22, 135, 148
Metre, 30
Mice, 98, 460
Midsummer Day, 218
Milkmaids, 75
Monkeys, 91
Months, names of, 214
Moon, 30, 66, 418, 444, 450
More, Sir Thomas, 285
Mourning, 304
Music, 210

Names, 466; of bells, 226; of birds, 167; of dances, 210; of dishes, 22; of fields, 333; of fingers, 24; of flowers, 333; of goodies, 466; of months, 214; of precious stones, 466; of stars, 6, 466; of taverns, 210; of toes, 24; of villages, 333; of words, 333
Napoleon Buonaparte, 185
Navy, 187, 418
Nelson, Lord, 187
Nest of Singing Birds, A, 440

Night-feast, A, 214
Nonsense-rhymes, 316
Noses, 358
Nursery rhymes, 1

Ormus, 396
Owl, 107, 109

Parrot, 400
Passing-bell, 368
Peel, John, 143
Phoenix, 163
Piggie's eye, 43
Pincushions, etc., 153
Pink, 42
Pomanders, 284
Precious stones, names of, 466
Preening, 8
Pronunciation, 302

Raleigh, Sir Walter, 285
Reading, 9, 30
Rhythm, 9, 30, 32, 40, 189, 202, 212, 249, 251, 385, 443
Riddles, ancient, 343
Robins, 102
Roc, 120
Rowan Tree, 135

Sabrina, 138
Sailors, 189
St Louis, 407
St Mark, legend of, 460
Salamander, 335
Samplers, 470
Schools, 35
Sea-flowers, 242
Shakespeare, Will, 19, 440
Shanties, sea, 398
Shepherd, A, 95
Ships, 418
Sidney, Sir Philip, 286
Sillabub, 22

Singing birds, 440
Singing-game rhymes, 41, 84, 259, 352
Sleep, 3
Sluggard, 4
Solitude, 168
Sonnet, 364
Sorrow, 51
Sparrows, 101, 120
Spelling, 126
Spenser, Edmund, 164
Stars, 6, 307, 470; names of, 6, 466
Stonehenge, 61
Stones, precious, 466
Street cries, 153
Sunrise, 442

Tamlane, 136
Tansy, 74
Taverns, 210
Thomas, Edward, 60, 105
Thomas of Ercildoune, 136
Toes, names of, 24
Tom o' Bedlam, 310
Totnes, 175, 199
Traherne, Thomas, 170
Twelfth Night, 258

Valentine's Day, St, 22
Vermin, 60
Villages, names of, 333
Virginians, 214

War, 177, 180
Watchman, 444
Whale, 396
Wheatear, 211
Winter, 260
Witches, etc., 335, 343
Words, 53, 407, 435
Wordsworth, Dorothy, 232
Wren, Jenny, 255

Index of Authors

The numbers are page numbers – those in *italic* referring to the notes in *About and Roundabout*.

Abbot, Claude Colleer, *388*

Abercrombie, Lascelles, 188, *840*

Allingham, William, 153

Anon, Thomas, 234

Armstrong, Martin, 131

Aubrey, John, *420*, *443*, *767*

Augustine, St, *780*

Bacon, Francis, *419*, *765*

Barnes William, *372*, *447*, 507, 517, 518, 718, *758*

Barnfield, Richard, 137

Bashford, H. H., 109

Batterham, Eric N., 492

Beaumont, Francis, 503, *764*, *766*

Beddoes, Thomas Lovell, *303*, 629, 705, *816*

Belloc, Hilaire, 237

Best, Charles, 599

Binyon, Laurence, 233, 250

Blake, William, 47, 48, 69, 94, 121, 126 143, 172, 196, 201, 235, *311*, *333*, *362*, *379*, 621, 706, 708, 709, 733, 735, 736, *868*, *888*

Blunden, Edmund, 108

Bottomley, Gordon, 661

Breton, Nicholas, 179

Bridges, Robert, 274, *307*, 510, 719, 734

Brontë, Emily, 263, 268, 514, 522, 705

Brooke, Rupert, 206, 497

Browne, Sir Thomas, *882*

Browne, William, 185, *772*

Bryant, William Cullen, 144

Buckhurst, Lord, 146

Bunyan, John, 121, 248, *395*, *450*, 707, *866*

Burns, Robert, 77, 222, *808*

Burton, Robert, *383*, *791*

Byron, Lord, 721, *822*

Callanan, Jeremiah John, 599

Campbell, Thomas, 117, 214, *425*, *870*

Campion, Thomas, 184, 225, *404*, 740, *759*, *822*

Carbery, Ethna, 553

Carew, Thomas, 186

Cartwright, William, 130

Cellini, Benvenuto, *792*

Chapman, George, *834*

Charles I, 724

Chatterton, Thomas, 500

Chaucer, Geoffrey, 39, *377*, *391*

Clare, John, 107, 244, *331*, *468*, 710

Cleland, William, 625

Coleridge, Mary, 79, 136, 228, 558, 601, 614, 720

Coleridge, Samuel Taylor, 49, *325*, *326*, *327*, *382*, *468*, 505, 572, 577, 579, 621, 632, 656, *817*

Colum, Padraic, 79

Constable, Henry, 596

Corbet, Richard, *390*

Cornford, Frances, *321*

Cornish, William, 42

Coulton, G. G., *322*

Cowley, Abraham, *345*, *408*

Cowper, William 67, 76

Crabbe, George, *457*

Cunningham, Allan, 215, 279

Dalmon, Charles, 243, 600

Daniel, Samuel, 197

Darley, George, *407*, 571, *849*
Davenant, Sir William, 30, *761*
Davidson, Frances, 110
Davies, Sir John, *414*
Davies, William H., 31, 64, 123, 178, 486, 653
Davison, Edward L., 205
De Bary, Anna Bunston, 193
Dekker, Thomas, 485, 518
De la Marche, Olivier, *347*
De Quincey, Thomas, *336*
De Tabley, Lord, 610
Dixon, Richard Watson, 260, 263
Dobell, Sydney, 58, 70, 557
Donne, John, *769*, *822*, *841*, *881*
Doughty, Charles M., 164
Drayton, Michael, *381*, *395*, *775*
Drinkwater, John, 488, 537
Drummond, William, 197, *458*, 485, *771*
Dunbar, William, *344*
Dunn, Dr Courtenay, *313*

Elizabeth I, *392*, *415–19*
Elliot, Jean, 223
Ellis, Havelock, *380*
Ellis, Vivian Locke, 617
Emerson, Ralph Waldo, *406*

Farjeon, Eleanor, 150, 209, 275, 716, 722
Ferguson, Sir Samuel, 155
Flecker, James Elroy, 66, 631
Fleming, Marjorie, *865*
Fletcher, John, 606, 695, 713, *761*, *764*, *879*
Francis, Colin, 623
Freeman, John, 65, 207
Frost, Robert, 51, *370*, *460*
Fuller, Thomas, *362*, *440*, *450*
Furse, Margaret, Cecilia, *406*

Garstin, Crosbie, 733
Gibson, Wilfrid, 654, 667
Gifford, Humphrey, 202
Godwin, Mary Wollstonecraft, *317*

Goldsmith, Oliver, *844*
Googe, Barnabe, 119, *807*
Gosse, Edmund, 559
Graves, John Woodcock, 171
Graves, Robert, 139, 269, 658
Gray, Thomas, *871*
Greene, Robert, *303*
Grey, Viscountess, 151

Hall, Edward, *415*, *853*
Hamilton, John, 272
Hardy, Thomas, 34, 50, 210, 211, 509, 537, 712
Hawes, Stephen, *766*
Hayman, Robert, 224, *430*
Hemans, Felicia, 75
Henry VIII, *392*
Herbert, George, 42, 707, 741
Herrick, Robert, 183, 245, 253, 257, *312*, *316*, *342*, 507, 530, 706, *821*, *865*
Heywood, Thomas, 31
Hodgson, Ralph, 140, 185, 711, 743
Hogg, James, 173
Hood, Thomas, 49, *454* 534, 538, 607, 656
Hopkins, Gerard Manley, *793*
Howe, Julia Ward, 203
Howitt, Mary, 122
Hudson, W. H., *339*
Hume, Alexander, 177

John, Gwen, 279
Johnson, M. M., *361*, *839*
Jonson, Ben, *419*, 484, 560, 596, 719, *876*

Keats, John, 137, 160, 258, 270, *378*, *389*, 489, 520, 628, 726, *847*, *878*, *884*
Killigrew, Henry, 725
King, Henry, 508
Kingsley, Charles, 264, *872*
Kipling, Rudyard, 536
Kirk, Robert, *799*

Lamb, Charles, *324*

Landor, Walter Savage, 611, *763*, *770*

Lindsay, Lady Anne, 608

Longfellow, Henry Wadsworth, 57, *828*

Lovelace, Sir Richard, *363*

Lucas, E. V., *402*

Lydgate, John, 227, *305*, *902*

Lyly, John, 40

Lysaght, Sidney Royse, 80

Macaulay, Thomas Babington, *429*, *890*

MacGillivray, W., 133

Macleod, Fiona (William Sharp), 675

Macneill, Hector, 60

Mahony, Francis ('Father Prout'), 247

Mandeville, Sir John, *361*, *825*

Mangan, James Clarence, 216, *429*

Manning-Sanders, Ruth, 141, *582*

Maplet, John, *842*

Marriot, John, 505

Marryat, Frederick, *428*

Marvell, Andrew, 127, 182, *369*, 630, *832*

Masefield, John, 52, 84, *839*

Meredith, George, 573, *836*

Mew, Charlotte, 549

Meyer, Kuno (trans.), 96, 125, 229, 271, *366*, *904*

Meynell, Alice, 252, 722, 730

Meynell, Viola, 660

Milton, John, 35, 162, 251, *829*, *866*

Monro, Harold, 33, 154

Montgomerie, Alexander, 28

Moore, T. Sturge, 176

More, Sir Thomas, *767*

Morris, William, 723, 739

Munday, Anthony, 111

Nash, Thomas, 40, 494

Newbolt, Sir Henry, 78, 212, 252

Noyes, Alfred, 184

Odoric, Friar, *845*

Ogilvie, William, *334*

O'Keefe, John, *439*

Opie, Amelia, *422*

O'Riordan, Conal, *779*

O'Sullivan, Seumas, 233

Overbury, Sir Thomas, *353*

Owen, Wilfred, 207

Patmore, Coventry, *414*, *467*, 731

Patmore, F. J., *373*

Peacock, Thomas Love, 242, 502

Plotinus, *311*

Plunkett, Joseph, *405*

Poe, Edgar Allan, 88, 561, 580, 612, *880*

Polo, Marco, *846*, *905*

Pope, Alexander, 506

Raleigh, Sir Walter, *358*, *766*

Ramal, Elizabeth, *783*

Ramsay, Allan, *810*

Ravenscroft, Thomas, 149

Reese, Lizette Woodworth, 513

Reid, Forrest, *410*

Rhodes, Hugh, *756*

Rock, Madeline Caron, 499

Rossetti, Christina, 483, 515, 516, 597, 615, 731, 741, 745, *817*, *823*

Rossetti, Dante Gabriel, *846*

Rowlands, Richard, 46

Rowley, William, 622

Ruskin, John, 867

Sassoon, Siegfried, 205

Scot, Reginald, *791*

Scott, Alexander, 606

Scott, Sir Walter, 208, 220, *431*, 515, 570, 602, *851*

Scott, William Bell, 564

Shakespeare, William, 30, 102, 149, 151, 163, 175, 236, 246, 262, 286, 287, *294*, *439*, 501, 607, *785*, *826*, *830*, *849*, *863*, *870*, *875*, *904*

Shanks, Edward, *458*, *572*

Sharp, William (Fiona Macleod), 675
Sheldon, Gilbert, 655
Shelley, Percy Bysshe, 32, 189, 190, 247, 261, 265, *354, 375, 379, 411,* 484, 487, 490, 583, 598, 654, 715, 721, *808, 872*
Shirley, James, *833*
Shorter, Dora Sigerson, 511
Sidney, Sir Henry, *768*
Sidney, Sir Philip, 597, 720, *763, 767*
Sitwell, Edith, 234
Skelton, John, 62, *842*
Sleigh, Bernard, *383*
Southey, Robert, *424*
Southwell, Robert, 282, 492
Spenser, Edmund, 187, 226, *415,* *581, 750, 769, 815*
Squire, J. C., 628, 675
Stephens, James, 89, 124, 192
Stevenson, Robert Louis, 52, 56, 66, 82
Suckling, Sir John, *443*
Surrey, Earl of, 730
Swinburne, Algernon Charles, 603

Temple, Sir William, *438*
Tennyson, Alfred Lord, 134, 138, 152, 265, *449, 554, 827*
Thomas, Edward, 81, 131, 144, *338, 371, 394, 717, 732*
Thomas the Rhymer, *385*
Thompson, Francis, 496, 522, *835*
Thomson, James, *887*
Thurlow, Lord, *453*

Tomlinson, H. M., *420*
Topsell, Edward, *367, 883, 907*
Traherne, Thomas, 195, *412*
Trench, Herbert, 204
Trevisa, John de, *367*
Turberville, George, *455*
Turner, Walter J., *533, 623, 659*
Tusser, Thomas, *296*
Tynan, Katherine, 77

Vaughan, Henry, *394, 521, 780*
Vautor, Thomas, 134

Waller, Edmund, *771*
Walton, Isaac, *308, 376*
Watts, Isaac, 29
Webb, Mary, 35, 135, 174
Webster, John, 497, 502, 503
Wedderburn, John, *762*
Whitman, Walt, 213
Wither, George, 239, *443*
Wolcot, J., *307*
Woods, Margaret L., *369*
Wordsworth, Dorothy, 257
Wordsworth, William, 132, 259, 273, 276, *345, 432, 512, 712, 870*
Wotton, Sir Henry, 41
Wright, Elizabeth M., *359, 402*
Wylie, Elinor, 276

Yeats, W. B., 535, 552, *783*
Young, Filson, *827*
Young, Francis Brett, 120

A PUFFIN BOOK OF VERSE

Edited by Eleanor Graham

This anthology is intended simply to give pleasure, and it is hoped that every boy or girl who browses among its pages will find something to enjoy.

It ranges from nursery rhymes and nonsense poems to verses whose meaning has to be thought about: but whether the poems are simple or more difficult, they have been chosen partly for that beauty of rhythm and language which makes lines linger in the mind after the book that contains them has been put aside.

A PUFFIN QUARTET OF POETS

Edited by Eleanor Graham

This unusual anthology contains a selection of poems from the work of only four poets, but four of the finest who are writing verse for children today. A substantial amount from the work of each is given, enough to show their individual quality and special characteristics. The quartet is made up of Eleanor Farjeon, James Reeves, E. V. Rieu, and Ian Serraillier.

A CHILD'S GARDEN OF VERSES

Robert Louis Stevenson

There are more than sixty famous verses by Robert Louis Stevenson in this book, and they are illustrated with many drawings by Eve Garnett. 'These are rhymes, jingles,' the author wrote to a friend. 'I don't go in for eternity and the three unities.' They are rhymes about his childhood, divided into three sections – *The Child Alone*, *Garden Days* and *Envoys*.